Robert Ardrey was born in Chicago, majored in natural sciences at the University of Chicago and thereafter became a successful playwright and screen writer. In 1955 he began his African travels and studies. **African Genesis** is the impressive result of these pursuits. Mr. Ardrey's latest book, also the result of these pursuits, is **Territorial Imperative.**

AFRICAN GENESIS

by ROBERT ARDREY

A Personal Investigation into the
Animal Origins and Nature of Man

 Drawings by Berdine Ardrey

A Laurel Edition

Published by
Dell Publishing Co., Inc.
750 Third Avenue, New York, N.Y. 10017

First printing—June, 1967
Second printing—December, 1967
Third printing—September, 1968
Fourth printing—April, 1969
Fifth printing—October, 1969
Sixth printing—January, 1970

Printed in U.S.A.

to the memory of
Eugène Marais

Contents

AFRICAN GENESIS

Chapter 1
The New Enlightenment

Not in innocence, and not in Asia, was mankind born. The home of our fathers was that African highland reaching north from the Cape to the Lakes of the Nile. Here we came about—slowly, ever so slowly—on a sky-swept savannah glowing with menace.

In neither bankruptcy nor bastardy did we face our long beginnings. Man's line is legitimate. Our ancestry is firmly rooted in the animal world, and to its subtle, antique ways our hearts are yet pledged. Children of all animal kind, we inherited many a social nicety as well as the predator's way. But most significant of all our gifts, as things turned out, was the legacy bequeathed us by those killer apes, our immediate forebears. Even in the first long days of our beginnings we held in our hand the weapon, an instrument somewhat older than ourselves.

Man is a fraction of the animal world. Our history is an afterthought, no more, tacked to an infinite calendar. We are not so unique as we should like to believe. And if man in a time of need seeks deeper knowledge concerning himself, then he must explore those animal horizons from which we have made our quick little march.

2

In the past thirty years a revolution has been taking place in the natural sciences. It is a revolution in our understanding of animal behaviour, and of our link to the animal world. In sum, therefore, the revolution concerns that most absorbing of human entertainments, man's understanding of man. Yet not even science, as a whole, is aware of the philosophical reappraisal which must proceed from its specialists' doings.

Assumptions concerning the nature of man, today unquestioned by education, by psychiatry, by politics, by art, or even by science itself, are being eroded by the tiny streams set loose from obscure scientific springs. And few of us, scientists or laymen, know.

That the contemporary revolution in the natural sciences has proceeded thus far in almost total silence must not be regarded as too great a wonder. Other and noisier revolutions have overwhelmed our unquiet time. As compared with the fortunes of the totalitarian state, of nuclear physics, of anti-biotics or the long-playing record, the fortunes of the palaeontologist may seem remote from our daily life. And the work of the revolution has been accomplished by such extreme specialists that it has been recorded only in such inaccessible pages as those of the *American Journal of Anthropology* or the *Biological Symposia*. Such heralds gain few hearers in the modern market-place.

Still more important than the obscurity or specialization of the revolution has been its suddenness. When in 1930 I emerged from a respectable American university as a respectably well-educated young man, no hint had reached me that private property was other than a human institution evolved by the human brain. If I and my young contemporaries throughout the following years wasted much of our fire on social propositions involving the abolition of private ownership, then we did so in perfect faith that such a course would free mankind of many a frustration. No part of the curriculum of our psychology, sociology, or anthropology departments had presented us with the information that territoriality—the drive to gain, maintain, and defend the exclusive right to a piece of property—is an animal instinct approximately as ancient and powerful as sex.

The role of territory in general animal behaviour lies today beyond scientific controversy; then it was unknown. We of the Class of 1930 had to emerge into a world of tumultuous evaluation without benefit of this most salient observation. Similarly, we could not know, as we bemused ourselves with the attractions of the classless state, that hierarchy is an institution among all social animals and the drive to dominate one's fellows an instinct three or four hundred million years old.

There is a classic experiment which may be performed with sword-tails, those darting red fish that decorate many a tropical tank. Half a dozen male swordtails gathered together in a tank will rapidly arrange themselves in a straight-line hierarchy, each through strength and pugnacity and determination finding those he may dominate and those to whom he must submit. His rank determines many a prerogative, whether access to food or to females or to an undisturbed corner of the tank, and his defence of that rank will remain his most belligerent preoccupation. Just how profound is the instinct for dominance in the swordtail may be tested most simply. Let the water in the tank be gradually cooled. The time will come when the male will lose all interest in sex; but he will still fight for his status.

We of the Class of 1930 could not know of the experiment with swordtail fish, for it had not yet been performed. And it would be almost ten years before the head of my own zoology department at the University of Chicago, Dr. W. C. Allee, would publish his *Social Life of Animals* and establish the thesis, today no matter for controversy, that dominance in social animals is a universal instinct independent of sex. By that time, however, I was a practising playwright no longer *au courant* with what the natural scientists were up to. Any convictions which I may have held concerning such human tendencies as tyranny, aristocracy, or keeping up with the Joneses had been formed without knowledge of the ways of my animal ancestry.

Many were the unblemished fallacies that the well-educated young man of my generation took with him into a rambunctious world. From the time of Darwin, for example, it had been assumed by science that man evolved from some extinct branch of happy apedom not radically different from contemporary species. No assumption could have been more reasonable, since without exception every modern primate, whether gorilla or macaque, chimpanzee or vervet monkey or gibbon or baboon, is inoffensive, non-aggressive, and strays no farther from the vegetarian way than an occasional taste for insects. And so our psychology, sociology and anthropology professors had no reason to believe that the human ancestor led a life less bland. Yet within a decade African palaeontologists would demonstrate beyond doubt the presence on that continent of a race of terrestrial, flesh-eating, killer apes who became extinct half a million years ago. Within another decade the human emergence would be demonstrated as having taken place on that continent at about that time. And the final decade of the contemporary revolution would establish the carnivorous, predatory australopithecines as the unquestioned antecedents of man and as the probable authors of man's constant companion, the lethal weapon.

We, the approximate Class of 1930, today furnish trusted and vital leadership to world thought, world politics, world society and to whatever may exist of world hope. But we do not know that the human drive to acquire possession is the simple expression of an animal instinct many hundreds of times older than the human race itself. We do not know that the roots of nationalism are dug firmly into the social territoriality of almost every species in our related primate family. We do not know that the status-seekers are responding to animal instincts equally characteristic of baboons, jackdaws, rock cod, and men. Responsible though we may be for the fate of summit conferences, disarmament agreements, juvenile delinquents and new African states, we do not know that the first man was an armed killer, or that evolutionary survival from his mutant instant depended upon the use, the development, and the contest of weapons.

We do not know these things, since they are conclusions to be drawn from the contemporary revolution in the natural sciences. We should know, however, that acquired characteristics cannot be inherited, and that within a species every member is born in the essential image of the first of its kind. No child of ours, born in the middle twentieth century, can differ at birth in significant measure from the earliest of *Homo sapiens*. No instinct, whether physiological or cultural, that constituted a part of the original human bundle can ever in the history of the species be permanently suppressed or abandoned.

The ineradicability of a cultural instinct finds a fair example in the history of beavers on the River Rhône. A beaver colony creates its dams and ponds and lodges by communal effort, and does so only when the numbers of its society are at moderately full strength. From ancient days the European beaver was hunted for its fur until it very nearly became extinct. A few stragglers hung on in a few tiny colonies, but they built nothing. For centuries beaver dams were unknown in western Europe. Then the French government extended protection to a scanty beaver population in the Rhône valley. Slowly, through several decades, their numbers grew. And at last the beavers went back to work. For the first time in many hundreds of years dams and ponds and lodges appeared in the tributaries of the River Rhône. And they differed in no least degree from the dams and the ponds and the lodges built five thousand miles away by distant Canadian cousins.

The problem of man's original nature imposes itself upon any human solution.

I have attributed the silence of the contemporary revolution to the distractions of our time. Yet so brilliantly is every modern circumstance illuminated by the revolution's flares, that the reason seems inadequate. I have attributed the silence to the obscurity of such highly specialized scientific findings; yet the even more specialized endeavours of the nuclear physicists have scarcely gone unnoted. I have attributed the silence to the newness of the revelations, and lamented an educated generation born too soon. Yet the approximate Class of 1960, thirty years later, emerging from its respectable universities as respectably well-educated as were we, has been taught not a whit more.

The contemporary revolution in the natural sciences has proceeded in something more striking than silence. It has proceeded in secret. Like our tiny, furry, squirrel-like, earliest primate ancestors, seventy million years ago, the revolution has found obscurity its best defence and modesty the key to its survival. For it has challenged larger orthodoxies than just those of science, and its enemies exist beyond counting. From seashore and jungle, from ant-heap and travertine cave have been collected the inflammable materials that must some day explode our most precious myths. The struggle towards truth has proceeded, but as an underground intellectual movement seeking light under darkest cover.

Is man innocent? Were we in truth created in the image

of God? Are we unique, separate and distinct creatures from animalkind? Did our bodies evolve from the animal world, but not our souls? Is man sovereign? Are babies born good? Is human fault to be explained successfully in terms of environment? Is man innately noble?

The contemporary revolution in the natural sciences, unorganized, undirected, and largely unrecorded, has with a strong instinct for survival challenged the romantic fallacy in a voice unlikely to be heard. When a strident voice from southern Africa has repeatedly lifted itself in challenge, science itself, as we shall see, has unwittingly combined to mute, to divert, or to discredit the call.

A certain justification has existed until now, in my opinion, for the submission of the insurgent specialists to the censorship of scientific orthodoxy. Such higher bastions of philosophical orthodoxy as Jefferson, Marx, and Freud could scarcely be stormed by partial regiments. Until the anti-romantic revolution could summon to arms what now exists, an overwhelming body of incontrovertible proof, then action had best be confined to a labyrinthine underground of unreadable journals, of museum back rooms, and of gossiping groups around African camp-fires.

For six years I have lived with that underground. Why a dramatist should have become the accountant and interpreter of a scientific revolution is a paradox that need not divert us here. The rare reader who finds himself unbearably curious is invited to turn to Chapter Seven and to get his impatience over with. What need only concern us at this point is that a dramatist is a specialist, in a sense, in human nature. In another sense, however, he is a specialist in nothing, and therefore a generalist. And while the generalist may be the most suspect of creatures in the view of the modern, specialized human animal, a generalist was what a revolution of specialists demanded. And a generalist was what it got.

For the task of this account, I have brought a fair experience with the human condition; the innocence of the Class of 1930; a willingness to trade the theatrical posture of the playwright for that of the audience; and no too great disinclination for adventure. Departing from theatrical procedures, I have been a touring, one-man audience on an endless series of one-night stands. I have listened to geologists, ecologists, and zoologists in America; anthropologists, palaeontologists, and meteorologists in London; archaeologists, anatomists, and biologists in South Africa; primate specialists in Central Africa, reptile specialists in California and the Transvaal, mammal specialists in Pretoria and Nairobi, game wardens in the vast reserves of Uganda, the Congo, South Africa and Kenya. And everywhere, surprisingly, I have been welcome. I have been entertained by old foetuses, and older bones. I have been dragged through limey caves; I have beheld peculiar animals; I have drunk more tea than I can mention. Why a prowler as suspicious as myself should have been received with such kindness, I do not know. Perhaps a generalist was what these specialists yearned for. Or perhaps they were merely lonely, and there was no one about but myself.

In any event, it is a dramatist who must first record, synthesize, interpret and evaluate a scientific revolution striking deep at the human circumstance. And the man of science, confronted for the first time by the arrayed achievements of the various specialized natural sciences, must be tolerant of the dramatist lurking behind the pages: the weakness for lights and shadows, for mystery and irony and situation and adventure, for the rude joke or the great story. Similarly the general, informed reader, for whom this book is written, must tolerate the scientific discipline lying upon the dramatist. He should recall that much of the material, as unfamiliar to the scientist as to himself, must be presented with authority and detail. He should recall that the psychiatrist, for example, faced with scientific evidence casting doubts on certain of his profession's premises, will demand degrees of proof for which the general reader will not ask.

All readers, lay or professional, confronted by a new interpretation of man's origin and nature, must be obliged continually to ask the question: Why should I believe this? To aid the reader in this evaluation, I have arranged the material according to its order of controversy. In the remainder of this opening chapter I present a brief history of the contemporary revolution. I then proceed through following chapters to present those factors of animal behaviour which, unassimilated though they may be by modern thought and undigested by orthodox science, still lie beyond authoritative dispute. And I analyze the romantic fallacy in terms only of the indisputable.

To that point, none of the material presented in the account can be regarded as today controversial within the ranks of advanced specialists. Beyond that point, however, we encounter the stormy channels of our African genesis, and the final animal mark on man. Here the disagreement of specialists has in the past been the rule. The discovery on July 17, 1959, of a single fossil skull near the bottom of a dry gorge in Tanganyika's dusty Serengeti plain, leading undoubtedly to new discoveries, new riddles, and new controversies, should at least end most of the old ones. I choose in any event to regard all material relating to man's predatory origins as essentially controversial, demanding special investigation, special evaluation, and special proof. And so, before the reader is presented with a final interpretation of the contemporary human predicament in terms of our total animal legacy, he may judge for himself that portion of our legacy on which not all specialists yet agree.

3

Previous to 1930, only two scientific cries heralded the revolution to come. One came from South Africa, from the throat of a clamorous Australian anatomist. This challenge was universally rejected. But the other cry, with which we begin our story, was in fact a quiet statement from an English bird-watcher, and it was widely heard, widely accepted, and widely misunderstood. It nevertheless marks the opening of the contemporary revolution in the natural sciences.

Eliot Howard was the English bird-watcher. Until 1920 he possessed a narrow face as supreme authority on the British warbler. But then he published a book called *Territory in Birdlife*, and there will be small hope for a United Nations that fails to take account of his work. For what Eliot Howard had observed throughout a life-time of bird-watching was that male birds quarrel seldom over females; what they quarrel over is real estate.

So far as I know it was Howard who introduced the term, *territory*, to zoölogy. In the 1860's a German scientist named Altum had recognized that the notion of males competing for females—at least among birds—was an error of observation. The English bird-watcher, however, knew nothing of Altum's work, and I find no evidence that the German's radical observation had the least impact on scientific thought. But Eliot Howard's pronouncements were another matter. With infinite detail and infinite patience he observed the pattern of bird competition. Rarely did males compete for females. Instead, the male seizes a territory. He defines its boundaries by the pugnacity of his individual nature, and warns away all others by his song. On this territory he will mate and breed, but the seizure and struggle take place before the coming of the female and without consciousness of sexual significance.

What Eliot Howard had done, of course, was badly to upset Darwin's "law of battle", and to introduce into scientific thought the possibility that in evolutionary progress the romantic struggles of sexual rivalry might not be the beginning and end of all things. A superb naturalist—and a realist uninfluenced by any temptation to project the supposed nature of man on the supposed conduct of animals—the British bird-watcher studied species after species, migratory birds and resident birds, land birds and sea birds. And always there was the same conclusion, that a male bird who has acquired his territory will have small problems in gaining or holding a female.

Farther along in the account of the new enlightenment we shall consider the enchanting details of Howard's work. What need concern us now is simply that in the 1920's Howard's theories were accepted by most authorities as a remarkable characteristic of bird life alone. Birds had funny ways. By the 1930's, however, it was becoming evident in many an obscure scientific paper that it was not just birds.

A growing host of naturalists were going out to field and sea, to Siam and to Panama and into the Congo fastness, looking all of them about with a hard, new eye. Lizards, jewel fish, seals and muskrats revealed the same primary passion for a place of one's own. One cannot say that the urge to seize and hold a territory was unveiled as some universal law of life. Many a species showed sleepy indifference to the problem of *lebensraum*. But what could not be denied was that in vast segments of the animal world natural selection of the most qualified individuals took place not by competition for females but by competition for space.

It was an astonishing discovery, well worthy of headlines. But no headlines appeared. In the later years between the wars our attention was being diverted by the more dramatic endeavours of economic depression and militant nationalism. A scientific thesis the overtones of which lent support to the defenders of private property could scarcely, in such a time, be considered popular reading. Similarly, we were most of us during that period convinced that wars were made by munition-makers; and we saw no reason to look into the matter more deeply.

But work progressed in its silent way. An American zoologist, Dr. C. R. Carpenter, brought matters perilously close to home. His patient studies of ape and monkey societies in a state of nature are classics of modern science. And they show that among our closest relatives territoriality is a universal law. Even more important, they reveal the inner workings of that more sophisticated institution, the social territory—one held and defended by a group. It was Dr. Carpenter's work that inspired the grand old man of British anthropology, Sir Arthur Keith, to make one of the few political deductions so far published on the subject. In his last essays Keith reflected that if one seeks the origins of nationalism, of patriotism, and of war, one need look no further than to territoriality.

I should suggest today that Sir Arthur writing in the mid-1940's spoke too soon. The more recent revelations of our African beginnings have contributed factors more starkly terrifying than simple territoriality to the animal instincts directing our behaviour. In contrast, the drive to gain and defend a territory, even to live in undying hostility with one's neighbours, must be interpreted as we shall see as a conservative force in the broad panorama of species.

Eliot Howard's observations of birds upset the time-honoured assumption that the male animal has little on his mind but females. Many a zoologist today, after a generation of accumulated studies, will flatly assert that the territorial compulsion is more pervasive and more powerful than sex. But the observations of a revolutionary generation revealed that it was not just territory, either. The chief target of such zoologists as Carpenter and Allee, and of such naturalists as Konrad Lorenz and Eugène Marais, was animal society. Investigations revealed the obligatory dependence of territorial defence upon social order, and the exquisite relationships of social order to acceptance of responsibility by the dominant hierarchy, to acceptance of domination by the rank and file, to group defence of the individual and the young, to division of duties and communication between social partners, to the minimizing of sexual conflict, to the development of a dual code of behaviour—amity for the social partner, hostility for the territorial neighbour—and to the enlarging role of the female as sexual specialist to counteract the tendency of social males to be preoccupied with activities other than reproduction.

Man is a primate. All primates are social animals. As social animals, all primates have developed to one degree or another such instinctual bundles as guarantee the survival of their societies. There is no reason to suppose that man in his African genesis inherited from primate ancestors a bundle less complex. It will be worthy for you to recall when next you transport your troubles to the psychoanalyst's couch, that the science of Freud's day acknowledged no human instincts other than sex and individual survival, and no social inheritance larger or more complex than the family group. If you are encouraged to believe that all your troubles can be traced to the repressions of sex and family relationships, then this is the reason why.

Two basic discoveries have powered the revolution in the natural sciences. One—to which we shall now turn—was that the main stage for the dramatic emergence of man from the animal world was the continent of Africa. The second—inspired by a British bird-watcher—was that conclusions regarding animal behaviour are valid only if confirmed by observation in the wild. Freud's generation knew nothing of the broader patterns of animal instinct, because science of that time confined its observations to captive animals. And zoos offer no territories. Only in a state of nature can we be sure that we are observing true animal behaviour. If today we say that almost nothing is known about the much-observed chimpanzee, then what we mean is that almost nothing is known of his behaviour in a state of nature. Modern zoology is building as rapidly as it can a new knowledge of the animal based on Eliot Howard's inspiration and Dr. Carpenter's techniques.

Unrelated though the two basic discoveries may seem,

still both lead the natural scientist to the opportunities and hazards of the African continent. Here the palaeoanthropologist works against time to unearth the fossil history of man's beginnings. And the zoologist, drawn by the last vast reserves of wild life remaining on the planet, works also against time to learn what he can of our animal ways, while still he may. On a magnificent, awesome, natural stage both wings of the contemporary revolution meet and encounter a third revolutionary force, one with consequences ironically dovetailing their own. The African independence movements are rapidly converting a continent into something approaching a political state of nature, where primitive human behaviour may be observed not as we should wish it to be, but as it is.

I had the opportunity in 1960 to experience with both scientific wings, in the same portion of the African arena, the impact of the new force. Two of the most significant primates, in terms of human behaviour, are the gorilla and the chimpanzee. But as almost nothing is known of the chimpanzee in the wild, so almost nothing is known of the gorilla. And so, since I had been able to find little trustworthy scientific literature on gorilla behaviour, I went early in the month of June to a village named Kisoro on the Congo-Uganda border. Above the village is a towering volcano with bamboo forests still sheltering a few of the vanishing mountain gorilla. And in the village is a tiny hotel called Travellers Rest, dedicated to madmen and scientists. While no literature may yet exist on gorilla ways, at the hotel dining table and nowhere else in the world one can at least hear gorilla gossip.

The area about Kisoro marks the little-known hinge of the African continent. A hundred miles to the south lies blue Lake Kivu, a hundred miles to the north rise the misty, legendary Mountains of the Moon. A hundred miles to the east spreads sprawling and enormous the cynically smiling face of Lake Victoria, poisonous with disease, crawling with crocodiles, the probable focus of our earliest human experience; while off to the west into the Congo march the volcanoes, three miles high, peak after perfect, symmetrical peak. For several weeks I lived not only at the hinge of Africa, but at the heart of the contemporary revolution. Just beyond Lake Victoria, in Tanganyika's Olduvai Gorge, Dr. L. S. B. Leakey and his wife excavated from sunrise to sunset for further remains of the dawn creature, *Zinjanthropus,* which they had discovered the previous season. And high on a saddle between two peaks a few volcanoes to the west perched Dr. George B. Schaller of the New York Zoological Society. For a year he had been living with the mountain gorillas, and his reports when they are published will constitute our first, only, and for the time being last authoritative observation of gorilla behaviour.

On the thirtieth of June—the Congo's Independence Day—my wife and I left the border. Dr. Schaller was still on his Congo perch.

4

When I was a boy in Chicago I attended the Sunday School of a neighbourhood Presbyterian church. The church is gone now, a victim I must believe of wear and tear. It was a wonderful Sunday school. A modern critic might demur on grounds that it did nothing for juvenile delinquency other than to bring it indoors. But I cannot share such a view. My class met not only on Sunday morning but on prayer-meeting night too, and I recall our Wednesday night meetings with the simplest nostalgia. While in the church above, the more devout adults of our congregation would be gathering for quiet song and prayers, we would meet in the basement. The meeting would as a rule be of a business sort given to sport programmes and reports, collections and the like. A new member or two would be initiated, and if injured seriously helped home to his mother. Then the meeting would close, always with the same devotions. There would be a short prayer, and a shorter benediction. And we would turn out all the lights and in total darkness hit each other with chairs.

It was my Sunday-school class in Chicago, I believe, that prepared me for African anthropology. North of the equator the contemporary revolution has resembled the polite prayer-meetings in the church upstairs. It has been discreet, impersonal, colourless, courteous in its differences, seemly in its modesty. But below the equator it has been led by three unforgettable wild men all as vital as leopards, as durable as elephants, and as unpredictable as Kenya earth movements. Below the equator the contemporary revolution has been unseemly, indiscreet, a scientific basement shenanigan where a one-time Chicagoan could feel entirely at ease. But the greatness of its discoveries have given us the outline of the origins of man.

Raymond A. Dart, the most famous of the three, was until his retirement in 1958 head of the anatomy department at the University of the Witwatersrand in Johannesburg. Australian-born, trained in Britain and the United States, he came to South Africa in 1922 to organize the Medical School's department of anatomy. Two years later he discovered *Australopithecus africanus,* the carnivorous ape of the high, ancient veld, and was plunged into scientific controversy from which he has never emerged. His was the other cry besides Eliot Howard's to break the pre-1930 stillness. And his was the strident, challenging voice from South Africa that orthodox science tried for so long to mute or discredit.

Dart is a small, compact man of far-reaching interests, far-gripping personal magnetism, and appalling durability. Until recent years he still gave lectures to his astounded class in comparative anatomy while brachiating cheerfully from the steam pipes over its heads. I recall an occasion a few years ago when the two of us were climbing a steep wall of the wild Makapan valley, in the northern Transvaal near the Limpopo River, to visit an unhappily situated cave. Halfway up my breath went out of me as from a punctured tire. We stopped. "Yes," said Dart, gently, compassionately, breathing as easily as a sleeping child, "it's a difficult climb." I reflected without pleasure that Dart was all of sixty-five years old. And he was smiling to himself in pleasant reminiscence. "Do you know," he said, looking about as if he had just discovered something, "this is exactly the place where old Broom always had to stop." I reflected with even less pleasure that Robert Broom, the second of the wild men, had not even entered the field of anthropology until he was seventy.

It was Raymond Dart's durability, tenacity, and unshakable belief in his own rightness that in my opinion made possible our present knowledge of human origins. The 1924 Taungs skull was that of an infant, and Dart's description violated every scientific preconception of the time. His grasp of comparative anatomy led him to project the adult creature as four feet tall, erect in its carriage, bipedal, with a brain still the size of a gorilla's: as an animal, in other words, halfway between ape and man. Dart further deduced from study of the creature's teeth and habitat that *Australopithecus africanus* had been carnivorous and had led a hunting life. The ape-man had been a transitional being possessing every significant human qualification other than man's big brain. The discovery in the view of the discoverer pointed to Africa as the scene of the human emergence.

But science in the 1920's was still convinced that mankind had arisen in Asia. A famous expedition of the period was fairly sifting the sands of the Gobi desert for signs of the missing link. Since no fossil background for Dart's creature had ever been found in all Africa, the Asian presumption prevailed. With equal justification science dismissed the claim that the man-ape had been a carnivore. As we have already noted, flesh-eating primates were unknown to science, and therefore could not exist. A third preconception, however, was even more important than these logical two. Anthropology, for the most mysterious of reasons, was convinced that the big brain had been the first, not the last of man's evolutionary endowments. All human characteristics such as posture and diet and way of life had proceeded from the original gift of brain. Such

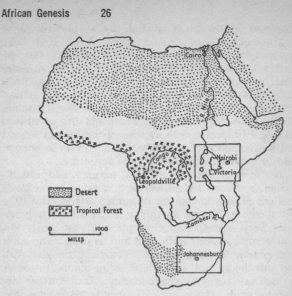

Lake Victoria quadrangle: p. 254

Johannesburg quadrangle: p. 182

a creature as Dart's, with a human body and ape brain, managed to get things all backwards.

The animal, like the griffin, was a scientific impossibility. Other factors may with reason have affected the verdict. Sweeping claims had been made on the basis of a single, infant skull by a young anatomist without previous experience in anthropology. Dart had compounded his sin by giving the creature a name which no one, I am sure, could pronounce. And the judgement of the northern prayer-meeting, I also suspect, was not entirely uninfluenced by the discovery's source in the church basement. Anything coming from below the equator has always, to the northern nose, borne the suspicious odour of someone hailing from the wrong side of the tracks. Whatever was the ambiance of the verdict, the unanimous body of northern science including such great ones as Keith, Hrdlicka, Woodward and Elliot Smith dismissed Dart's southern ape as a young anatomist's fancy. And the young anatomist, in his citadel on Hospital Hill at the wrong end of the world, went right on writing about his discovery as if all the world agreed with him.

Such was the situation twelve years later when the second wild man found himself drawn by Raymond Dart's unyielding conviction. This was Robert Broom, with whom we shall become better acquainted at a later stage in this narrative. Broom was a fellow South African, seventy years old, who through a long and remarkable career had established himself as one of the world's greatest zoologists. Now in 1936 he emerged from retirement, and on a Sunday morning visited a cave not an hour's drive from Johannesburg. Like Dart, he was a small man, but unlike Dart his appearance was exceedingly formal. In his black hat and his black tie and his stiff white collar he investigated the cave with care. A week from the following Monday, just eight days later, he found the skull, teeth and brain case of an adult australopithecine. And they confirmed in every detail Dart's projection based on the infant skull.

Subsequent discoveries have given us the fossil remains of more than one hundred individual australopithecines from five different South African sites. More is known today about nature's last animals than is known about nature's first men. But Broom's 1936 discovery was enough. The case against Dart began its slow collapse.

What Broom had proved was that the Taungs infant had been neither a freak nor an anatomist's fancy. In the meantime two thousand miles away to the north in the Lake Victoria area the third wild man of African science was busy demolishing the Asia fixation. L. S. B. Leakey is Kenya-born and is today curator of the Coryndon Museum in Nairobi. We shall return to Leakey, as we shall to Broom, much later in this narrative. But beginning in 1930 the Kenyan produced example after example of quadruped terrestrial fossil apes from Lake Victoria fossil beds, any one of which could have been ancestral to the erect-walking apes of the south. The australopithecines flourished on the Transvaal high veld three-quarters of a million years ago. The terrestrial apes of the *Proconsul* family had frequented Kenya lake shores in Miocene times, twenty million years earlier.

The scientific objection that no fossil background for Dart's discovery existed on the African continent had been a point well taken. But now Leakey was exploring that background. Six hundred examples of the terrestrial ape have now been found. During a period antedating the known presence of apes on any other continent, the *Proconsul* family was as common in East Africa as the antelope today. Throughout all the 1930's and 40's massive evidence for man's African origin piled up in museums and laboratories. But even yet, any interpretation of the southern ape as man's evolutionary halfway house faced anthropology's mystical conviction that the big brain had been the first of man's evolutionary awards. And that most elusive preconception remained intact until 1953.

When scientists at the British Museum proved Piltdown Man to be a hoax, they created one of the most sensational scientific stories of the century, and Dr. Kenneth P. Oakley's fluorine tests became world-famous. But while the revelation of the fraud may have reverberated through the world press, the significance of the tests did not.

Piltdown Man combined perfectly the elements visualized by anthropology—by English anthropology in particular—as essential to threshold man. There was the ape jaw, and there was the bulging human cranium, source of all future evolutionary glory. The unknown perpetrator of the fraud had provided science with just what science wanted. And so the true significance of the London disclosures lay not in Piltdown Man's fall from scientific glory, but in the fall of the big-brain-first thesis from philosophical respectability. No discovery in the African earth has advanced our knowledge of human origins more than Oakley's tests in a London laboratory.

Why had English anthropology been so devoted to the notion that intellectual capacity had been the evolutionary foundation for the human being? It is the sort of question that will haunt the later stages of this narrative. It was a question, most certainly, that haunted Oakley. Even after his tests had demonstrated that Piltdown's brain case and jaw belonged to different creatures, an eminent British scientist confided to him the wistful expectation that the first human being, when at last discovered, would despite all resemble Piltdown Man. Not for another three years did Dr. Oakley, as he has described it to me, come on any kind of an answer to the puzzle. Then, during the course of a lecture in the United States on quite another subject, the answer flashed without warning in his own large-domed head: "Of course we believed that the big brain came first! We assumed that the first man was an Englishman!"

Only when we come to the latter half of this account shall we consider in detail how the combined yet highly individualistic efforts of Dart, Broom, Leakey and Oakley have established the rough but indisputable outline of the human emergence on the African highland. It is L. S. B. Leakey, however, who has made the discoveries that will tantalize the future. Dr. Leakey and his wife, Mary, have been the finders beyond equal, and they have uncovered in East Africa enough significant remains of man's origin to keep a regiment of analysts busy for a generation.

For the last thirty years the Leakeys have been finding crude pebble-tools, the most primitive evidence of human culture, in the Lake Victoria area. They dated from a period more or less contemporary with the australopithecines in South Africa and predated by hundreds of thousands of years the earliest stone artifacts known on any other continent. As the remains of terrestrial apes, twenty million years old, pointed to East Africa as the scene of the emergence of the human stock, so these pebble-tools, almost a million years old, spoke of the emergence of man himself in the same area. Then the Leakeys began their investigations in Tanganyika's nearby Olduvai Gorge.

The Olduvai Gorge is a twenty-five-mile-long dry canyon inhabited exclusively today by such unpleasant thugs as the cobra, the rhino, and the black-maned lion. In the exposed beds of the canyon walls the Leakeys found layer upon layer of ancient lake shores containing evidence of human occupation. In the bottom beds were the ancient, crude pebble-tools. And, in the later, higher beds could be read the continuous evolution of stone implements to the last sophisticated efforts of final stone-age man. The Olduvai Gorge is the Grand Canyon of Human Evolution. With the stunning discovery there, in 1959, of the remains of the first maker of stone tools, L. S. B. Leakey established his prize preserve as the world's most important anthropological site.

With that discovery in Tanganyika's Olduvai Gorge, the two wings of the contemporary revolution collided. For three decades zoology had been pressing forward our knowledge of animal behaviour. For three decades anthropology had been pressing backward, in point of time, our knowledge of human history. And near the bottom of a dry East African canyon they met. The creator of our human culture had not been a man but an animal.

New riddles have been posed by the Leakeys' discovery, and we shall explore them. New controversies must be born where old ones have died, and we shall anticipate them as best we can. But the link between the world of man and the world of the animal has been definitely established. The African highland was humanity's cradle. And man was born of the southern ape.

5

In March, 1955, I sat for the first time in Raymond Dart's office on Hospital Hill in Johannesburg. We could not know that events within a few years would prove the southern ape to be the human ancestor. We could not then, with any sense of scientific responsibility, regard the relationship as more than probable, and to describe the creature simply as the last known animal before man. Even within such limitations, however, a claim of Dart's for which he was at that time preparing to present evidence loomed like a thundercloud over the panorama of our animal past. To inspect it we must go back another six years.

In 1949 Dart had dropped the other shoe. He had published a paper in the *American Journal of Physical Anthropology* claiming that *Australopithecus africanus* had gone armed. Study of some fifty-odd baboon skulls from various sites associated with the southern ape had revealed a curious, characteristic double depression. Dart concluded that the baboons had met sudden death at the hands of the southern ape; that the man-ape had used a weapon and that his favourite weapon had been the antelope humerus bone.

The use of weapons had preceded man.

The blast set off by Dart's claim in the dignified corridors of northern science could not even be called a controversy, since there was no one on Dart's side at all. The reception allotted to his infant skull, exactly a quarter of a century earlier, seemed in comparison a hymn of praise. But Dart as usual persisted as if none disagreed. And in 1953 he published a paper that may some day rank with the *Communist Manifesto* among those documents which have contributed least to man's ease of mind.

The Predatory Transition from Ape to Man was a paper that no regular scientific journal would touch, and so it appeared in *The International Anthropological and Linguistic Review*, published in Miami. The stricken editor of this remarkable journal tacked a foreword to Dart's work disclaiming responsibility for the author's deductions, and even for the australopithecines themselves. The foreword ended with a pitiful sigh: "Of course, they were only the ancestors of the modern Bushman and Negro, and of *nobody else*." (Editor's italics.)

What Dart put forward in his piece was the simple thesis that Man had emerged from the anthropoid background for one reason only: because he was a killer. Long ago, perhaps many millions of years ago, a line of killer apes branched off from the non-aggressive primate background. For reasons of environmental necessity, the line adopted the predatory way. For reasons of predatory necessity the line advanced. We learned to stand erect in the first place as a necessity of the hunting life. We learned to run in our pursuit of game across the yellowing African savannah. Our hands freed for the mauling and the hauling, we had no further use for a snout; and so it retreated. And lacking fighting teeth or claws, we took recourse by necessity to the weapon.

A rock, a stick, a heavy bone—to our ancestral killer ape it meant the margin of survival. But the use of the weapon meant new and multiplying demands on the nervous system for the co-ordination of muscle and touch and sight. And so at last came the enlarged brain; so at last came man.

Far from the truth lay the antique assumption that man had fathered the weapon. The weapon, instead, had fathered man. The mightiest of predators had come about as the logical conclusion to an evolutionary transition. With his big brain and his stone handaxes, man annihilated a predecessor who fought only with bones. And if all human history from that date has turned on the development of superior weapons, then it is for very sound reason. It is for genetic necessity. We design and compete with our weapons as birds build distinctive nests.

Not in our stars and not in our hearts had we ever considered such a possibility. In the century that had elapsed since Darwin all of our most searching thought concerning the nature of man had been premised, as we have already noted, by the assumption that the human family had arisen from the neutral, non-aggressive, vegetarian forest ape, or from some common ancestral primate more or less in his likeness. But now we had australopithecus, and he was a a carnivore and a predator. And we had this newest claim, that he was armed.

What Raymond Dart faced was more than the mortal howls of northern science or prejudices concerning things from the wrong side of the tracks. What he faced was the solid phalanx of modern thought. His theory of the predatory transition might or might not be susceptible to proof, and surely other factors would be revealed as contributing to the human condition. But a world dedicated to the manufacture of explosive playthings could scarcely afford in its regard for his theories the luxury of neglect. And so, in 1955, I visited him. For six years Dart and his students had been patiently developing the evidence that australopithecus had been a systematic, purposeful user of weapons. I examined the evidence and found it overwhelming. And now we sat in his office at the wrong end of the world while Dart looked out of his window at thunderstorms chasing each other across the African sky. There was an occasional rattle in the gold-workings a mile beneath us. There were skulls on his desk. In my hand was the jawbone of a twelve-year-old southern ape found a few years earlier at Makapan. The jaw was broken on both sides. The front teeth were missing. There was a dark, smooth dent on the chin where the blow had landed; and the boy had died of it, for there had been no time for the bone to knit.

What if a weapon had done this deed? What if I held in my hands the evidence of antique murder committed with a deadly weapon a quarter of a million years before the time of man? What if the predatory transition should be susceptible to proof, and accepted as the way we came about?

Could we afford to surrender, in such desperate hours as those we now lived in, our belief in the nobility of man's inner nature?

I asked Dart how he felt, from a viewpoint of responsibility, about putting forward such a thesis at such a time. I said that I understood his conviction that the predatory transition and the weapons fixation explained man's bloody history, his eternal aggression, his irrational, self-destroying inexorable pursuit of death for death's sake. But I asked, would it be wise for us to listen when man at last possessed weapons capable of sterilizing the earth?

Dart turned from his window and sat down at his desk; and somewhere a tunnel collapsed, a mile down, and skulls jiggled. And he said that since we had tried everything else, we might in last resort try the truth.

Four months later Dart presented his evidence to the body of northern science. And if the verdict of a hundred authorities had been other than what it was, then I doubt that a dramatist would now feel impelled to review the findings of a scientist's revolution.

6

In the early eighteenth century an Italian monk named Vico recorded a simple but radical statement: "Society is the work of man." It was a statement of immense revolutionary import, in its time, for it denied all medieval dogma concerning divine intervention in mundane affairs: the divine rights of kings and governments, divine ordinance over man's becoming postures, his birth, his fate, his daily life, his aspirations and lowliest submissions. The Enlightenment was no more than a broad elaboration of the Neapolitan's single phrase.

Society is the work of man: the human being, uninfluenced by gods and devils, holds exclusive power over the character of his society. It proved a meaty enough thesis to power a generation of eighteenth-century thinkers and political revolutionaries. Thrones and altars fell in rational dust. The winds of the Enlightenment blew new nations into being, and old dogmas into obscurity.

But then, in the following century, human thought became infatuated with the converse of Vico's phrase: *Man is the work of society*. To Rousseau's preoccupations with the nobility of the savage we added a variety of explanations for all that man is: poverty begets crime; imperialism begets war; the class struggle begets political institutions; early emotional relationships beget later unfriendly dispositions.

The basic fabric of modern thought is woven from one or the other of the two theses: that society is the work of man, or that man is the product of society. Yet whether we bow to the rationalism of a Voltaire or to the romanticism of a Marx, we are accepting guidance from thinkers who knew nothing of the animal role in human affairs. They thought too soon. Because gods, devils, and witches could be driven from the temples of man's concern, they assumed the illimitability of human sovereignty.

Long is the story of the natural world, and we are a page that turns. Glory is written on us, for we are kings. But our kingship is a limited sovereignty; we are part of all things. We stand upon creatures lost in pre-Cambrian slimes. Our genes still reflect their ambitions. We may anticipate species unborn, times beyond prediction, sovereignties beyond *Homo sapiens,* and beings that we shall never know. But we shall be part of them, influencing their destinies as others have influenced ours.

We are a shining link in a chain beyond knowing, for a portion unknowable remains yet unforged. But our gift to that chain will never be lost, for we were the questioning animal, the first animal conscious of self. And if tomorrow we are possessed by a blinding vision or consumed by a blinding flash, then the one will scarcely be the answer to all things, nor the other their end. We shall have our inheritors, who may perhaps know the animal compulsions of their nature better than did we.

Chapter 2
One Tiger to a Hill

The belated recognition by science of territorial behaviour serves in many ways to confirm the clear eyesight of poets and peasants. A century and a half before Eliot Howard, Oliver Goldsmith meditated that one rarely saw two male birds of a single species in a single hedge. And "one tiger to a hill" is a folk observation of equivalent discernment. But while peasant and poet may apprehend a truth, it is the obligation of science to define it, to prove it, to assimilate its substance into the body of scientific thought, and to make its conclusions both available and understandable to the society of which science is a part. It is an obligation which the sciences fulfil with the most conscientious discipline in any matter concerned with the blowing up of man; yet in matters related to understanding the fellow, there has been a tendency to accept responsibility more lightly.

Whether or not behind human behaviour there stands an all-powerful instinct for territorial possession is a question not to be kept in the ice-box. But no library in the world will offer either the general reader or the scientist himself a title devoted to the subject. No encyclopaedia so far as I know offers the briefest discussion under the heading, "territory." The word does not appear in the dictionary with a biological connotation. Only prime sources, such as we shall investigate in this chapter, will permit us to squeeze out for ourselves a definition, a comprehension, and an evaluation of one of science's most significant discoveries. But before we quite lose ourselves in the animal world, let us take a brief glance at the price we pay when science fails to digest its own fruit.

Sir Solly Zuckerman is one of the world's most distinguished scientists. Like Raymond Dart he is an anatomist who has spent most of his career as the head of an anatomy department, that of Birmingham University. Like Dart also, his interests have been far-ranging and his fame was established in a field other than that of his main career. When Zuckerman was a fairly young man he published a study of primate behaviour establishing sex as the basis of animal society. Few scientific books of the century have commanded such wide or lasting authority. But its conclusions were based largely on zoo observations.

There is a delightful story—too good, undoubtedly, to be true—told by Zuckerman's Bloomsbury friends of the period. The young scientist was a South African who had not yet acquainted himself with all the nuances fluttering like pigeons around the staider British institutions. When his horrified friends learned that the new book was to be called *The Sexual Life of the Primates*, they whispered to him a fact of life: Primates, in England, could refer to nothing but the hierarchy of the Established Church. The book appeared under the title, *The Social Life of Monkeys and Apes*.

Whether or not the story is true, a hard truth emerges from it. The original title accurately described a book which is a masterpiece of observation of primate sexuality, even though conducted under the abnormal conditions of captivity. But if we read it as an analysis of primate society, then fallacy undermines all. In the London Zoo there are no animal societies other than artificial.

The book was written in 1932 before the difference between animal behaviour in captivity and that in a state of nature had become apparent. The famous anatomist cannot be blamed for presuming that the sex-obsessed activities of London baboons reflected true primate behaviour, or for drawing the logical conclusion that the powerful magnet of sexual attraction must be the force that holds primate societies together. But over and over we shall encounter in this narrative the disastrous consequences of applying utter logic to a false premise. And Zuckerman's premise was false. The creature whom we watch in the zoo is one denied by the conditions of his captivity the normal flow of his instinctual energies. Neither the drives of hunger nor the fear of the predator stir the idleness of his hours. Neither the commands of normal society nor the demands of territorial defence pre-empt the energies with which nature has endowed him. If he seems a creature obsessed with sex, then it is simply because sex is the only instinct for which captivity permits him an outlet.

Disastrous for your life and mine were the philosophical consequences of Zuckerman's conclusion. Anthropology—the science of man—accepted zoology's word that primate society is based on sex, and reasoned most logically that since human society is not, then society as we know it must be of human invention owing no allegiance to biological evolution. Then sociology—the science of society —accepting anthropology's word that our society is of human invention, reasoned logically that the more unpleasant aspects of our social life, such as war and crime and a general reluctance to love our neighbours, must arise from special conditions of the human circumstance. And so you and I, accepting the word of a variety of authorities who should know what they are talking about, tend to reason that if the pressure of economic want, for example, could be erased from the world scene, then we should witness a marked diminution of crime, an inevitable relaxation of warlike moods, and a release of social energy for love's harmonious purposes. The hounds of our anxieties bay at old, cold traces, while nature's foxes watch amused.

The romantic fallacy, which we shall investigate in its proper place, is something as old as Rousseau; it can scarcely be attributed to a handful of London baboons. But science's unwillingness to reappraise the evolutionary basis of human society in the light of observations later and more realistic than Zuckerman's, has done much to keep the doctrine of human uniqueness a going concern to this very date. And for you and for me it has been a great pity, since Zuckerman's conclusion became obsolete exactly two years after it was presented.

In 1934 Johns Hopkins University published the classic monograph by the American zoologist, C. R. Carpenter, *The Behavior and Social Relations of Howling Monkeys*. For eight months, over a period of two years, Dr. Carpenter had kept under systematic observation the activities of some twenty-three troops of howling monkeys on an island in Gatun Lake, in Panama. During the course of his study he created and perfected techniques for the observation of animal behaviour in a state of nature which were to become standard in modern zoology. But he did far more than that. He discovered the role of territory in primate society.

Any reader of Dr. Carpenter's monograph must gain one impression overwhelming all others: that never again could science rest content with conclusions formed solely in zoos. But science rested content. Just how content, and for what an astonishingly long period, may be judged from an article appearing in the *Scientific American* in September, 1960. The article is by the American anthropologist Dr. Marshall B. Sahlins, and concerns the origins of human society. It appears as one section in a general survey of the story of man reflecting the most authoritative views and information to be published on the subject in many years.

"Comparison between the findings of primate sociology with anthropological research," writes Dr. Sahlins, "suggests a startling conclusion. There is a quantum difference, at points a complete opposition, between even the most rudimentary human society and the most advanced subhuman primate one. The discontinuity implies that the emergence of human society required some suppression, rather than direct expression, of man's primate nature. Human social life is culturally, not biologically, determined.

"The decisive battle between early culture and human nature," Dr. Sahlins goes on, "must have been waged on the field of primate sexuality. The powerful social magnet of sex was the major impetus of subhuman primate sociability. This has been long recognized. But it was the British anatomist, Sir Solly Zuckerman—whose attention to the matter developed from observations of the almost depraved behaviour of baboons in zoos—who made sexuality the key issue of primate sociality."

Dr. Sahlins' conclusion is startling to no one but himself. It is a scientific restatement, 1960-style, of the philosophical conclusion of an eighteenth-century Neapolitan monk: *Society is the work of man.* It is just another prop, fashioned in the shop of science's orthodoxies from the

lumber of Zuckerman's myth, to support the fallacy of human uniqueness. And as we pass now into an exploration of the territorial instinct, it will be wise for us to keep in mind the explosive nature of the materials we are handling, as it will be wise for us to seek other than zoo-inspired authority on a subject which cannot be observed in a zoo.

In 1940 Dr. Carpenter published another monograph, *A Field Study in Siam of the Behavior and Social Relationships of the Gibbon,* no copy of which exists today even in the immense libraries of the British Museum. In this rarely-read work, at this early date in the contemporary revolution, it was possible for the American zoologist to state on the basis of his own studies and those of others: "It would seem that possession and defence of territory which is found so widely among the vertebrates, including both the human and subhuman primates, may be a fundamental biologic need. Certain it is that this possession of territory motivates much primate behaviour."

It was a pure scientist's confirmation of Walter Heape's inspired guess, made in 1931 in the classic *Emigration, Migration, and Nomadism.* Evidence was scanty in those days, but Heape had the courage to state: "There can, I think, be no question but that territorial rights are established rights among the majority of species of animals. . . . In fact, it may be held that the recognition of territorial rights, one of the most significant attributes of civilization, was not evolved by man but has ever been an inherent factor in the life history of all animals."

It is to the validity of such statements that we must direct our attention.

2

How prevalent in animal life is the territorial instinct? What natural purposes does it serve? How is territory gained? Defended? Against whom? What is a territory, anyway?

Mrs. Margaret Morse Nice, writing in 1941 in *The Midland Naturalist*, gave a definition of territory which remains today as good as any. "The theory of territoriality in bird-life is briefly this: that pairs are spaced through the pugnacity of males towards each other of their own species; that song and display of plumage are a warning to other males as well as an invitation to the female; that males fight primarily over territory, and not over females; that the owner of a territory is nearly invincible on his own ground; and finally, that male birds who fail to secure a territory form a reserve from which replacements come in the case of death of territorial owners."

What holds for birds holds by and large for all those vertebrate species in which competition for territory is on an individual basis. In such species it is sometimes difficult to separate territorial from sexual rivalry. But when we come to social species in which a group defends a territory against other groups, then no sexual objective can play a part. The territorial compulsion stands cleanly on its own. Why, then, does it exist?

When Eliot Howard published his observations concerning the relation of bird-life to territory and introduced to the natural sciences a new concept of animal behaviour, he believed that the sole motive of the male bird in seizing and defending an area of land was the protection of food supply for his nestlings. But questions arose. A rare species like the marsh warbler, possessing abundant food in relation to a small population, will fight as fiercely as any on behalf of property's privacy. Or we may consider the cuckoo. The female cuckoo lays her eggs in somebody else's nest. Parental concerns, with this single, happy gesture, become anybody's problem but the cuckoo's. Yet the nestless cuckoo asserts rights of territory.

Why is the male animal so singularly devoted to a place of his own?

The suggestion has been advanced that an instinct insuring the proper spacing of individuals will not only protect food supply but will also provide a check against the spread of disease. Yet certain species of fish defend watery territories in the commonly infectious seas. And fiddler crabs, fed and menaced by the same impartial tides, line the sands with their burrows centred each on a tiny, sandy estate approximately two yards wide.

That the territorial drive confers benefits on breeding and safety of the young must be obvious. Paul Errington's studies of muskrat colonies in the American Middle West show that the number of breeding pairs tolerated by a given habitat tend to remain similar from year to year. Droughts, hard winters, plagues, or an access of foxes may cast notable shadows on the pleasures of muskrat life. But it is as if for any specific area there exists some threshold of security, and behind that threshold life goes on. The laws of territory make sure that muskrat families will divide up the area in no greater number than the threshold of security can sustain.

Good times may come to the muskrat community, and over-population threaten its future. The foxes may relax; but the demand for territory never. Surplus muskrats are driven out of the home range to find new ones for themselves in the unfamiliar countryside. Some succeed. But a variable number continue their footloose, hazardous wandering, and of them Errington paints a sad picture: "A harassed and battered lot, they congregate about the fringes of areas dominated by muskrats already in residence. Transients, they form a biological surplus largely doomed by one medium or another."

Nature, by instilling in the individual a demand for exclusive living space, insures two consequences: First, that a minimum number of individuals in any population will be enabled to breed in relative security and pass on in fair certainty the conformation of their kind. And second, that the surplus will be cast to the wolves; to the owls, to the foxes, to the plagues and famines and lonely, unfamiliar places, there to make the most of perilous conditions or to die.

What might be called the economic benefits of territory are plain. As easily glimpsed are the advantages of a familiar homeplace to an appetizing creature preoccupied by defence against hungry predators. There is an old axiom, the more the cats, the fewer the mice. But like many other axiom, it is not quite true. Soviet ecologists have given us a statistical determination of the territorial factor in prey-predator relationships.

One Russian field study was made in Siberia, the other in the Caucasus. The first considered the rate at which newly arrived predator birds—hawks and owls—killed off such local rodents as voles and hamsters The study revealed that in one month the rodent population in a Siberian field was reduced from fifty-eight per acre to nine. But then a surprising thing happened. Despite the best efforts of hawks and owls, the voles and hamsters were reduced little further.

The second study considered the fate of field mice and came to comparable conclusions. Although predator birds ate up mice at the alarming rate of one-and-a-half per cent of the mouse population per day, still a time came when the hunting got thin. Catches became rare and the remaining mouse population virtually constant. Natural cover had proved sufficient to protect the survivors. The best burrows and the most secret runways had provided sanctuary for the wise ones who knew their homeland best. Territory protected the selected few, and the hawks went hungry.

Rules that apply to the hunted should apply equally to the hunter. The predator possessing a hunting territory should possess also the best chance for dinner. But the absence of authoritative scientific literature on the behaviour of carnivores is as startling as it is stark. The ways of leopard and lion and wolf may have gripped the imagination of ordinary men since the time of our oldest records; they have failed singularly to grip the attention of contemporary scientists. And so, since the behaviour of captive predators holds small significance and the voluminous anecdotal literature of wild ones small reliability, I have found it necessary to supplement the observations of science with certain observations of my own. But even as the reader is alerted to the significance of predator behaviour in the light of our own predatory origins, he must also be warned that the evidence here presented is derived from that most dubious of sources, the author.

South Africa's famous game reserve, the Kruger National Park consists of nine thousand square miles of bushveld bordering on Portuguese East Africa. In the southern areas of the park around the Lower Sabie River the game has been so conditioned by the presence of tourist cars that its behaviour cannot be accepted as normal. North of the Olifants River, however, in the less visited area from Shingwidzi camp to the Limpopo River, conditions as in the great Central African reserves differ little from that of an unpenetrated state of nature.

Game wardens in the Kruger reserve estimate that an adult lion must consume on an average one fair-sized antelope a week. Yet the antelope population of the reserve is not over half a million, while the lion population is more than two thousand. Competition, any arithmetic must reveal, makes the life of a lion not so easy as it looks, and an exclusive hunting territory a valuable property. Every lion pride, normally a single family, maintains and defends such an exclusive domain. In the northern regions of the Kruger reserve it averages six miles in radius, varying in accordance with the size of the pride. The territory will be defended against the invasion of another pride by all adults, regardless of sex. Death from territorial conflict must be placed second among causes of lion mortality. But whether or not that most nerve-shattering of sounds, the night-time roar of the African lion, like bird-song is a territorial warning, I do not know. It may partially serve this end, although its function seems more likely to derive from the subtle tactics of the kill, which we shall inspect in another context.

Most abstract of all territories that we shall investigate, that of the lion occupies no fixed spot. In South-West Africa the springbok and in Tanganyika the wildebeest migrate with the rains and the fresh, green grass over enormous areas. Each antelope herd maintains and defends a moving territory determined by available grazing and the pressure of competitive herds. The lions follow, maintaining and defending their own moving territories determined by the available lion food and the pressure of competitive lions. The moving territory may seem a complicated piece of real estate to a business man, but so far as I know it is accepted as simple enough by the lion.

There is another type of hunting territory of a circular and less complex sort that may exist in western Uganda. There, below the Mountains of the Moon and lying directly on the equator, sprawls flat, vast Queen Elizabeth Park, vista upon vista of grass and brush and euphorbia trees like a landscape over-stylized to suggest some lonely theme. In such an equatorial situation lion food remains fairly stationary. And it was against this setting that a warden in the park told me a strange story. A few years ago, over a fairly long period, a lion pride appeared regularly, every three weeks, in the vicinity of Mweya Lodge. Mysteriously it would appear, remain a few days, then mysteriously vanish. So regular were its appearances that observers seeking a glimpse of lion could schedule a visit to the lodge in advance with fair probability that lions would be there. The warden had no explanation.

I remembered, however, a rare predatory study made by Frank Illingworth. Wolf packs pursue a circular territory from twenty to a hundred miles in circumference. The pack moves about the circuit a few miles a day, denning up at night, leaving the circumference only to make a kill. So regular is its movement that a hunter knowing the habits of a pack can time its arrival at a given point sometimes to the half-hour. Had the lions of the Queen Elizabeth Park patrolled such a circular territory, then their appearances at the lodge would be explained.

Among the exotic types of animal possession is the double territory of the hippopotamus. No animal society is so cuddlesome or so fixed in its territorial location as the hippo by day. A hippo school in an African river consists of a tightly pressed mass of blubber not over fifty feet in diameter containing from five to thirty separate and distinct monsters. I cannot suggest why the hippo should so adore the touch of his fellow hippo, or why the entire school should show such devotion to its particular portion of watery home-land. In the game reserves of southern Africa, where the hippo is rare, a school will be found in such a river as the Crocodile or the Luvuvhu. Game authorities may safely construct a road miles long to an observation point above the school. The hippos will stay put, this year, next year, and for years thereafter.

The hippopotamus, however, is a grazing creature who must overwhelm vast quantites of fodder to sustain his bulk. And so he comes out of the river at night to feed. In southern Africa he has little competitive problem. But in Central Africa tens of thousands of hippo, around such Uganda lakes as Edward and George and the connecting Kazinga channel, and around such Congo rivers as the Rutshuru and Ruindi, must travel miles every night to compete for grazing. On such grounds he will establish and defend a second territory, of a moving character like the antelope's, its location determined by available grass and hippo competition.

The territorial instinct may be fulfilled in many a way, depending upon the nature of the species. And a territory solely possessed may confer many a benefit on its proprietor: assurance of food supply whether for carnivore or vegetarian; spacing of individuals in a habitat; sorting of the fit from the misfit; attraction for mates; security against the predator. But while we may speak of benefits and purposes, the animal staking out a claim seizes simply for reasons of seizing. If man is so rarely conscious of the ultimate reasons for his actions, it seems highly improbable that the animal should be better informed. And he will fulfill his territorial instinct, as has been spectacularly demonstrated, whether or not benefit will accrue.

During the course of his studies of primate societies, Dr. C. R. Carpenter settled 350 rhesus monkeys from India on a small island off Puerto Rico. It was a famous experi-

ment combining the behaviour of animals in a wild state
with conditions of laboratory study and control. Many conclusions were derived from the experiment, and we shall
refer to others in the course of this narrative. But the
startling conclusion concerning territory will concern us
now.

The monkeys had been gathered from random sources
in India. They survived the misfortune of a bad sea voyage
on which conditions prevailed that can only be described as
animal anarchy. But arriving at Santiago Island they entered what any primate must regard as a monkey Utopia.
There was ample space, thirty-six acres for a few hundred
individuals. No leopards haunted their nocturnal hours, or
pythons their day-time excursions. There was food in
abundance distributed daily and evenly by the island care-
takers. Yet within one year the whole monkey community
divided itself into social groups, each holding and defending a permanent territory and living in permanent hostility
with its neighbours.

3

When Eliot Howard confronted his critics in the early
1920's with the radical observation that male birds conduct
their competitive struggles not on behalf of attractive females, but rather on behalf of attractive properties, romance died hard. He cited the case of migrant species.
Among these, the males arrive in advance of the females.
In a bird-world undistracted by female presence claims
are staked, quarrels fought, conquests trumpeted, and the
weak cast out. When the females arrive, the struggle is
over.

There was an answer: that the male conducts his territorial conflicts with the image of the female in mind.

It was not a very good answer, but one must remember
how important was the principle at stake. In any event,
Howard met the objection with the case of a resident bird.
During the winter the lapwing flocks associate cheerfully
on neutral feeding grounds. When breeding time nears, the
males desert the flock to establish territories in the breeding
area. Here conditions of warfare promptly prevail. Until
each successful male lapwing has established his claim

there is nothing but conflict. But if, in the midst of the struggles, a few males return to the feeding flock *containing females*, peace instantly returns. In the presence of females there is only amity amongst male lapwings. In the absence of females, on the territorial battleground, there is only conflict.

To this there was no answer, not even a poor one.

The urge to assert exclusive possession over a territory, as I have stated, is a thing apart. It may or may not be associated with the seasonal stirring of sexual forces. It may or may not have direct connection with the assurance of food supply, or the protection of the nestling brood. It may or may not reflect an instinctual defence against that ever-present animal nightmare, the predator. The drive to possess and to protect what is one's own is an instinct on its own.

The reed bunting seems a sensible enough bird, as birds go. Yet Howard once observed a pair of reed buntings in a state of extreme commotion. They had a nest, and young; and the object of their anxiety was a weasel. They chorused their hysterical disapproval of the invader, flew at him, sought to distract his attention from their nest. The weasel was not to be put off by either insults or the wind of wings. He lingered. The hysteria mounted. Male and female alike resorted to all those diversionary tricks for which birds are famous. Yet three times during the course of the incident the male bird turned from his attack on the weasel to drive off a third reed bunting seeking to invade his territory. The territorial command worked in opposition to, and took precedence over, the command to protect his young.

Before we consider the methods by which various birds establish territories, let us glance at the seal. The migrant bulls, like male birds, arrive first at the intended rookery. There is a deal of shoving and hauling and roaring and gouging. Territories are established. Only then do the females arrive. Now bulls acquire harems that vary in size according to the extent of their real estate holdings, an extent already determined by the relative power and pugnacity of the individual bulls.

The seal's polygamous disposition presents him with domestic headaches unsavoured by the decently monogamous bird. He is immediately surrounded by squabbling females. Neither does he receive any proper reward for conquest and glory. The females have arrived regrettably pregnant. While gestation is polished off and the young are born and reared, the male must content himself with barking at his fellows and driving off bachelors whose invasion of his territory can hardly be motivated by a desire to share his paternal role. Only when the rookery ceases to be a nursery and all infants are found seaworthy, does the female become sexually responsive. Now at last the harem may test the validity of territorial boasts.

Migratory birds establish their territories in a manner little different from the seal. The males have as a rule a fortnight before the arrival of the females in which to settle their differences and establish freeholds. Then the females come. The male without a holding is ignored. The propertied male advertises his advantages and secures a mate worthy of his holding. Family life begins.

For the resident bird, however, the same process is a little slower, a little more complex, and far more revealing. Reed buntings, for example, winter on bare, arable land, or on seed fields, or near watercourses. Flocks are small and behave without regard for individual sexual differences. It is a monotonous life searching for food on the winter acres, and hazardous, too, when the freeze strikes hard. Predators develop a hunger the equal of their prey. Survival, one would think, would surmount all other instincts until spring. And yet, towards the middle of February, the males desert the flock. They isolate themselves on marshy ground perhaps still frozen. There the male selects some willow or alder, sings, preens himself. Now and again he seeks the feeding ground. But gradually he spends more and more time on his selected territory until finally it becomes his only home.

The yellow bunting pursues a similar course. One discovers them frequently in winter's early dusk roosting in flocks half-hidden in a roadside hedge. Then in early February, even before the reed bunting, the male takes leave of the flock. He finds his freehold and his particular perch—a gate, a bush, a railing, a fence-post—and gradually it becomes the central point of his life. By persistent song he announces to the world of yellow buntings that this place is his. By persistent, darting flight he drives off all intruders.

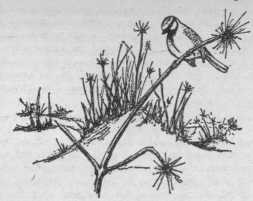

The chaffinch, too, when instinct stirs, must leave his flock no matter what the weather. His time comes later, towards the end of February, but seldom even then has the cold relaxed its grip. He is a friendly, sociable creature; all through the winter you may find the chaffinch, as the early dark comes on, perched in cheerful flocks in some holly tree or other. With the last week of February the dark comes little later, the bitter wind little less icy, the food no more abundant. The nesting season lies still many weeks ahead, yet for no apparent reason the male will forsake the congenial holly to seek his acre and his oak. With all the dark days yet ahead, and food still short, he will spend what energy he has to insure his isolation.

As late as 1923 it was still possible for a competent naturalist to write that "birdsong is an expression of the joy of life, and the mocking bird, above all, is the most joyous." Just fourteen years later the anti-romantic revolution could make possible the statement from another competent naturalist that "birdsong exists either seldom or never as an expression of peace or pleasure; all or most is produced for practical purposes."

Birdsong takes place when and if the male gets his territory. So long as buntings are joined in flocks on the neutral feeding ground, the male never sings. Only when he finds that perch which will be the advertisement of his territorial existence—his alder, his gate, his willow bough—does the will to sing enchant him. Male lapwings fight and sing, and sing and fight, as they establish their freeholds apart from the flock. As we have seen, on those occasions when males return to neutral ground their hostility is suspended; so likewise is their song. Eliot Howard once kept track of a flock of turtle-doves numbering upwards of a hundred. They fed on an eight-acre stretch of field where seeds were plentiful, while flying back and forth to a nearby range where territories were being established. Not on a single occasion did Howard hear their characteristic coo anywhere but on the territorial range.

Birdsong from the female is unquestionably an announcement of sexual readiness. But it occurs in response to the male's announcement of territorial readiness. Furthermore it is an error of observation to associate birdsong exclusively with the mating season, for it begins when the male deserts the female and goes to seek his fortune. Then and for some time he will sing as the cock crows for male ears alone. Habitually—whether before or after the arrival of females—he sings from that particular perch which he makes his throne and from which he proclaims his sovereignty. When the male leaves his territory—whether before or after mating—he rarely sings. But immediately upon his return he goes directly to his throne and announces that the king is again in residence.

Mrs. Nice has given us a careful description of a territorial conflict between two male song sparrows which she observed in Ohio. One was the owner, the other the challenger. Mrs. Nice had premised her observations by banding 343 song sparrows seeking territories on forty floodplain acres near the city of Columbus. When the struggle for living space was concluded, each successful male had acquired a realm of approximately three-quarters of an acre. But this left a considerable surplus of unpropertied outcasts. And it was one of these proletarians who chose to challenge a member of the privileged class.

The challenger approached the disputed territory in watchful silence. The owner, on watchful guard, sang. The challenger, darting from bush to bush, explored all approaches while the champion, likewise darting about, blocked every avenue. Now and again the challenger made a foray onto the disputed freehold; he was repelled. Again and again he attacked; again and again he was beaten off. At last the challenger accepted defeat and retired to the mortal doom of the surplus, unmated, unpropertied male, while the champion returned to his fruitful throne. Through all the long engagement the proprietor had never failed to sing eight to ten times a minute. The challenger in no single instance had broken his silence.

The male bird sings of his possession. His call is distinctive throughout all his species since it is directed to the ears of his species alone. He sings to all other males that he is a bird of property and is prepared to defend what is his own. When he sings to the female, it is not to advise her that he is sexually ready—since he is a male his readiness may be assumed—but that being a bird of property he is worthy of her notice. It is a piece of information essential to the female ear.

Eliot Howard, in all his long career, never knew of a male bird, with territory, to lose a mate; nor of a male bird without territory to gain one.

4

By what means are the boundaries of a territory defended? And why should the proprietor almost invariably win?

Natural selection has through all its long history shown a mighty open-mindedness towards any new idea that works. Random mutation may present the kudu with horns like elongated corkscrews, the impala with horns like a bent-in lyre, the waterbuck with horns like a graceful pitchfork, and the gemsbok with horns like lances. None fail to perform the necessary function, so all have been tolerated. And natural selection has been no more dogmatic in the evolution of territorial character, size, or means of defence.

We have inspected the moving territory of the lion, the circular territory of the wolf, and the double territory of the hippo. The intensely territorial domestic dog defends a property coinciding precisely with his master's fence lines. Seasonal variations affect the moose. In winter he confines himself to a restricted "moose yard". In summer he expands his territory to include from three to ten square miles. Arboreal creatures such as birds and primates determine three-dimensional territories by volume. The gibbon will defend from thirty to one hundred acres according to the heights of the trees. A squirrel will defend three large trees or five small ones. Any variation in the size or character of a territory will be tolerated by natural selection so long as the variation acts in the interests of species survival. Even neutral territory, if it is to provide survival value, will be encouraged.

Antelope observe the neutrality of the water-hole. Most resident birds establish individual territories only through the breeding season, and observe the neutrality of the feeding ground throughout the winter. It serves the interest of dogs to affect two different personalities: to be a hostile belligerent on his master's territory, and an amiable tail-wagger in the neutrality of the street. But the crowded conditions of seal rookeries have produced neutral territories of the most startling order. Narrow corridors of access lead from the sea to properties boasting no riparian rights. It is to the interest of the species that such corridors exist, and their neutrality is respected by every jostling bull in the rookery.

As anything goes that works, concerning the character of a territory, so anything goes that provides its means of defence. It is the male, for example, who almost invariably is the bearer of the territorial instinct, although his mate may assist in territorial defence. But natural selection has tolerated exceptions even to this all-but-universal law.

The phalarope is a water-bird related vaguely to the sandpiper and it frequents the Arctic in summer. It is a freak. Some chance mutation once affected the phalarope's ancestral line and in consequence certain sexual characteristics suffered reversal. The male is dun-coloured, the female brightly feathered. The female arrives first at the breeding grounds and conducts the territorial scramble. The male arrives later and incubates the eggs while she defends the home place. The system works and evolution shrugs.

Another exception to the universal rule that the male conducts territorial defence is that of the Cuban lizard. Unlike the phalarope, however, the male has everything arranged his way. The Cuban lizard is the master of a territory no more than ten or twelve square yards in extent. Like the seal he is polygamous, and on his territory he rules a harem of three or four females. But the little lizard wastes no energy on hostility's eternal demands. By the most ingenious system known to nature he allots to the female the role of territorial defender, and guarantees her co-operation by the simplest of means. He displays enormous appetite for every passing female. The harem responds to his philandering fancy by guarding the territory with a vigilance beyond anything that nature might normally demand.

For an inquiry into more normal means of territorial defence, however, we may turn to the work of the Austrian naturalist, Konrad Lorenz, whose studies have become familiar to many readers through his endearing book, *King Solomon's Ring*. There Lorenz describes the establishment and defence of a territorial boundary by that formidable fish, the European stickleback. It is a charming portrait applicable to many a belligerent male in the animal world.

The stickleback, like the Siamese fighting fish, is a species in which the male, not the female, undertakes the building of the nest and the care of the young. Such behaviour in the bird-world stamps a species a freak; it does not, however, in the world of fish. One may wonder, nevertheless, if both European stickleback and Siamese fighting fish might not better leave such duties to the ladies; for the males of both species nurse, besides the young, the vilest of dispositions.

The stickleback is a dangerous-seeming creature constructed apparently for mortal combat. His back is decorated with a deadly spine. His aggressiveness appears uncompromising. His approach to family responsibilities is of a stern order, and he entertains no romantic impulses until he has dug a hole in a sandy bottom, constructed in it a nest built of plant fibre and cemented by kidney secretion, and established in the neighbourhood an unassailable territory. There is a difference, however, between the combativeness of the European stickleback and of his eastern counterpart. The Siamese fighting fish, more frequently than not, leaves either himself or his opponent a tattered corpse at the end of a watery duel; the stickleback, on the other hand, is capable of compromise. In this characteristic he is fairly typical of aggressive masculinity in the animal world. Lorenz never knew of a stickleback that died of his convictions.

"The basic principle of his fighting," writes Lorenz, "is that my home is my castle." The fighting inclination may be stated with mathematical exactness: it decreases in direct proportion to the distance from the nest. The stickleback having built his castle prowls the adjacent water glaring about in a search for intruders of his own species. He encounters one. It is a male stickleback who has likewise finished a castle on an adjacent territory. The less-than-mortal battle is joined.

The intruding stickleback has ventured too far from home. He flees. Our stickleback pursues him with every apparent intention of ramming him with the formidable spine and disposing of the intolerable neighbour for good and all. But a mysterious thing happens. As the panic-stricken neighbour approaches his own castle, his courage returns. Simultaneously the courage of our own stickleback begins to wane; it is as if, suddenly, he began to wonder how things were going back home. As suddenly the roles are reversed. The pursued neighbour becomes the pursuer. Our stickleback is in flight. Now they return deep into our stickleback's territory until again the roles reverse. Courage rises in the one, wanes in the other. The combat turns again.

It is a process all but interminable. Yet with each death-defying excursion into enemy territory, the courage of the pursued stickleback returns perceptibly sooner, even as do the second thoughts of the pursuer. The alley of battle shortens. The fish turn more quickly. At last there is no more flight and pursuit. The sticklebacks, weaving menacingly, glower at each other through an invisible wall. It is their territorial boundary. A balance of courage—or of cowardice—has been struck.

Dr. Carpenter in 1934 published a similar observation in his revolutionary monograph on the howling monkey. For eight lonely months, as we have seen, he observed twenty-odd communities on Barro Colorado Island in Panama. But the months, while lonely, could scarcely have been boring, for the eminent American zoologist had found an animal worthy of his patience.

The howler, like a character in a good farce play, achieves the greatest hilarity when he is at his most earnest, and suggests the most universal implications when he is at his most hilarious. He is a creature almost black, with an old-time comedian's bare face and chin whiskers. Although he is nearly as large as the baboon, he leads a life entirely arboreal. Like most New World monkeys, he has a prehen-

sile tail, and he uses it with equal facility to anchor himself at night when he sleeps, to brush away insects, and to manipulate his own or the next monkey's genitals. For all-round, unashamed, disgraceful conduct the howler acknowledges no equal in the animal world.

The howling monkey draws his name from a most antisocial habit of greeting the day, each dawn, with a cry as mournful as it is deafening. The Spanish conquistadores were the first to lead depressed lives in consequence. As far back as the seventeenth century we find colonial administrators regretting that they had ever left Spain, and recording their doubts as to the likelihood of ever being able to massacre the last of their melancholy neighbours. These were the days, of course, when birds sang for the unbearable joy of life, while howlers mourned its sadness.

The howling monkey distributed worse things than gloom from his home in the tree-tops. The early Spaniards, in their misery, frankly recorded all; and so a second trait became part of the howler's tradition. This was his unwholesome habit of urinating or even defecating on intruders beneath his tree. Carpenter found the trait no myth; frequently the objects of his observation used him as a target. Howler apologists had evolved the hypothesis that the presence of man produced fear in the animal, and fear an emptied bladder. Carpenter disagreed. On too many occasions he spotted a male who in turn had just spotted him. He observed the unscrupulous animal making his way through the branches—now and again camouflaging the movement by tearing off leaves and pretending to eat—until he had got the zoologist's range. Carpenter could testify to the purposefulness of the manoeuvre, to the time required, and sometimes, unfortunately, to the accuracy of the gunnery. With an objectivity admirable under the circumstances, Carpenter concluded that an average time of sixty seconds between the sighting of an intruder and a physiological consequence was a little too long to be attributed to fear. The howler repelling a potential enemy simply subscribes without inhibition to the doctrine of any means to an end, and so makes use of those meanest weapons with which nature has endowed him.

Not all the howler's ways, however, can be regarded as deplorable; some we may even admire. The creatures live in social groups of twenty or thirty, defending each a social territory of approximately three hundred acres. The dawn-and-dusk vocalizing serves as warning to all neighbouring groups as to the home group's location. If the chorus is loud, it is because the territory is large. If the mood seems to human ears one of unendurable melancholy, then its quality must be ascribed more to the disposition of man than to the disposition of the howler. He is in fact an amiable sort of fellow. Seldom does physical violence mar his day. He has even developed through vocal ability a defence for his territory by means short of war.

Unlike the baboon troop which scatters far and wide in search of food, the howlers' society clusters close all day feeding in two or three trees. In the course of a month the group moves from tree-camp to tree-camp throughout its territory. Carpenter mapped the movements, and found that the closer to the territorial centre the clan is disposed, the more certain is the direction of its movements. But as the group nears the fringes of its territory, a zigzag quality appears on the chart. Familiar paths beckon; unfamiliar repel. In its hourly course the clan falls more and more into vocal dispute, into hesitation and into uncertain leadership. And when it reaches the actual border of an adjacent territory, the group sharply and invariably turns back on itself. As the stickleback draws courage from his castle, the howler draws confidence from the familiarity of his territorial heartland.

There were twenty-three clans on Barro Colorado Island when Carpenter studied the community, and each had its fixed estate. But while a border might be recognized by the pressure of strangeness, it was established by contact with adjacent clans.

In all his studies of primate societies, Carpenter never

observed two adjacent groups living in anything but total hostility. The howling monkey is no exception. But whereas the baboon, for example, must express his hostility by violent action, the howler like the stickleback has found means of non-violent compromise without loss of belligerent satisfaction. He vocalizes.

No flights of human invective pioneered by modern diplomacy and displayed so engagingly in the United Nations' Security Council can touch the howler in his older and more sophisticated substitute for war. When two groups sight each other, each on the fringe of its territory, all break into total rage. Males, females, juveniles and infants become ants on a hot plate, leaping through the branches, scudding through the tree-tops, screeching, barking, chattering in frenzy. The forest cathedral becomes a green asylum for its insane habitants, and the howls of apparent melancholia become the shrieks of the truly demented. For thirty minutes rage has its way; then both sides retire from the field of glory. Losses have been nil; territory has been held inviolate; anger has been magnificent and satisfaction for both sides a maximum. Carpenter records that if an intrusion has indeed taken place, then the home team always wins.

The stickleback and the howling monkey has each through its history developed means of territorial defence which offer the greatest possible delight to the soul with the least possible damage to the body. The same cannot be said of all species. Even so, physical conflict between the proprietors of adjacent territories tends to be at a maximum during the period of establishment. And establishment tends to be permanent, except among species which hold territories only during the breeding season. When Carpenter returned to Barro Colorado Island the second year he found little change in the positions of the various howler clans. And there is a record of a South African farmer who faced for thirty-five years the same troop of baboons raiding his orchards.

Permanence of territory acts as a factor reducing conflict. But also there prevails throughout all territorial animals a varying respect for the rights of the neighbour. The respect exists despite the universal law that territorial neighbours live in eternal and unremitting hostility. The bird attacks an intruder not with the objective of destroy-

ing him or of seizing his territory in reprisal. Victory is accomplished by driving him away.

A heron will fish at a definite location. His neighbour will fish at another location. But the first heron will not trespass on the next preserve, even when the neighbour is absent. Certain predator birds have hunting territories, among them the golden eagle. This mighty hunter will on occasion condescend to share his territory with the raven. But the raven respects the sovereignty of the eagle and will not hunt while the eagle is hunting.

To use the anthropomorphic term, respect, is of course inexact. If a herd of hartebeest in Kenya grazes to a certain line and no farther, it is out of instinctual certainty that in any conflict on an opponent herd's territory the home team, as Carpenter has pointed out, has always the best of it. A South African naturalist named Fitzsimons reported in the days before the use of the term, territory, that on blue wildebeest feeding grounds each herd had an area of its own sharply marked; that trespassers were driven away; and that the promptness of a trespasser's retreat would seem to indicate some consciousness of having been caught in the wrong club-house. It is again the story of the stickle-back; courage wanes in foreign parts, waxes in familiar places.

How powerful and mysterious is the pull of the home-place on animal behaviour has been the subject of many a human meditation. Some of us may recall from childhood the quickening pace of our grandfather's horse when at the end of a day's shopping in the village the turn of a single corner set a course for home. Or tales may have come to us of the dog banished to a new home a thousand miles away who unexpectedly turns up, one bright morning, on his former master's doorstep. Or we may puzzle over the inexplicable capacity of the salmon to spend years in the seas, then to return unerringly to his natal brookside, there to spawn and die. We may even meditate on the ill-defined, unremarked, rarely guessed influences of a force called nostalgia as it affects human affairs.

Eugène Marais, an untrained South African naturalist, once performed a homely experiment that by careful laboratory extension might give us a quantitative measurement for the power of animal nostalgia. Marais observed two columns of red ants moving along an African roadside. They proceeded in opposite directions, as ants do, one towards the nest and one away from it. The column leaving the nest was unburdened; each ant of the returning column carried from a neighbouring field a seed very nearly as large as itself.

To begin his experiment, Marais scratched a narrow ditch across the path of the two columns and filled the little ditch with water. On either side of the ditch there immediately gathered a milling mass of frustrated ants, confused as only ants can be when they encounter an unexpected obstacle. Marais then offered them a way. He placed a straw across the ditch for a bridge. And then he sat back to observe the startling climax.

The unencumbered ants proceeding *away from the nest* tried the bridge, hesitated, explored its uncertainties again, backed away, and in the end rejected its hazards. But the column of ants each handicapped by the burden of a gigantic seed hesitated not at all and proceeded nimbly and with confidence across the swaying straw. They were going home.

Territoriality is a vertebrate instinct touching fish and amphibia, reptiles and mammals and birds. While it therefore must be several hundreds of millions of years old, still it came into being after the evolutionary separation of the ancestral insect line from our own. The red ant like other insects establishes and defends no territory. But the pull of the home-place is a force that pervades us all. And there can be no doubt but that the superior power of the territorial proprietor, while benefiting from superior knowledge of familiar terrain, still finds its most profound convictions in the ancient, mysterious and perhaps unknowable headwaters of animal nostalgia.

The world of the animal is a world full of fear. There is an old saying that in a state of nature the object of existence is to obtain one's dinner without providing someone else with his. In such a world the creature who has established a trusted territory has made for himself a trustworthy ally. The alliance may benefit him in any of numerous ways, determined by the particular problems which afflict his species: it may guarantee his food supply; it may shelter his young; it may give him an edge on the leopard that inflicts delirium on his nights. Or territory may give him status in the eyes of the female, a creature necessarily dedicated to the long view of things; and so he may gain a better mate and more worthy young. Whatever the advantage that an individual animal or a particular animal society may gain from the powerful territorial drive, it is evident that chances for survival are bettered. And natural selection, as blind as a cave fish concerning ultimate purposes yet as shrewd as a cat concerning the moment's situation, lays the long finger of survival on those in whom the drive runs strongest and the thumb of death on the remainder. So an instinct flowers.

Chapter 3

The Society of Animals

Tragic, unknown Eugène Marais, the South African naturalist whose little experiment with the red ants I recorded in the last chapter, was the purest genius that the natural sciences have seen in this century. And no discussion of animal societies can open without homage to his name.

Marais began his work at the turn of the century and was the true pioneer of all that may lie ahead of us in our new understanding of ourselves. His was the first eye to see clearly and with only occasional anthropomorphism the behavior of man in the behaviour of animals. His were the first studies of both insect and primate societies to be made in terms of their relevance to the origins of our own. His was the first mind to grasp without inhibition at that taboo subject, the evolution of the human soul. And his were the first prolonged observations of primate behaviour to be made in a state of nature. But that I have not included his studies in the history of the contemporary revolution is for a very simple reason. They remained, with one extraordinary exception, unknown to science, for they were written in Afrikaans.

Marais was many things besides a naturalist. He was a poet, an advocate, a journalist, a partially trained doctor, a morphine addict, and a suicide. He came from one of the oldest of Afrikaner families, and at the outbreak of the Boer War was in London studying for the Bar. He was interned. He completed his studies and somehow managed to get out of England. War's end found him in Rhodesia smuggling arms and ammunition to the exhausted Boers.

The defeat of his people left as heavy a scar on Eugène Marais as it left on his country. Superb though his command of the English language may have been—and I have read many of his letters—still on only one or two occasions did he ever publish in any language but Afrikaans. And so deep was his depression immediately following the war that indicating that one more abandoned tunnel had collapsed renouncing the society of men he retreated to the Waterberg, a mountain fastness in the northern Transvaal, and accepted the society of animals. From a dramatist's standpoint, it is the ironical premise of Marais' tragic life that a single action created of a sensitive man the century's greatest naturalist and at the same time condemned him to lifelong obscurity.

Marais went to live on a farm near Doornhoek in a high mountain valley. The year, one must calculate, was 1903. The valley was a lonely wilderness. In a hidden kloof along the ledges of a rocky, towering krans, a troop of three hundred baboons made a sleeping place protected from view by the massive limbs of a giant wild fig tree. Now once more the effects of the Boer War acted as a determinant in Marais' life. The local farmers were still prisoners of war. For years the baboons had heard no gun fired, and to an extent had lost their fear of men. Marais could approach them. And he built a hut at the entrance of the kloof.

For three years—the longest sustained period of observation ever made of an animal society in the wild—Marais lived with and studied his troop. One by one the farmers returned from their prison camps and Marais found himself in the position of advocate for three hundred of nature's most congenital bandits. Out of his personal funds he compensated local farmers for damage done to their orchards. The guns remained still. But after three years baboon thievery at last surpassed human financial resource, and the study ended.

Marais published his observations as short essays in an Afrikaans newspaper. They remained untranslated and uncollected until 1939 when some appeared as a slim but unforgettable book, *My Friends the Baboons*. What had been revolutionary observations shortly after the turn of the century still remained revolutionary observations thirty-five years later. But by then Marais was dead.

One must evaluate with extreme care, however, all animal observations made at the earliest stage of Marais' career. He could not at the beginning be described even as a self-trained naturalist, for his self-training had only begun. Anthropomorphism unquestionably colours some of his conclusions. But his mind trained for law was disciplined and self-sceptical, and his intuitions were of the order of genius. The observations of baboon social behaviour made by a lonely, depressed, drug-addicted lawyer in the Waterberg fastness have stood up against the erosions of time rather better than have those of another South African, highly trained and world-famous, in the London zoo.

It was after his time with the baboons that Eugène Marais performed experiment after experiment with the most irreproachable scientific finesse. He became absorbed in the way of the insect, and spent years observing the mysteries of termite society. And his theories, constituting perhaps the highest flight made by any scientist of the century into the thin air of remote animal behaviour, are known in every corner of the world. But whether by coincidence or otherwise, we do not associate them with Marais' name. Not until the same year as *My Friends the Baboons,* when his *The Soul of the White Ant* was likewise published in London, did the strange circumstance become known outside of South Africa. In her preface to this volume Dr. Winifred de Kok, his translator, wrote:

"His years of unceasing work on the veld led Eugène Marais to formulate his theory that the individual nest of the termites is similar in every respect to the organism of the animal, workers and soldiers resembling red and white corpuscles, the fungus gardens the digestive organs, the queen functioning as the brain, and the sexual flight being in every respect analogous to the escape of spermatozoa and ova.

"About six years after these articles appeared, Maurice Maeterlinck published his book, *The Life of the White Ant,* in which he describes this organic unity of the termitary and compares it with the human body. This theory aroused great interest at the time and was generally accepted as an original one formulated by Maeterlinck. The fact that an unknown South African observer had developed the theory after many years of indefatigable labour was not generally known in Europe. Excerpts from Marais' articles had, however, appeared in both the Belgian and French press at the time of their publication in South Africa. Indeed, the original Afrikaans articles would have been intelligible to any Fleming, for Afrikaans and Flemish are very similar."

Marais, indeed, had sued the Nobel prize-winner, alleging that page after literal page had been taken from his writings and that Maeterlinck's scientific naivete had been such that he had even used terminology invented by Marais under the impression that it was common scientific language. Such an international law-suit was however beyond Marais' means to press, and so we cannot judge the merits of the case today. All we can record is the South African's deepening obscurity.

After 1915 he seems to have done little more scientific work. He continued as an off-and-on journalist and wrote some of the finest of Afrikaans poems. But morphine's evil magic now enclosed his life. Then at last in 1935 the English translation of his early primate stories was undertaken in London by Dr. de Kok.

I have read Marais' letters to his translator, and their context must be kept in mind: they were written at approximately the date when Dr. Carpenter's primate studies were first opening the door to an evolutionary understanding of human nature; they were written by a man who thirty years earlier had apprehended truths which probably still remain unpenetrated; and they were written by a man who within months would be dead.

The letters are gay, witty, cleanly phrased. He may speak of a certain South African publisher who "thinks I am too big a fool to be trusted with any transaction of a financial nature. Well, he should be able to judge, since he has fathomed all the depths and shoals of my soul in this particular respect—always to his own pecuniary advantage!" Or he might reflect with diffidence on the essays to be published two years later as *My Friends the Baboons*. "I have always been rather ashamed of these tales, they lie so far outside of the sphere of what I have always considered my real work. They appeared as feuilletons in an Afrikaans newspaper and were never intended to assume a more enduring apparition."

In his letters he reflects without bitterness on the Maeterlinck case, and without regret on his fatal preoccupation with the Afrikaans language. In the latter connection he reminisces about his earlier tutor, a missionary of the Church of England, about his life in London, and being called to the Bar in the Inner Temple after abandoning the results of a four-year medical course. "You will perhaps be astonished at what my psychological reactions were to this jumble. The most enduring result was that it made me far more bitter about the war than men who took part in it at a more advanced age and who had less to do with the English. It was for purely sentimental reasons that I refused to write in any language except Afrikaans, notwithstanding the fact that I am far more fluent and at my ease in English."

His English prose, which to his ruin he had refused to write, made the schoolboy efforts of American or English scientists seem a halting, clubfooted thing. But while Marais in his time had been the pioneer mind of modern zoology, alone and unarmed by vaguest precedents exploring the blue distant hills of future understanding, yet like every other Boer he had been above all a territorial animal. And no human consideration or rational demand could compete with the compulsions of an instinct so frustrated.

It is the later pages of the correspondence that one has the breathless sense of Eugène Marais again catching the scientific fire. He becomes absorbed in plans for the translation and publication of a second book, *The Soul of the White Ant*, which Dr. de Kok indeed fulfilled at a later date. This was to consist of his pre-Maeterlinck termite studies. And one finds him confiding to his translator the hope that he may assemble from old field notes and unpublished studies the material for another, a book which he had always anticipated as his greatest work, *The Soul of the Ape*. In one letter in late 1935 he deplores his bad health and inability to work: "I am writing this in bed under the spur and inspiration of pain." Then in the next letter he is transported. And no one reading his inspired letter a quarter of a century later could fail to be transported with him.

"You see that your kindly enthusiasm has infected me! ... You must know that a great deal of the work I did and my interpretation of the results will be new to science. No other worker in the field ever had the opportunities I had of studying primates under perfectly natural conditions. In other countries you are lucky if you catch a glimpse of the same troop twice in one day. I lived among a troop of wild baboons for three years. I followed them on their daily excursions; slept among them; fed them; learned to know each one individually; taught them to trust me and love me—and also to hate me so violently that my life was several times in danger. So uncertain was their affection that I had always to go armed, with a Mauser automatic under the left armpit like the American gangster! But I learned the innermost secrets of their lives. You will be surprised to learn of the dim and remote regions of the mind into which it led me. I think I discovered the real place in nature of the hypnotic condition in the lower animals and in man. I have an entirely new explanation of the so-called subconscious mind and the reason for its survival in man. I think I can prove that Freud's entire conception is based on a fabric of fallacy. No man can ever attain to anywhere near a true conception of the subconscious in man who does not know the primates under natural conditions. ... Please don't worry about the health business. It was silly of me to write in that strain—just a period of avernal gloom to which I am occasionally subject. Accept my thanks and salutations—Eugène Marais."

It was the last letter. The next, several months later, was from a friend in Pretoria informing Dr. de Kok of Eugène Marais' suicide. It recalled certain details of his stormy, drug-ravaged life, and closed: "I am sorry that you never had the privilege of meeting him. He was a handsome, well set-up man and a veritable courtier. We who were privileged to call him friend can never forget him."

As no gallery of modern art can fail to be haunted by the burning eyes of Vincent van Gogh, so the pages of no future science can fail to be haunted by the brooding, solitary, less definable presence of Eugène Marais. His was the first human mind to penetrate the secrets of the wonderful world of the animal, and to apprehend the legitimate mysteries of the wonderful world of man.

2

The most famous of all animal societies is that of the insect. More has been written about the life of the bee, of the ant, and of the termite than about all other prehuman societies combined. It is faint wonder that the mystery of insect behaviour so fascinated Marais at an early stage in his career. And so as we turn our investigating eye on those animal societies which may or may not have relevance to our evolutionary origins, let us begin with the insect so that we may dismiss him. He has virtually no relevance at all.

The studies and theories of insect societies presented to the world by Maeterlinck laid the foundation early in the century for some of the most hair-raising observations of animal behaviour ever to become part of our literature. One may turn today to Dr. Karl von Frisch's experiments with the honeybees' means of communication through dances for the most recent of the bewildering revelations. But my encounter in Kenya with a less-known insect than the bee provided me with at once my own most speechless moment, and my reason for dismissing the insect so briefly from the pages of this account.

There is a creature native to Kenya called the flattid bug, and I was introduced to it in Nairobi, some years ago, by the same great Dr. L. S. B. Leakey who today is churning up prehuman remains from the Olduvai Gorge by the bucketload. But to speak more precisely, what Dr. Leakey introduced me to was a coral-coloured flower of a raceme sort, made up of many small blossoms like the aloe or hyacinth. Each blossom was of oblong shape, perhaps a centimetre long, which on close inspection turned out to be the wing of an insect. The colony clinging to a dead twig comprised the whole of a flower so real in its seeming that one could only expect from it the scent of spring.

My real moment of astonishment, however, was yet to come. I had never seen anything comparable to the insect-flower before, but such protective imitations exist widely in nature. The stick bug provides so perfect an imitation of a twig that it even has thorns on its back. There is a moth that conceals itself among leaves and has wings equipped with a pattern of leaf veins. Among other moths unbelievable mimetic qualities, as they are called, have been developed. Some moths of a flavour congenial to birds have developed wing patterns in precise imitation of those bitter-tasting moths which birds fail to enjoy. How random mutation can account for such imitations must be left for geneticists to worry about. But imitation exists in the natural world, and to demonstrate my sophistication I expressed my admiration for the flattid bug, but threw in a few comparable examples.

Leakey listened with amusement, and agreed with me, but then mentioned an off-hand fact. The coral flower that the flattid bug imitates does not exist in nature. And my moment of speechlessness began. The flattid-bug society had *created* the form.

While I was suffering mental indigestion from the extraordinary statement, the eminent Kenyan—who two years later would discover the dawn-creature, *Zinjanthropus,* and start depositing new riddles on science's doorstep—now contributed further material to my flattid-bug bewilderment. He told me that at his Coryndon Museum they had bred generations of the little creatures. And from each batch of eggs that the female lays there will always be at least one producing a creature with green wings, not coral, and several with wings of in-between shades.

I looked closely. At the tip of the insect flower was a single green bud. Behind it were half a dozen partially matured blossoms showing only strains of coral. Behind these on the twig crouched the full strength of flattid-bug society, all with wings of purest coral to complete the colony's creation and deceive the eyes of the hungriest of birds.

There are moments when one's only response to evolutionary achievements can be a prickling sensation in the scalp. But still my speechlessness had not reached its most vacant, brain-numbed moment. Leakey shook the stick. The startled colony rose from its twig and filled the air with fluttering flattid bugs. They seemed no different in flight from any other swarm of moths that one encounters in the African bush. Then they returned to their twig. They alighted in no particular order and for an instant the twig was alive with the little creatures climbing over each other's shoulders in what seemed to be random movement. But the movement was not random. Shortly the twig was still and one beheld again the flower. The green leader had resumed his bud-like position with his vari-coloured companions just behind. The full-blown rank-and-file had resumed its accustomed place. A lovely coral flower that does not exist in nature had been created before my eyes.

A year or so later I was spending a night in a South African village with a party of scientists. One in the party was Dr. C. K. Brain, an amazing young man from the Transvaal Museum. Brain is a scientist's scientist, and I know of none so young on any continent who has acquired from achievements so varied a reputation quite so wide. He is a Rhodesian, from a family related to that of Eugène Marais. He has a long, distinguished face and his mode of expression, unlike my own, is as a rule one of long, distinguished silences. Brain was twenty-seven at that time, and had taken his doctorate in geology. He had followed this with three fruitful years in anthropology, in which time he had furnished palaeontology with its only comprehensive geological survey of all five australopithecine sites; had developed techniques of ancient dating never thought of before by anyone; and with his uncovering of primitive stone handaxes at Sterkfontein had made a discovery ranked by Dr. Kenneth P. Oakley of the British Museum as one of the anthropological milestones of the century. And now, at twenty-seven, to the dismay of anthropology, Brain was shifting his attention to zoology. He preferred, he said, living things to dead ones.

It was well after midnight in Potgietersrus that we sat still absorbed by late drinking and talking. And I brought up the flattid-bug, a properly mysterious subject for such an hour. None had ever heard of it. I described it in detail, and recalled my own sensations. How could such wonders be? All sat in silence. Then at last Brain stirred.

"What we have to face," he said, "is that the insect is a good three hundred million years older than we are."

The mammal has a history of little over a hundred million years. The insect goes back four hundred million. Evolution has had an extra three hundred million years in which to perfect the intuitions, the communications, and the social patterns of insect life. When we wonder at the societies of flattid-bug or bee, we stand in the position of

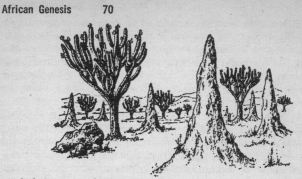

an infant race of superior endowment, struck with astonishment at the accomplishments of inferiors who we tend to forget are most definitely our elders.

Insects embarked on their own evolutionary course at a moment far back in the history of living things. We may study, if we will, the insect's individual behaviour, his collective psyche, and his society designed as a single organism in which the individual exists as a fraction of the whole. And our study must produce in us great wonder at what nature, given time, can construct from so little. But as we explore the natural world in search of those horizons of animal behaviour genetically related to our own, we may all but ignore the societies of insects. Their path took leave of ours too long ago, and has pursued its singular course through aeons beyond our infant comprehension.

The antiquity of insect society is a factor neglected in the meditations of many political minds. Some among us may regard the termitary as the perfect model of the modern state, and insect social behaviour as the ideal pattern for men. Even granting the wisdom of such an ideal, we must inspect the qualities of our patience. To perfect the subtle pattern of instincts which insect societies require took nature an extra three hundred million years.

3

Man is a vertebrate—which is to say that he possesses an articulated backbone, an evolutionary development that came about too late to affect the insect stream. It came about too late, likewise, to affect the destinies of squid and octopus, lobster and clam. And so we may say that the behaviour of a clam, for example, which boasts no backbone, is of less significance to man than the behaviour of a goldfish, which does. And when we find a characteristic prevalent among all branches of the vertebrates, such as the instinct to maintain and defend a territory, then we must mark it a significant instinct indeed.

Man is more especially a mammal. We do not lay eggs and our bodies are warm. The age of the mammals may be put at one hundred million years, and the behaviour of mammals must be of greater significance to the human investigator than the behaviour of vertebrates as a whole. And so the way of the lion and wolf, of the antelope and mouse, must light with greater intensity than the codfish the way of men.

But man is above all a primate. And so that arboreal family of living beings which emerged from the general mammalian background seventy million years ago, and to which our evolutionary history has been confined for an equal length of time, must concern us most. When we consider the social behaviour of apes and monkeys, we are looking at something very close to home. And when we consider as we shall do in later stages of this narrative the behaviour of the hunting primate—that predatory subfamily of which man is the only living example—then with one important difference we shall be looking at man himself.

What is a primate? It is of all animals the most difficult to define. At various stages of primate evolution various branches of the family have made themselves conspicuous. At one time it was the tree-shrews, at another the tarsiers or the lemurs. Monkeys and apes have for varying periods been those primates best illuminated by evolution's restless spotlight; and for the time being, at least, it is man. We shall consider with greater definition the character and the history of the primate family when we come to consider the emergency of the human stock. For the present it is enough to say that primates as a group are distinguished by their lack of specialization. One anatomical feature alone have they all developed beyond the common animal lot: the brain. From tree-shrew to man it would seem to be the secret of primate strength that he has combined an ex-

traordinary, oversized brain with a commonplace, under-
sized body. It is a body capable of doing any task, however, and it is handicapped by neither massiveness nor
special necessities, by neither hoofs nor horns nor monstrous appetites. But so unspecialized are we as a family
that when one seeks for a quick means of distinguishing
monkey from ape, one can only say that the ape swings
from the bough that the monkey runs on; that monkeys
have tails, the apes none.

Besides the enlarged brain, we primates possess another
trait—a physiological trait—held commonly and exclusively in the animal world. This is our freedom from the
sexual constraints of seasonal heat and rut. Female periodicity is a characteristic of all living primate species; and
not only that, but the menstrual periods is in all species of
approximately the same duration. The chimpanzee's is of
34-36 days, the rhesus monkey's of 28, the baboon's of
30-40. And while at one time in the best Du Chaillu tradition it was believed that the brutal, frenzied, simian male
took his female even during her periods of menstrual taboo,
we now have a higher regard for his general good taste.
He mounts her, it is true, but he does not attempt to
penetrate her. As Carpenter has said, it is no more than a
friendly gesture.

It has been fashionable as we have seen to relate primate
society solely to the primate's unique opportunity for year-
round sexual satisfaction. But other unique factors are of
comparable importance. There is the enlarged brain, with
its superior capacity for learning. There is the generalized
body so vulnerable to predators that it even lacks claws to
fight with. And there is the territorial instinct, probably
the most critical of all. Every primate species so far studied
—with the significant exception of the gorilla—maintains
and defends territories.

All four factors—sex, territory, the enlarged brain and
the vulnerable body—have entered into the evolution of
the primate's complex society. We shall consider a fifth factor, dominance, in the next chapter. And the final factor,
of course, was the predatory way, the contribution of the
australopithecines. This we defer.

The opportunity for the male to enjoy feminine companionship on a year-round basis has undoubtedly contributed to the development of the permanent primate family

so characteristic of the apes. But among many species of birds, the male, with small chance of sexual satisfaction, still takes his mate for life. The male lion pleases himself with a permanent harem; his pleasures if plural are still seasonal. Other factors than sexual satisfaction must induce the males of many species, primate and non-primate, to accept lifetime sexual arrangements. And among monkeys and apes those arrangements are so varied and sometimes so complex that one cannot say with any confidence that even the primate's permanent family, let alone his permanent society, rests entirely on sexual foundations.

The gibbon, most active and numerous of the four living apes, lives in south-east Asia. He takes unto himself a wife, and lets it go at that; he is monogamous. Less is known of the behaviour of his Indonesian neighbour, the orang-utan; he may or may not be monogamous. Unlike the gibbon, however, he seems to find the hazards of feminine companionship less than appealing. Although he maintains a permanent family he avoids it as much as possible, brooding by himself in some separate tree. The two African apes, the chimpanzee and the gorilla, find no virtue in monogamy. Each takes a harem as large as he can handle, but usually no more than two or three. In the spring of 1960, however, our estimate of the gorilla suffered abrupt enlargement. A few weeks before I arrived in Uganda a giant male died on the slopes of Mt. Muhavura. He left a half-grown son and five widows. The son still clung to the dead giant and is today in the London Zoo. The five widows, deserting both child and dying mate, had embarked as a body on a frantic, ten-day search for another husband. They found him, an ageing creature with one female and one child. And so the widows today are somewhere on the slopes of a Uganda volcano, contributing their portion to a harem of six. There is reason to believe that throughout the primate world the size of a male's harem is not invariably determined by male choice.

The primate family, particularly among apes, may begin with the permanent sexual arrangements of a male and one or more females. But it does not end there. The size of the group is extended by a characteristic of primate young: they grow up slowly. The ape matures in the tropics at about the same rate as man. And the slowness of physical development is complicated by another factor keeping the primate child for so long a part of the family unit. Certain of his instincts are poor. He must learn by experience.

Marais once performed a revealing experiment to test the relative powers of instinct and experience in lower and upper animals. From its mother's nest he obtained an infant otter; and at the same time, from its dead mother's arm, an infant baboon. The otter like the dog is one of the brightest members of the non-primate world. The baboon, largest of all the monkeys, is the only common primate to live a successful life on the ground. While physically the ape is a little more closely related than the monkey to our human line, still the baboon is the most significant of all the primates. His terrestrial life gives him problems of survival more closely akin to our own.

Marais' infants were newly born. He raised both far apart from their natural habitats. The otter never saw water, except to drink. The baboon never saw the mountains which had been its intended home. Neither had contact with its own kind, or tasted food which should have been a part of its normal diet. After three years Marais returned each to its own, the otter to its river bank, the baboon to its troop. And both were returned hungry.

For the very first time the otter confronted that natural medium of an otter's existence, water. He hesitated for perhaps thirty seconds, then took the plunge and within a very few minutes caught a fish. Instinct ruled. But for the poor baboon there was quite a different story. He blundered about. For him the customary items of baboon diet—roots, prickly-pear fruit, maize cobs, orchard fruits—carried no more meaning than broken pebbles or logs of wood. The sight of a scorpion—that supreme delicacy of the baboon table—gave him appetite for nothing but panic flight. The unfortunate, starving creature, his life cursed by a misspent youth, wound up the sad experiment by eating poisonous berries which no normal baboon would have dreamed of touching, and by having to be rescued from nature by the naturalist himself.

The famous story of the young lioness, Elsa, told so magnificently by Joy Adamson in *Born Free*, is a case in point. Before Elsa could be returned to her native bush, she had to be taught to kill. But that is about all that a young lioness need be taught, for the rest is left to instinct. The lion family, or pride, is a hunting unit. The elders assume responsibility for shaping the skill of the young towards the pride's single social objective, the kill. No other function is performed. In the Kruger reserve the first source of lion mortality is competition for food between mature and juvenile members of the pride. From the moment of being weaned, the cub receives no further aid or protection from the lioness. He is on his own, and frequently dies of it.

The problem of the primate is of a different order. Elsa was three when she was returned to the wild. A chimpanzee growing up in the tropics will not mature until eight or ten. And here the enlarged brain enters our social evolution. While it will make possible immense yields of learning to the primate, still that same brain weakens the instincts. The young primate cannot be turned loose on the world until he is educated. And so the family, that basic building block of primate society, is extended by a long train of juveniles of varying sizes and conditions of idiocy. The male orang-utan, brooding in his separate tree, has perhaps accepted the permanence of mateship while rejecting its catastrophic consequences. But the orang has other depressing matters to brood upon: the shrinkage of his domain that once extended as far as China and is now confined to a few islands in the Indonesian archipelago; the rarity of his kind, and the paucity of male fellowship; the eternal scarcity of fruit in sufficient quantity to nourish his overdeveloped body, and the consequent necessity for continual migrations inland away from his congenial, swampy riversides. It is not a happy life being an evolutionary failure, and a father, too.

Whatever attitude the orang may take to the family as a social institution, the remainder of the primate world embraces it with cheer. So valuable do they find it as an answer to living needs that few primates content themselves with the association of their own females and offspring. Rather, they extend the group to a chattering horde, the permanent and frequently intermingled association of several or many families, the true primate society.

3

As recently as 1927 the famous anthropologist, Malinowski, could declare that "the family is the only type of grouping that man takes over from the animal." The statement does not deny the gregarious primate nature. It implies, however, that all prehuman social ties and conflicts involved sex or its consequences. His statement and earlier comparable deductions have had profound influence upon modern psychiatry. Yet the statement is flatly false.

The rare orang-utan keeps as a rule to solitary family units. Evolution, however, exhibits him as no prize winner. The successful gibbon, the most perfect of acrobats, likewise accepts a society confined to mate and children. But beyond these two examples, one can find in the world of monkeys and apes no example of a creature who regularly maintains in a state of nature a society as simple as the one-family unit.

A group of howling monkeys contains on the average three adult males and six or eight adult females. Spider monkeys in Panama live in a permanent society containing, as a rule, about eight males and fifteen females. A troop of rhesus monkeys carefully observed by Carpenter in Siam contained six males and thirty-two females. I have never myself observed a troop of vervet monkeys in Africa numbering less than forty.

The chimpanzee is difficult to observe, and habits seem to vary. Niels Bolwig told me in Kampala that his observations in western Uganda indicate a tendency towards one-family societies. But of twenty groups studied by Nissen in French Guinea, six contained two males or more. Observation of the gorilla in the past has likewise been so sketchy that room was left for the preconception of the gorilla as a one-family creature. But George Schaller's study of mountain gorillas in the Congo volcano chain will include prolonged observation of permanent groups as large as twenty-seven including seven adult males and nine females.

The hamadryas baboon, in the Sudan, lives in troops as large as three hundred. Marais' troop of chacma baboons likewise numbered three hundred. Fitzsimons once observed a troop of chacma baboons numbering an extraordinary five hundred. Because of its terrestrial life the baboon, as I have suggested, pursues an existence more resembling the human than any other of our primate relatives. But we need not lean on that environmental likeness to press from the baboon some human equation. With the exception of the gibbon and the orang, *all* upper primates tend to cluster in societies larger and more complex than the family unit.

What Malinowski's generation of natural scientists (and Freud's) failed to grasp is that primate society is rarely confined to a single family. And while Zuckerman and his contemporaries corrected this error and granted the existence of a wider social life among sub-human primate species, still they perpetuated the sexual fallacy by limiting observation to the protected cages of the zoo. They failed to consider the role of the predator in the life of a creature with a vulnerable body, as they failed to evaluate territorial behaviour exhibited only outside of zoos. In a natural state, sexual opportunities and obligations may have served to create the ever-present primate family, but territorial advantages, opportunities, and necessities have evolved the larger primate society.

The male gibbon has been favoured by a tree-top environment natural for defence, and he needs no allies to defend his territory against other gibbons or his family against natural enemies. A battleground poised a hundred feet above the earth offers a mighty alliance to the swinging creature who knows his boughland best. Carpenter observed Siamese gibbons make downward leaps on their own territory of forty and fifty feet. It is a dangerous life and a high percentage of all gibbon specimens ever collected show evidence of healed bone fractures. The survival rate among those who defend a territory must be markedly higher than among those who invade it.

The male gibbon had been likewise favoured by a primate peculiarity more astonishing than monogamy. His sex-drive is low. He copulates infrequently, produces few parental responsibilities, and with a small family can afford to go it alone. In his disdain both for gravity and for plural marriage, the lean grey acrobat of the high green places resembles more the bird than his fellow primates; and like the bird, he shares his territory with none but the family group. Even so, faced by a natural enemy such as man, the gibbon can acknowledge the defensive advantage of numbers. Carpenter on one occasion found his presence disturbing three gibbon groups at once. All males instantly joined in a concerted bluffing movement. When Carpenter withdrew, all returned to their normal territories.

If of all the primates the secure gibbon enjoys the

maximum alliance of habitat, body accomplishment, and temperament, then the baboon enjoys the least. He inhabits the pitiless earth where mercy is extended only to specialists. And the baboon has specialized in nothing but thievery. The zebra may outrun his enemies; not the baboon. The badger may outdig his enemies; the baboon can dig no deeper than his favourite root. Throughout millions of lavish years, the leopard has developed a particular appetite for baboon tastiness; the baboon cannot match him in strength, or in stealth, or in speed. Since most ancient times the python has nourished a particular fancy for baboon babies; but nature has presented the baboon with few places of refuge not equally accessible to all those like the python who wish him less than well. To add to his discomfort, nature has presented him with an uproarious sex-life. The beset baboon must somehow seek survival not only for himself but for a mob of wives and children.

The baboon, of course, is not without resource. He is fairly powerful. Like all primates he lacks claws but his nails are formidable. He has canines like daggers. And he has wits. If while he is plundering a man comes out of a farm-house, he will flee. If a woman comes out, he will ignore her. But if a determined male human enemy dresses in woman's clothes, the baboon will instantly take to the woods. And South African farmers are convinced that the baboon can count to three. When a troop of chacma baboons raids an orchard and the enraged farmer appears, the troop will withdraw to return of course the instant he leaves. If three farmers enter the orchard, and two withdraw, the baboons are not to be deceived; they will keep their distance. Only if four farmers enter the orchard, and three withdraw, will the baboon's mathematics fail him. He will return to the orchard and fall into an ambush.

Such cleverness, however, does not truly swell the total of baboon security, for it means only that he has added man to that already imposing list of natural enemies against whom he is no match. One might wonder why there are any baboons left in the world, with such odds placed against them. And yet the baboon is an evolutionary success of an outrageous order. He flourishes. He adapts himself to the most marginal conditions of climate and terrain. The bandit of Africa, he is all but ineradicable as any farmer can testify. How has he survived? The most defenceless of animals, a grounded primate, the baboon has preserved himself by developing to a high degree nature's most sophisticated instrument of defence: society.

It is no evolutionary accident that the secure gibbon can maintain a society as small as any in the primate world, and that the insecure baboon maintains societies amongst the largest. A baboon troop may contain scores of individuals, or hundreds. Typically, it will contain a dozen or more adult males, each with his harem and train of dependents. Typically, it will also contain a varying number of bachelor males, tolerated for their contributions to plunder and defence and living in varying degrees of romantic frustration. The dominant baboon is a practical sort of animal who seems sufficiently convinced that in numbers there is strength to take a few calculated risks on the integrity of his family life.

The troop maintains a territory based on whatever advantages the terrain may afford, and defends that territory against others of its kind. As a society it demonstrates all those hostile traits normal to the individual territorial proprietor and so isolates itself from the world of baboons. But a group of baboons is a society of individuals; it is not a colony of insects. The baboon cannot draw on a wealth of social instincts four hundred million years old in the evolving to compel his collective behaviour. Yet the individual baboon if he is to survive must see his society survive. He must suppress many an instinct of individual expression in favour of the good of the group.

Baboons—and all other primates—found the complexity of their social institutions on the simplicity of the ancient territorial drive. As members of a group are isolated from all others by territorial animosity so they are welded together by territorial defence. The stranger must be hated, the fellow protected. For the foreigner there must exist no measure of tolerance or charity or peace; for the countryman one must feel at least rudimentary loyalty and devotion. The individual must protect the group; the group, the individual.

For many years the famous authority on captive anthropoid behaviour, W. Kohler, experimented with chimpanzees at his station at Tenerife, in the Canary Islands. It was an early observation of his that if one chimpanzee had to be punished, the keeper risked the reprisal of all. Zuckerman noted the same problem at the London Zoo. For several years a collection of hamadryas baboons was kept there in an area called—by a flight of imagination which could only have been human—Monkey Hill. From this area the removal of a dead baboon offered considerable difficulty for the keepers: the baboons would defend even a corpse.

Groups assembled under conditions of captivity are of a superficial order, yet even so defend the individual. In the wild they will do so at definite risk. One of the greatest of African game wardens, Stevenson-Hamilton, once surprised a troop of baboons in the bush. The troop immediately retreated, but one of its number had been left isolated in a tree. The lonely, panic-stricken baboon cried for help. The troop partly returned. It would not leave him. Stevenson-Hamilton captured the isolated baboon, and still the troop would not leave. Only when one of its number was shot did the troop at last take flight.

African hunters have recalled incident after incident of altruistic behaviour. A baboon troop in flight has been recorded as carrying off an injured member. One hunter having killed a baboon found himself facing the entire group. It had surrounded the corpse and would not retreat. And there is the story of an ambushed troop that left several dead in its flight. One was a mother with an infant clinging to her corpse. Another baboon returned, snatched up the infant and fled. How many of such stories are accurate one cannot judge. Examples of sheer self-sacrifice or anything resembling true heroism must certainly be rare. And to describe such behaviour by the anthropomorphic term, altruism, is dangerous indeed. Neither, however, can it be denied that all individuals who are members of groups show to varying degrees a group-survival response in answer to any outside threat. And sometimes that response can be extraordinary.

Eugène Marais recorded an incident which one can find no grounds to question. In a few of his early observations, as I have indicated, one feels that he may have fallen into the anthropomorphic trap. But in his record of one terrible dusk in the Waterberg there can be found no flavour of amiable speculation or human identification. Interpretation plays no part. Things happened; and they happened in a certain sequence; and that was all.

The baboon fears man as the most recent addition to his list of natural discomforts. It is unfortunate for the baboon that his appetite for fruit and maize cobs, combined with a disposition that can scarcely be described as law-abiding, leads him so frequently into disagreements with local farmers. From time to time he has been officially declared a pest. Bounties have been placed on his scalp. The shooting of baboons has become in desperate times a kind of patriotic deed performed in behalf of home and country. Yet it is not on an enemy so recently acquired as man that the baboon lavishes panic. This he reserves for his more ancient enemy; the leopard, at nightfall.

The Waterberg was a lonely place in the years after the turn of the century; and still is, for that matter. Night comes on like a silent express train, and the dark becomes quiet with the listening of animals. In the hour before dusk baboon troops throughout all Marais' area would come scampering back from their scattered feeding grounds to the security of home and numbers. One fortunate troop, for example, slept in an almost inaccessible cave five hundred feet high on a sheerest cliff. There was a way to the cave, a ledge half a mile long and in places only six inches wide that overhung like the cave itself a fall as fatal for baboons as for baboon enemies. In the hour before nightfall the ledge would be crowded with the troop seeking safety. Marais would watch, and marvel at the orderly movement. Caution for once stilled baboon chatter. Adult males led, then childless females, then females to whose backs and bellies clung infants. Marais noted that peril might still the baboon voice, but not the play of baboon young. At the most dangerous corners children could not resist the temptation of pulling the convenient tails of their neighbours. But at last the cave would fill, and the ledge would clear. Night would fall, and death would move on unheard feet through wood and bush and clearing. Cold stars, brutal in their impassivity, would make of the sky an emptier thing. But at least one society of animals was safe, and would sleep in peace.

Other troops in the Waterberg, such as Marais' own, possessed no strongholds of comparable strength. Yet to all, whatever their insecurity, night brought the same spectre. Marais could always tell when a leopard was in the neighbourhood of his own band. Protected by nothing but the rocky hollows in the krans and concealed only by the limbs of the massive wild fig, the troop would begin to move uneasily. He would sense the restlessness, and then hear a particular cry of disturbance. Helplessly the troop would wait for unseen death to pass unseeing. But one night the leopard came early.

It was still dusk. The troop had only just returned from the feeding grounds and had barely time to reach its scattered sleeping places in the high-piled rocks behind the fig tree. Now it shrilled its terror. And Marais could see the leopard. It appeared from the bush and took its insolent time. So vulnerable were the baboons that the leopard seemed to recognize no need for hurry. He crouched just below a little jutting cliff observing his prey and the problems of the terrain. And Marais saw two male baboons edging along the cliff above him.

The two males moved cautiously. The leopard, if he saw them, ignored them. His attention was fixed on the swarming, screeching, defenceless horde scrambling among the rocks. Then the two males dropped. They dropped on him from a height of twelve feet. One bit at the leopard's spine. The other struck at his throat while clinging to his neck from below. In an instant the leopard disemboweled with his hind claws the baboon hanging to his neck and caught in his jaws the baboon on his back. But it was too late. The dying, disemboweled baboon had hung on just long enough and had reached the leopard's jugular vein with his canines.

Marais watched while movement stilled beneath the little jutting cliff. Night fell. Death, hidden from all but the impartial stars, enveloped prey and predator alike. And in the hollow places in the rocky, looming krans a society of animals settled down to sleep.

4

Sex is a side-show in the world of the animal, for the dominant colour of that world is fear. Only behind the fences or moats of a zoological garden shall we see sex take its place in the main arena. For as there are no territories in zoos, so there are no predators, and there is no fear. And all those delicate instinctual mechanisms evolved by natural selection to promote the survival of individuals or the survival of species are alike suspended. Only sex and a hearty appetite remain for us to see. But how delicate may be the instinctual social responses in a state of nature has been recorded by many an observer. Even in the zoo some still may be seen.

When Kohler observed the likelihood of chimpanzee group reprisal he also noted that defence occurred only if the punished chimpanzee gave a definite, characteristic cry. Zuckerman observed the same odd behavior among the baboons on Monkey Hill. The group would come to the defence of a member, but only after a particular cry had been given. Stevenson-Hamilton noticed similar behaviour among baboons in the wild. A group response in a primate society is aroused not by the plight of an individual member, but by a particular vocal signal.

Zuckerman also noticed that whenever keepers attempted to remove a body from the Hill—a corpse of any sort, whether that of an infant from its mother's arms, of an elder gone to his reward, or simply of some over-abused victim of baboon disagreement—the defence of that body would be preceded by a chorus of deep, distinctive barks. To Zuckerman it seemed most unlikely that the baboon is capable of some special recognition of death, and I believe that I agree with him. The group defends a corpse as it would defend a living fellow, without recognition of its special estate. Death is not a tangible thing but a generality, a deduction, a name which man gives to a particular abstract state of non-being, and it would seem to me improbable that the animal is capable of response to such a conceptual condition. But there is a catch to all this. In the depths of the Waterberg over half a century ago Marais heard and described the same low, distinctive baboon bark. Lying in his bed in the middle of the night, he would hear the deep chorus, deep in the mountain. And he would know with certainty that in the morning he would find the body of a departed friend.

There is much that we have not yet learned about the animal, much that we shall know before very long, and much that we shall never know. If I agree with Zuckerman concerning the unlikelihood of an animal society's vocal response to the presence of death in its midst, then I do it on principle, and because not enough evidence has been gathered, so far, to endanger that principle. But I do it with sure knowledge that for those authorities on animal behaviour who subscribe most firmly to doctrines of animal limitation, history has provided the most lamentable of fates.

A society of Central American howling monkeys, so far as I know, provides no vocal response to death. But the individual howler communicates his reaction to nine distinct situations with nine definite and distinctive cries, each with meaning to the society. It is precisely the same number as the cries of the gibbon and the siamang in the Far East. The most characteristic of the howler cries is a signal that the territory is threatened by invasion, and has the approximate effect on a group of howling monkeys that the cry of "Remember the Alamo!" has on a group of Texans. Another cry, quite different, amounts simply to one of suspicion. It is an alert, gathering the group's attention to the possibility of disturbance. The emotional consequence of this cry, quite the opposite from that of the war-cry, is expressed by silence. Another vocal expression of less dramatic order might simply be interpreted as "Let's go this way." It occurs when a male in the clustered, feeding group develops restless ideas of his own. If it is taken up by the group, then all follow him. But as often occurs another male may repeat the cry to express his own version of the group's proper progress. The dispute that follows will, in straight-forward howler tradition, be of minimum violence and maximum racket. Sooner or later the group comes to vocal agreement with the winner, and all move.

Lorenz had long experience with a society of jackdaws, a small, intelligent and beguiling variety of the European crow. He found in jackdaw society a cry comparable in its meaning, and sometimes in its consequent arguments, to the howler's "Let's go this way." Jackdaws, however, have another cry quite distinct in its sound and significance: "Let's go home." Still another characteristic jackdaw cry comes about as a result of a species peculiarity: the baby jackdaw has no instinctive recognition of natural enemies. A jackdaw chick, as innocent as an apple, will favour an approaching cat with the most benign attention. Nothing but the particular cry of his fellows disturbs his composure. It is that cry, not the sight of the enemy, that teaches him who in his world is malevolent, who benevolent.

Birds, like primates, have a superior capacity for learning by experience. Nature has taken advantage of this capacity to deposit in jackdaw society, not in the jackdaw individual, awareness of danger. Each generation of jackdaws communicates to the next through the warning cry, the accumulated wisdom of jackdaw history. When a new peril appears in jackdaw life, it becomes apparent just how much more selective and more adaptable is the mechanism of social experience than the inflexible apparatus of individual instinct.

The jackdaw, for example, has a very special rattling,

warning cry distinguished from the general awakening to danger. It can be interpreted only as: "Creature approaches bearing dead jackdaw." The cry arises at the sight of a man bearing anything black and small in his hand. Lorenz, hanging out a new pair of black swimming shorts, was once set upon by his own jackdaws. The reaction was instant, violent, and needed few instances of association to become permanent. Lorenz holds the conviction, based on the experience of a friend, that had he continued to favour black swimming shorts for only a few days, he would have been finished as a keeper of jackdaws.

Lorenz' Austrian friend had a tame crow, and wild crows have a comparable cry. He appeared in the open with the tame crow on his hand on just a few occasions but these were enough to mean the end of any civilized relation with local crows. From that time onwards, no matter where he went, no matter how far he walked, and no matter how he dressed, the friend was the unhappy object of rattling, angry, circling flocks.

Not by the gun on his shoulder but by the dead black bird in his hand does crow observation distinguish the hunter from less predatory fellows. His personal identification is permanently imbedded in the consciousness of every individual member of the flock by means of the rattling cry. Other flocks, which have not themselves witnessed the murder of their kind, will hear and take up the cry; and so the hunter's bad reputation may spread through a whole region. He may change his hunting ways. He may lose his gun in a poker game. Even so, generations of crows yet unborn will learn that this particular man has a crow record, and must be regarded for all time as a bad risk to crow welfare. So animal society becomes the permanent repository for animal experience, surviving the death of individual members.

Among the howling monkey's vocabulary of perils must be placed the infant's fearful squeal, which attracts his mother's attention; and another group cry which must be translated as "Infant dropped from tree." At this very particular cry which may be set up by the mother or any other member of the howler society, every adult in the clan springs into action. The howler does not regard the earth below as a favourable sort of place. And only the reaction to territorial defence can be compared to the instant, unanimous and compulsory group rescue of an infant dropped from a tree.

In primate societies as in jackdaw society the individual comes to the aid of the group or the group to the aid of the individual through the machinery of language. The cry must precede a social response. But there is one supreme difference between animal and human language. Specialized though the animal call may be—as specialized as the howler's "Infant dropped from tree!"—it is never purposeful. Never does the animal cry out with the motive of enlisting aid. The cry is simply an expression of mood, and the mood catches.

The yawn, among humans, is an expression of mood comparable to animal language, and it carries the same contagious quality. I grow sleepy; I yawn. Then you yawn, and you grow sleepy. For a dramatist to write a scene in which a character yawns repeatedly would be to commit artistic suicide; the entire audience would be put to sleep. Coughing can be likewise an expression of human mood, as every actor or playwright knows. An audience does not cough because the weather is bad and everyone has colds. It coughs because it is bored, and the cough is like an animal expression of wishing to be home in bed. One cougher begins his horrid work in an audience, and the cough spreads until the house is in bedlam, the actors in rage, and the playright in retreat to the nearest saloon. Yet let the action take a turn for the better, let the play tighten up, and that same audience will set in a silence unpunctuated by a single tortured throat.

Animal language is a contagious expression of mood effecting communication between social partners. Something happens: a disturbance in the bush, the fall of an infant, the sight of something black in a man's hand. A mood is generated in the observing animal: fear, concern, anger. The mood is expressed by a particular cry. The cry is contagious. It is promptly taken up by all. And as the mood in the individual has produced the cry, the cry echoed by the society reproduces the mood in all its members. Now all act as one in whatever response the species has devised, throughout its history, as that best calculated to insure its survival.

5

Society is the primate's best friend. In group response
he has found a weapon that multiplies the number of his
eyes, the weight of his muscle, the ranks of his fighting
teeth. Through his social mechanism the primate has made
sure that he will get the greatest return from his own superior endowment, the brain; and suffer the least disadvantage from his inherent vulnerability, the all-around weakness of his body.

There is order in all the wild animal world. We stand
before a cage in a zoo and observe what seems to be a
kind of happy or disgruntled anarchy. In any case it is a life
free of rules, and perhaps that is why we so like to go to
the zoo. But in a state of nature, the life of the animal is
not so. He follows the rules and regulations of territorial
behaviour. If he is a social animal, then he obeys the rules
and regulations of his society; and his personal inclination
must, on occasion, yield to the necessities of his society.
In this the animal accepts and subscribes to a kind of
primal morality.

The wild animal is not free. If he be monkey or ape,
then order is imposed on his conduct by the survival of his
young, which must be educated as well as fed and defended; by the demands of territorial defence; and by the
laws of dominance which we shall soon inspect. Above all,
since he is an animal who depends on social mechanism
for survival, order is imposed on his inclinations by the
demands of his society. The primate is a most well-regu-
lated fellow. But let one factor—territory—be absent from
his life, and anything can happen.

At an early point I spoke of C. R. Carpenter's resettle-
ment of some 350 Indian rhesus monkeys on Santiago
Island, off Puerto Rico. That long, carefully controlled experiment was perhaps the most revealing of any ever performed in the observation of primate conduct. But one
phase of the observations came about not quite according to plan.

The animals were transported by sea. Their transfer to a
new habitat meant that they had to be accustomed to a new
diet. To force them to accept a new diet, it was necessary

to feed them most sparely, and keep them for a time continually hungry. This stage of the conditioning was planned to take place through the sea voyage. But at sea, unfortunately, the monkeys had no territories. In India territorial behaviour had been part of their evolutionary tradition, and on Santiago Island they would establish new territories and organize new societies. On shipboard, however, there was no such opportunity. And without the machinery of their social life the hungry monkeys descended into anarchy and lost the most primitive reflexes of their moral order.

One would think that a mother's defence of her young would be an instinct so profound that it would carry on despite any departure from normal life. Nothing could be less true. Without the disciplines of territory and society, mothers scrambled for food without regard for their infants. Time after time the mother fought her own child for possession of a scrap. No male, it goes without saying, rose to the defence of mate or offspring. Without territory, there was only terror. And by the end of the voyage ten infants were dead.

It took about a year, as I have mentioned, for the rhesus monkeys to divide Santiago Island's thirty-six acres into territories each with its newly organized society. During that year there was no shortage of food, since a caretaker distributed it daily. There was a shortage of nothing, indeed, but society. That, however, was enough. By the end of the first year on Santiago Island, more rhesus monkey infants had been killed by adults than died of all other causes combined. Then conditions stabilized. Territories were affirmed, societies isolated and unified. Females regained their mother-love, and males their respect for the rules and regulations. Infant mortality ceased promptly to threaten the survival of the rhesus monkeys.

There are birds like the swallow and jackdaw, and fish like the herring and cod, who form societies based on other than the territorial urge. But in the family of primates to which our human stream has been confined for seventy million years, to be deprived of territory is to be deprived of society; and to be deprived of society is very nearly to be deprived of all.

Chapter 4
Who Pecks Whom

Every organized animal society has its system of dominance. Whether it be a school of fish or a flock of birds or a herd of grazing wildebeest, there exists within that society some kind of status order in which individuals are ranked. It is an order founded on fear. Each individual knows all those whom he must fear and defer to, and all those who must defer to him. Self-awareness in the limited sense of consciousness of rank seems to have appeared at some very early moment in the evolution of living things.

Whether or not in such societies as the antelope herd every individual has a separate rank, we cannot yet say. Too little study has been done. In some societies there may be classes themselves ranked which an individual achieves or to which he is relegated. But determination of rank by birth is a characteristic of the insect world alone. Among the vertebrates, from fish to apes, status is competitively determined fairly early in the individual's lifetime. That rank is rarely lost, and rarely improved upon.

Dominance occurs when two or more animals pursue the same activity. It is a type of behaviour long-observed, since all animals—wild, captive, or domesticated—pursue it. But not until zoology turned its attention to the natural state did we begin to comprehend the unyielding fabric of dominance in the texture of animal societies. The social animal does not merely seek to dominate his fellows; he succeeds. And succeeding, he achieves a status in the eyes of the other. That status will be permanent; and oddly enough satisfying as a rule to all parties.

In the halls of science there are many doors, and the one with the sign that reads *Animal Dominance* is one that we have scarcely opened. We have learned much: that it is a force at least as old and as deep as territory; that like territory it benefits sex but stands independent of it; that among social animals it is universal, and among our primate family the source of society's most mysterious subtleties; and that among all animal sources of human behaviour, the instinct for status may in the end prove the most important. But while we may observe it, we still do not truly understand it. And that is why any new study of status in animal societies is apt to leave the most informed reader in a renewed state of stupefaction.

The jackdaw is an extremely intelligent bird who reaps the benefit, as we have seen, of a highly organized social life. It is logical, I suppose, that any animal who gains so much from the deathless wisdom of society will see to it that his society operates with the least possible friction. Natural selection would so decree. But I still find my credulity strained by the subtleties of the jackdaw social order. And were Konrad Lorenz a less experienced observer, I should probably wind up in stolid disbelief.

Every male jackdaw has his number, as it were. From Number One to Number Last there is not the least vagueness in the hierarchical position of the individual male bird within a flock. That position is settled upon at an early date in life. Even in chickhood a shuffling about for status begins. Food may be abundant, but quarrels flourish. Somebody pecks somebody, and gets pecked back; somebody retreats. Gradually the timid, the weak, the irresolute fall; gradually the strong and the determined rise. Before too long rivalry of body and character has determined the exact social position of every male bird in the flock. And he will keep that position, most probably, for life. Lorenz never saw a case of change in status caused by discontent from below.

Every barnyard has its pecking order, as every farmer

knows. Chickens like jackdaws establish a hierarchy. And the position of the individual chicken determines all pecking rights. Who may peck whom? No chicken may peck another ranking higher in the order. This is known in zoology as a straight-line hierarchy. The high-ranking chicken may peck left and right at the feeding pan; but there is always that lowly chicken who is pecked by all, and can peck no one in return.

As compared to the jackdaw the chicken is a crude sort of animal, and her barnyard society is an artificial thing. The jackdaw establishes his order of dominance not to nourish quarrels but to minimize them. The senseless autocrat of the barnyard may flourish her rank at every opportunity, and vent her anger on the lowliest. The high-ranking jackdaw rarely descends to such behaviour. If he enters a quarrel among the lowly, it is usually to settle it.

It seems to be a general rule of jackdaw conduct that while one may quarrel with one's hierarchical neighbours, one should not peck too far down the ranks. Number 4 may quarrel with Number 5 or Number 6, but Number 10 is out of bounds. Remarkably enough top jackdaws almost immediately upon achieving their lofty positions acquire a sense of social responsibility. Carpenter observed precisely the same response in rhesus monkeys. The high-ranking jackdaw stands aloof from flock disagreements. Numbers 1, 2 and 3 may have certain differences among themselves; they do not enter into differences with the masses. Occasionally such an aristocrat may enter a low-placed argument, but invariably he sides with the contestant bearing the lower number. It is as if intuitively he bears the weight of a balance of power. Lorenz can find no explanation for such conduct excepting in the prevalence of quarrels over nesting sites. By throwing his weight on the side of the lowest placed members of the flock, the jackdaw insures that all will find reasonably satisfactory nests.

Jackdaws mate for life, and like most birds who follow such a custom become engaged at an earlier date. Wild geese pair in the spring following birth, although sexual maturity does not come about for another year. And it is the same with jackdaws. The young males will have finished their status struggle when pairing begins and the jackdaw female promptly upon pairing assumes the social position of her male. His rights and restraints become her rights and restraints. Throughout all their lives, they will together defend that social position against any rare challenge. But should a female not secure a mate, then it becomes a sadder sort of story. She remains at the tail of all social things in a mournful, unclassified spot. She is last to the food and last to the shelter. She is pecked by the lowliest, snubbed by the least. No aristocrat descends to her defence, for she holds not even a minimum power to keep in balance; neither are there lesser jackdaws on whom she can vent her frustrations. One can well apprehend the jackdaw drive for status, even to gain the status of last in line, when one considers the fate of the sorry unnumbered. The spinster jackdaw has little to look forward to, not even the couch, someday, of the jackdaw analyst.

It was one of these sad, surplus females who revealed to Lorenz, through a train of circumstances, the full workings of the jackdaw social code.

Lorenz raised his flock from chicks. In the month before pairing and before rank order had been quite established one of the stronger males disappeared. At first Lorenz thought that the bird had gone off on an adventure and would return. But as weeks went by and he did not return, Lorenz checked the bird off as a probable victim of some watchful hawk. And he forgot him.

The flock proceeded with its social shakedown and the hierarchy was established. A strong, handsome young male secured the Number One position. Number Two argued for a while, then accepted his vice-presidential role. Distribution of rank moved quickly along until every male had a number. Then pairing proceeded. Just as worthy females in an individualist species look to territory as the mark of the eligible mate, so worthy females in a social species regard the male of high rank with special favour. Number One got a strong young female for his own, and together they made a handsome couple. On down the line the jackdaws paired, each male getting the approximate best that his rank could afford. And at the end of the line the completed pairing found two bedraggled females left over.

That was in the springtime. Mating would not take place for another year. The young jackdaw society settled down to the business of maturing: to the daily life of feeding and preening, of basking and growing, of praising one's fiancée and disparaging one's enemies. The top-ranking jackdaws found the aloofness proper to their aristocratic roles. The middle classes pecked at the lower classes, and the lower classes pecked at the unhappy spinsters. And then the vanished male returned. No hawk had got the strong young bird but only wanderlust. Where he had been Lorenz could not guess. But here he was, after almost six months' absence, returned to a society where order had already been established and pairing completed. The problem of rank came first in the prodigal's instincts. He fixed Number One with a bright, metallic stare.

There were few overt quarrels between the two birds. They ate together. They perched near each other. They looked at each other. It is Lorenz' opinion that the dominant relationship between two animals is established as much by the matching of energy, courage, and assurance as it is by strength. Perhaps the prodigal's adventures in far, desperate places had given him an assurance that no stay-at-home could match. Whatever were the determinants in the dignified struggle, there was little to observe. But by the second day it was all over: Number One had suddenly become Number Two, and the wanderer, Number One.

The problem of rank was settled; the problem of pairing remained. The new Number One assumed in the moment of his ascendancy all that aristocratic carriage which his eminence demanded. But he had no lady. He coud not accept an appropriate consort from among the females already paired; jackdaws are faithful. The new Number One could take only one course, and he took it with dignity. He paired with one of the leftovers.

A female, we recall, takes the rank of her male. All in a happy hour the scrubby little female had become the President's wife. All in a happy hour the unwanted spinster from the wrong end of the pecking order had taken her place at the head. The glass slipper fitted; the pumpkin coach arrived. And all in a most miraculous hour from which jackdaw fairy-tales might well be spun the skimpy little Cinderella found her days as a drudge behind her, the days of being pecked upon never to be repeated, the time of being last to the food, last to the shelter, of being snubbed, scorned, pushed about, crowded out, undefended, unloved, feared by none and rejected by all—it was a time that could be forgotten forever. But did she forget it? She did not.

Romance is one thing, reality another. Number One's wife became the worst behaved nouveau in the history of jackdaw society. She snubbed, she flurried, she pushed about, she displayed her dreary plumage, fluttered her skinny wings, and pecked, and pecked, and pecked. In the moment of his ascendancy jackdaw instinct had directed her male to accept the aristocratic jackdaw role. But from the moment of her ascendancy all she apprehended were her rights. And she neglected none. It took her a year to settle down.

Only one factor of social behaviour, in Konrad Lorenz' opinion, was more significant than the rejected female's immediate, intuitive grasp of all those prerogatives to which her new rank entitled her. And that was the immediate and equally intuitive grasp, on the part of every jackdaw, of the new social situation which each now faced. The creature whom all had pecked could now be pecked by none. Her flauntings were unnecessary. Her pecking and her posturing might appease those frustrations acquired through the long unhappy months, but they were quite unneeded to impress others with the grandeur of her new estate. From the hour of her ascendancy, every jackdaw by oldest instinct knew his new place, and hers. She was Number One.

2

Sage grouse in the American West have a curious institution known as the strutting-ground. In an area half a mile long and a few hundred yards wide the males here establish and display dominance. It is a competition very closely resembling the formal manoeuvres of the blackcock, an institution known to English ornithologists as the lek. A study of a sage-grouse strutting-ground in Wyoming has been described by W. C. Allee and demonstrates just how carefully natural selection may insure that only select male genes will colour the prospects of a future generation.

The study covered about eight hundred birds. After the males had sorted themselves out on the strutting-ground, the hens gathered at five mating spots each the size of a room. Dominance established 1% of the males as what Allee terms master-cocks, 2% as sub-cocks. Copulation occurred *only* at the invitation of the hen; in other words, female prerogative of choice was the next step in natural selection. And the result of that selection was that 74% of all matings were with master cocks, 1% of the total male population; and 13% with sub-cocks, representing 2% of the males. Rank order of dominance had insured that 87% of that season's crop of young sage grouse be fathered by only 3% of the male population.

The Uganda kob is one of the most beautiful of African antelopes, and one of the few species that has been even superficially studied. All over the flat, reaching plains of the Queen Elizabeth Park the long, graceful necks of the does rise up from the bush like periscopes of inquisitive submarines. And one may observe the selective qualities of dominance as clearly in the kob as Allee observed it in the Wyoming sage grouse.

A far-spread herd of Uganda kob divides itself clearly into family parties, each with a territory, and into parties of surplus dominated males made up both of the young and ambitious and of the mature but defeated. The family party consists invariably of a master ram and twelve or fifteen does. His sexual franchise is of an exclusive nature. But he shares his responsibility for defending the family with three or four sub-chiefs. These second-rank rams act as sentinels and will be found standing apart at the extreme corners of the territory. Unlike the sage grouse subcocks, they have no sexual rights whatsoever. But any failure of leadership on the part of the master ram will result in challenge by one of the sub-chiefs. And failure to meet that challenge successfully will see the master ram relegated to the party of surplus males; the sub-chief promoted to the post of the master ram; and a flurry of struggle among the young and ambitious to determine which will inherit the vacancy in the rank of sentinel sub-chiefs. Natural selection has woven the instinct for territory and the instinct for dominance into an orderly hierarchical society providing at once the best possible defence against the lion and the best possible genetic inheritance for future Uganda kobs.

The sorting process of status, affecting any species, differs little in its reproductive consequences from the sorting process of territory. A herd of male seals lands on some rocky Pacific outpost held dear in the memories of none but seals. Territories are fought for. Strength, pugnacity, courage, and resolution reward this male with this territory, that male with that. When the females arrive, the issue is already decided. Males will acquire harems of a size proportionate to their real-estate holdings.

A troop of baboons holds a territory in common. But within the troop the drive for dominance sorts out the males. Strength, pugnacity, courage, and resolution reward this male with this rank, that with that. And the male will hold a harem of size appropriate to the attractiveness of his rank.

But rank determines far more than access to females. When the male jackdaw returned from his travels he turned his attention first to social position, and only afterwards to a mate. The choice was no accident of personality conditioned by the poor selection of local females. Rank must come first in the preoccupation of any social animal, for rank tells all. How numerous will be those who come ahead at the table? Who will be listened to, who ignored? Who will do the pecking, and who get pecked? All is determined by the single acquisition of status.

When Monkey Hill was established at the London Zoo its original inhabitants were mostly males. These were baboons of the hamadryas species from Abyssinia and the Sudan. They have long manes, penetrating eyes, and bear a striking resemblance to old-fashioned after-dinner speakers about to address a series of clichés to some local political society. Certainly the hamadryas resembles little the South African chacma baboon, who never succeeds in looking like anything but a shaven-headed convict escaped only day before yesterday from the clanking life of the chain gang. A baboon, however, is a baboon. He may gain a semblance of respectability from a flowing mane, but when the enchantments of sex enter his life then his ties to the Conservative Association are ended.

Zuckerman was the observer when thirty adult females were introduced to the dignified colony of hamadryas baboon males on Monkey Hill. The consequent uproar shook the entire zoo. Within four weeks, half of the females had died in the scramble. The society of males, artificially organized, lacked the strict rank order of dominance which

would have made such an unholy death rate impossible in the wild. But it is a significant comment on the unshakeable practicality of the male animal that in the whole glorious mêlée of embattled baboons fighting in the great tradition for feminine fancy, the female, not the male, paid the price of romance. While fifteen out of thirty female baboons gave their lives in the sex battle, only three or four males out of fifty-six pursued their opinions to a mortal end.

In time, things got better organized on Monkey Hill, and firmer dominance conserved female lives. Various overlords arose from the ranks to assert dominion over female harems; but they faced, of course, a horde of bachelors. Sexual fights were not infrequent. Zuckerman recorded in detail such a sexual battle-royal, and as today we read the record carefully we find that it was not for the female that the overlord fought, but for his rank.

A sexual fight among captive baboons is one involving all the males. It has its beginnings as a rule some days before the actual outbreak. A bachelor starts shadowing a female, keeping in the meantime a wary eye on her overlord. She remains passive. Sooner or later the overlord gets too much, and routs the bachelor. That ends the first phase. But now—if a sexual fight is truly in the offing—a mood of rebellion spreads through all the males. It grows. It may grow for days. Bachelors who have been keeping their places begin staying close to the overlord's females. The females try to ignore them. The overlord does not. The tension grows. Then one day a bachelor seizes a female. The uprising is lighted. All bachelors close in on the threatened family. But now the overlord's attention is entirely on the males. A bachelor may mount the overlord's female, penetrate her, copulate with her. The overlord ignores the action. A fight may break out among the bachelors for the female pried loose from the harem. In such a struggle the female is usually killed. But the overlord by now pays not the least attention. He is fighting for one thing and one thing alone, his rank.

The power of dominance is so enormous that a single high ranking baboon can hold off for days attack after attack on the part of a mob of bachelors who without the inhibition of the dominated could kill him in moments. In the end he wins, and winning retains his position and consequently his surviving harem. Or he loses, and losing loses everything. He joins the ranks of the bachelors. But seldom, almost never, does the deposed tyrant lose his life.

Such observations as that of the sexual fight led Zuckerman to the conclusion that sex forms the major impetus for the organization of primate society. But our knowledge today of primate behaviour in a state of nature may lead us to a far different interpretation of the recorded observations in the London Zoo. Even under the lunatic conditions of captivity in which the highly-sexed baboon is denied a natural outlet for all those complex instincts directing his behaviour, he will under the most climactic pressure fight for status rather than sex. In a state of nature, of course, the preoccupations of finding food, of defence against natural enemies, of the protection of young and the guarding of territory will make sexual shenanigans such as Zuckerman observed a total impossibility.

Throughout three long years of baboon observation in the lonely Waterberg Eugène Marais never once witnessed anything resembling a sexual outbreak. His troop of three hundred baboons favoured monogamy somewhat more than does the average troop. (Bolwig has commented that baboon social practices can vary from troop to troop even as human customs vary from tribe to tribe.) Marais' baboons, therefore, had a better balance between overlords and bachelors than did the artificial society on Monkey Hill. Nevertheless there were still many unmated bachelors and occasional differences of opinion. But that the sexually disenfranchised should rise against an overlord and that females should die of such clashes were matters unheard of.

There has never to my knowledge been any observation of baboon sexual behaviour in the wild that remotely resembles the observations in the London Zoo. The male baboon in a normal society may not even place great value on an exclusive sexual domain. Bolwig observed a female on one spectacular occasion copulate thirty times in one hour with six different males, then disappear into the bush with the youngest of the six. Her overlord had taken his turns but had otherwise watched unmoved. He apparently considered the gay proceeding no challenge to his dominance. We shall encounter the same indifference in heavily-dominant mountain gorillas.

Dominance challenged, however, will almost never be toppled in a state of nature. The possessor of high dominant rank wields mysterious powers just as does the territorial proprietor. And so, since almost any dispute must be settled in favour of the highest ranking, disputes are few or are trivial. The young maturing male in the one-family gibbon society, for example, will never challenge the dominance of his father. When such a time of challenge becomes possible, no challenge is offered. The young one instead simply leaves the group to seek his fortune in the wide, high world. There he will find a female and establish a society of his own; or he will not, and he will live his life a solitary.

So far as primates are concerned, the tradition of the tyrant deposed and exiled is an utter myth. Observers in Central Africa may encounter a lone young chimpanzee but seldom an old one. In Central America a lone howling monkey may appear on the territorial fringes of a howler society. He will be attacked by force, not by vocalization. He will be driven away time and again but if he is determined he will still hang around; and sometimes, after months, he will be admitted to the troop. It is always a young howler, however, who wanders the lonely arboreal paths; old ones may move down the ladder of status, but they retain sufficient rank to remain in the society where they have lived their lives.

Baboons, for one reason or another, have special regard for the old. Marais' troop in the Waterberg vested a special dominion in its elders. These were animals far past their prime, but they exerted a final voice in the conduct of the troop. And sometimes such decisions could be of a most delicate order.

It is standard behaviour among baboons that when a pregnant female's time arrives, she seeks and receives complete privacy. I cannot think of an observation of baboon childbirth ever recorded in the wild; success at achieving privacy is that complete. The mate usually accompanies her, but how he aids her in any way other than keeping up her morale, we do not know. And it is an intimacy as carefully preserved from the eyes of the troop as it is from the eyes of man. One of Marais' females, however, through unfortunate circumstances very nearly broke all the rules.

Whether this female came too suddenly into labour, or whether her hunt for a private place was delayed by a pusillanimous disposition, Marais of course could not know. But one morning just at the hour when the troop customarily sought its feeding ground, her moment struck. She hurried over a low, rocky rise out of the sight of the troop with her overlord, trying to be helpful, loping just behind. But beyond the rise she had no time. She could do nothing but crawl under a scanty and most transparent bush. The male joined her. Then over the rise came the troop.

The bush under which the female had found cover stood directly on the path to the feeding ground. Marais watched through binoculars. The troop did not know what to do. The scantiness of her bush was such that to pass along the only path would be to violate irreparably the accouchement's privacy. But the troop had to eat. The mob of three hundred overlords, females, juveniles, infants, bachelors and old ones shuffled about unhappy and irresolute. Nothing in the pattern of baboon social behaviour could instruct the individual in this unexpected situation as to what to do next.

Then Marais saw the old ones separate themselves from the troop. He had witnessed such an action many times before. For quite some time they crouched, or shuffled about, or inspected themselves. And then as a group they moved off in a direction other than the normal path. The undiminished dominance of the old ones had taken charge.

How strong was that grip was evident from the elders' choice of path which the troop now followed without whimper. It would take the hungry horde to the feeding ground by a difficult climb and an additional two hours' walk.

3

A lion society is as permanent as any in nature. But it cannot be founded on sex, since the lioness is a seasonal creature. It cannot be founded on defence against enemies, for the lion fears none but man. It cannot be dedicated to the care and education of young lions, for while the juvenile is taught to kill, none cares for him from the moment of his weaning. Finally the lion society is not, in my opinion, welded by territory. He is a territorial animal and unlike the non-predator dies frequently of territorial conflict. But the pride's moving territory, abstract in its very nature, seems more a social expression than a social cause.

A lion pride is a hunting unit, and this would seem to be its sole reason for existence. And it is the extraordinary dominance of the male lion, and little else, that welds the society together.

As a hunter the lion has a weakness. While he strikes with flash and power unequalled by any other predator, he cannot run with any great speed or endurance. The cheetah can outrun any animal on earth and so finds it unnecessary to hunt in parties larger than two or three. But the lion can match none of his favourite prey in speed, neither zebra nor wildebeest nor impala nor waterbuck. And so he must take his prey with stealth and above all tactics. A lion pride is as much a tactical unit as a naval task force, and the dominance of its leader is as essential as the unquestioned authority of a naval commander.

The male lion rarely makes the kill. Such entertainments he leaves to the lioness. His normal position in a hunting pride is in the centre with lionesses spread out on either flank considerably in advance. Thus the pride will proceed into a shallow Central African valley. It is the function of the male to flush the game and drive it within range of the nearest lioness. I mentioned in another context that I did not believe the roar of the male to be like bird-song an announcement of territorial position. The devastating, brain-numbing sound seems to me rather to serve a double purpose of a different order. It terrifies the prey and focuses attention on the male, while at the same time it communicates to the silent lionesses the male's position.

If such an interpretation seems to attribute to the lion a tactical subtlety beyond animal probability, then we are simply underestimating the lion. Along the Lower Sabie road, in the Kruger game reserve, tourist cars have been a commonplace for the last generation. It took lion prides far less than that time to incorporate the car into their hunting tactics. While the car's occupants sit in frozen awe, the lioness on the road beside it will make use of the car as a screen between herself and her prey. We owe some of our finest lion photography not to human but lion accomplishment.

The most astonishing example of adaptability of lion hunting tactics however, is found on the western margins of the Kruger reserve. In February, 1960, South African authorities began the construction of a two-hundred-mile-long fence along that margin to protect livestock and grazing on adjacent farms. Within three months lion prides learned to drive wildebeest against the fence. Kruger game

wardens had wondered how they could prevent antelope herds from breaking the fence down. They now have complete confidence that the lion will teach the herds to stay away from it.

The tactical ruthlessness, skill, and subtlety of the lion hunting pride was excelled, we may assume, by the ruthlessness, the skill, and the subtlety of the australopithecine hunting band. But in the contemporary world of predators the lion has no superior other, of course, than man. And this is why to any investigator into the animal sources of human behaviour the way of the lion must bear such significance.

A system of dominance, I have suggested, is the welding force of the hunting pride. So enormous is the dominance of the male that although the female makes the kill she invariably retires from it no matter what her hunger. He eats at his leisure while the entire pride waits. Finished, he retires; and the lionesses, second in the rank order of the pride, appear to appease their hunger. But the juveniles, last in the pecking order, still must wait.

Dominance is the one profound instinct in the natural world that from the point of view of natural selection can sometimes get out of hand. Whereas territory acts invariably as a factor promoting the interests of individual and species, and whereas society furnishes creatures in a state of nature with their most striking instrument of survival, still dominance over-developed can do damage of an absolute order upsetting natural balances otherwise so carefully protected. The appalling death rate of juvenile lions, for example, as recorded in the Kruger reserve, can scarcely be regarded as in the long-run interests of natural selection or in the short-run interests of the pride. Yet the death-rate results from the conflict of juvenile appetites with the rigorous dominance of their elders. And while one may argue that the killing of juveniles by both lions and lionesses offers testimony to the value placed on hierarchy by the necessities of the hunting life, still nature in species less murderous evolves intuitive checks to restrain a valuable compulsion.

The way of the lion offers another example of social behaviour inimical to the interests of the species, and this too may be due to over-dominance. The example concerns size of pride. We know so little about lion behaviour that we still assume the hunting pride to be limited to the family unit. But it is not so. How large a lion pride may be came formidably to my attention one morning in the Congo's Rutshuru valley.

It was early. The mists of dawn were still lingering like night's reluctant ghosts on the winding river, among the trees along its shore, and in pockets along the vast, semi-circular amphitheatre of grassy lowland enclosed by a river bend. My wife and I stood on a rise looking down on the natural stage. A lone hippo still grazed on the lowland. A herd of a dozen elephant browsed near the river tearing loose branches of trees. Slowly they moved down-river, still browsing. The hippo continued to graze. And then out of the brush two hundred yards from where we stood emerged a pride of fourteen lion. They marched solidly, silently, shoulder to shoulder two or three abreast, eyes on the hippo.

It was a hunting pride. Only two were cubs, and their lioness immediately led them away. The remaining eleven, adults or nearly mature juveniles, settled low in the grass. But the killing assemblage proved more terrifying to its human observers than to the hippo. The grazing monster spotted them with its periscope eyes, lifted its head briefly, then returned to its late breakfast. Throughout the succeeding ten minutes the hippo without missing another bite grazed its way slowly to the river and vanished. The motionless pride watched from the grass as the lion banquet disappeared. Even eleven lion are helpless when they have been spotted.

On the plains above the Rutshuru River the sunscorched bones of departed hippo dot endless meadows like skeletons of a long-lost invasion fleet. Contrary to report, lion will attack adult hippo, and will attack them regularly and successfully. I could understand how a super-pride might form in hippo country, for to deal with prey so powerful with minimum risk to the predator a pride such as I had observed would be necessary. Under normal circumstances, however, a pride of this magnitude would face diminishing returns. A dead wildebeest does not go far when there are that many mouths to feed.

In the Kruger reserve one encounters such normal lion circumstance. Buffalo is the most dangerous animal that a pride may attack; and there are not many buffalo. Wildebeest and impala are the usual lion food, and for such prey the normal hunting pride of a male and two or three females forms an ideal unit. But the Kruger scientists and wardens regard my Congo observation as not at all unusual. Super-prides up to thirty-five have not been uncommon. And one of forty-five brought a fair sprinkle of grey hair to the Park administration. Simply to exist it destroyed all game in any area it frequented, thus damaging the natural balances of other species. And since the pride habitually roamed about less than fully fed, there was always the possibility that a careless tourist or two might be included in the pride's lean diet. To the relief of the Kruger administration, the pride recently vanished presumably into Moçambique, to become a Portuguese problem.

What force can assemble such frightening, organized, tactically unified predatory societies in the face of all sane laws of natural balance? I can only suggest, even at the risk of anthropomorphism, that in superbly successful predator species such as the lion or the human, dominance is a power that can get out of hand. The accident of an extraordinary endowment of dominance in the personality of an individual male lion may act as a magnet to effect coalition of prides into super-prides, and the creation of a hunting unit so efficient as to be self-defeating.

For an example of how such an excessively endowed male may affect the workings of an animal society—in this case, a non-predatory one—we must turn to the studies of C. R. Carpenter, and once more inspect the record of the rhesus monkeys transported from India to Santiago Island.

Among all the generalizations which one may tentatively put forward concerning tendencies in animal conduct, none rests more firmly on universal observation than Carpenter's own conclusion, that faced by territorial invasion the home team almost always wins. Warfare can be, and must be, continuous along territorial boundaries. Hostility for one's neighbour must be unremitting, and when one meets him at the fence line one must give every evidence of intended rape, pillage, and bloodiest invasion. But when the shouting is all over and perhaps a skull cracked here and there, it is the rule that both sides retire where they came from.

We cannot say that conquest never occurs in the world of animals. Our studies are too incomplete and have been so far too hit-or-miss to state that permanent conquest is a type of behaviour confined solely to that species currently most eminent in world affairs. A family of gibbons, we know, will conduct a grape raid into a neighbouring arboreal pasture; and a hawk, if he can get away with it, will sneak an occasional titbit from the next hawk's mouse field. But such disorderly conduct in the world of animals seems with rare exceptions directed towards an immediate objective with rapid retirement in mind from the beginning. The fundamental rights of territory are honoured even when they are being violated.

Despite our incomplete knowledge of animal affairs, one would be sorely tempted to state flatly that territorial conquest is a mode of animal behaviour so sporadic as to be of no evolutionary significance, were it not for an exception so carefully observed and so carefully analyzed as to causes, that one can only conclude that conquest as man knows it must occur in the animal world when conditions properly combine.

The rhesus monkeys transported from India, we will recall, were about three hundred and fifty in number; went to pieces morally on the voyage; and, resettled on the little Puerto Rican island, within about a year divided their thirty-six acres into territories, established their societies and regained their self-respect. In the light of what happened later one must keep in mind that these territories were new and perhaps lacked to a degree the authority over behaviour that older territories might exert. If this was so, however, it was not reflected in rhesus behaviour. Each group quickly established its proper hostility for neighbouring groups, and in customary isolation quickly welded its social life into an amiable, xenophobic whole.

One of the objects of Carpenter's study was dominance. He had developed in the course of other primate studies certain criteria for dominant behaviour: how often one male would be the leader in a move towards a new feeding place, and how often another; which made the first move towards food in the morning, and which towards rest at night; which took the lead in territorial disputes, or voiced the first call in an emergency. Such criteria compiled in the dossier of each male in a single society gave in sum the individual's rank order in the hierarchy. And it told more. It gave one an index of relative dominance that could be applied to a whole species.

Primates are not like jackdaws. There is no rigorous rank order in which every individual must always assume the same status in relation to every other individual. In primate societies there is simply a tendency for one male rather than another to take leadership in situations. Among gorillas that tendency is at its peak, so that one male rules and is never disputed. Among baboons the tendency is strong; a few males in the troop will make almost all the decisions, and the dominant rank of one male in relation to another will be quite distinct. The howler, for all his violent vocabulary, asserts the least rank in relation to his fellows. His is the closest to a co-operative, live-and-let-live, equalitarian society to be found in the primate world.

The rhesus monkey falls somewhere between the baboon and the howler. In a normal society containing half a dozen males, Number One will take the lead or win the argument on perhaps four or five times as many occasions as Number Last. And Carpenter found the ratio of dominance in his transported rhesus society on Santiago Island to be of such a moderate sort, differing little from that of untransported rhesus societies which he had studied in India and Siam. But while he was studying his various groups and making his calculations of dominance, an astonishing event took place. Group I embarked on conquest.

Group I seemed no different from any other troop on the island. It was average in size and contained the normal distribution of males, females, juveniles, and infants. Its territory was of the same order of magnitude, and the food supply—which as I have mentioned was distributed daily by a caretaker—was equally available to all. No reason for systematic aggression could at first be discovered. But conquest nevertheless occurred.

Daily Group I infringed on its neighbours—and got away with it. Daily, regularly, Group I made its feeding excursions on to the territories of not just one but five neighbouring societies. Group I was opposed, as it had to be opposed, by the injured societies. There was no weakness in the opposition. But Group I by some mysterious power broke that most fundamental of animal laws, that the home team wins. In this case the home teams, all of them, lost; and Group I had its way on opposition territory. The mystery, however, became quickly solved.

Group I contained a male of almost unbelievable dominance. He was Number One, of course, and his factor of dominance as compared to Number Last was about fifty. While a normal maximum in the rhesus would be about five, Number One had as great an advantage as that even over Number Two. That all-powerful natural accident, conception, had placed in the genes of a remarkable monkey such resources of strength, of energy, of courage, and of assurance that he had become a giant of dominance. And his very presence in a society amazingly enough communicated to all members of the society the resources of his nature. Group I was pervaded by its leader's character, and despite all laws of territorial behaviour acquired the capacity, as a society, to dominate its neighbours.

Carpenter removed the master monkey from the master society. The troop immediately fell back to its own territory. Not once during the exile of its leader did the society commit a single act of trespass. Then Carpenter restored the monkey to his fellows. Without hesitation Group I returned to its field of conquest.

I find it difficult to review Dr. Carpenter's careful study without recalling certain engimas of the lion and of man.

4

Nowhere in all the unexplored jungle of animal behaviour does the observer catch more fleeting glimpses of profound, suggested truths than along the shadowed paths of animal dominance. So little do we truly know that observations are frequently little but hints. A movement is reflected in a still pool; but when we look up, nothing is there. A face peers at us from the depths of a vine; but when we stir the leaves, the face is gone.

We may say with certainty that the instinct for hierarchy benefits many an animal society. Wild geese are assured that on their long flight south in escape from storm and winter the strong will fly first, breaking the wind, and that the ranks of the V will remain unbroken. A herd of migrating elephants may proceed with assurance that the strong and experienced will lead the way, and the weak and unwise will follow protected.

We may say with equal certainty, based on innumerable observations, that dominance brings many an unpleasantness to a society of animals. Punishment tends to be handed down, since pecking goes not to the deserving but to the next creature down the line. To be high in rank is to be privileged in all things, and to be low in rank to possess but one satisfaction, that there is probably someone worse off than yourself. Yet discontent with one's status is a scarce commodity in a state of nature. Hierarchy is a force too valuable for natural selection ever to have favoured the discontented.

We may say a few things with certainty, for they are logical, apparent, and have been thoroughly observed. But still one comes back to the fleeting faces beside the path and the startled movements reflected in ancient pools. One asks remote questions, and recalls strange stories.

How do dominated males in certain antelope species resign themselves so utterly to life without sex? And one recalls an observation from Asia, recorded by Fraser Darling, that answers the question not at all, and simply opens a wider one.

It is a very simple story. The owner of a small herd of water buffaloes had a bull incapable of serving all the cows. He bought two more bulls. Immediately the three bulls entered into a struggle for dominance. The original bull, perhaps benefited by his seniority, succeeded in so thoroughly dominating the new bulls that they became impotent. He, on the other hand, was now capable of serving the entire herd.

Can psychological castration be the lot of the dominated? We cannot say, we lack evidence. Can increased sexual potency be a reward for the dominating? Carpenter recorded a biological phenomenon among rhesus monkeys. Oestrus in the female primate consists of that part of her cycle in which she is sexually responsive. In her 28-day menstrual cycle, the normal rhesus female is sexually responsive for just eight days. But on Santiago Island the female consorts of dominating males showed definitely prolonged periods of oestrus.

What is the true relation of social status to sexual powers? What physiological forces are released by hierarchical attainment? We do not know. We have just these fleeting glimpses. But again, an obscure study of dominance is recalled to one's mind, answering no question but opening others.

A herd of dairy cows demonstrates a butting order almost as severe as the pecking order of barnyard hens. It gains nothing thereby, neither advantages of access to food nor bulls nor shelter. No physiological consequence results. An elaborate study of a large herd on a Louisiana experimental farm revealed that milk production among dominated cows differed not at all from the dominating. But let us reflect. A butting order will be established by cows themselves the product of artificial insemination who never in their lives will glimpse a bull.

What dark wonders of animal nature does the hierarchical instinct serve?

Alex Forbes, headmaster at Ecole Internationale at Geneva, has described to me a forest pool called Fairy Springs in his native New Zealand. Trout inhabiting the pool wait for visitors to throw in food. They wait in files, each file with a territory, each trout with a place in his file. The water is so clear, and the pebbles on the pool's bottom are so varied in their patterns, and the speckled markings of each trout are so distinctive, that the exact position of an individual fish may be marked in the visitor's mind. Then food is thrown in. The tranquil pool is afflicted by a storm of fish. But when the storm has passed and the water has cleared, there again one finds the trout each file to its territory, each fish to its proper position in relation not only to the file but to the pebbles on the bottom of the pool.

What advantage does a society of fish gain from such a rigorous rank order? High rank confers no favour in feeding. We do not know what relation dominance may bear to breeding in a school of fish, but any advantage would seem obscure. The society's protection is scarcely advanced; and while the trout by their disciplined behaviour may thereby collect more food from awed tourists it seems doubtful that nature has designed their conduct towards that end.

One may conclude that in the eternal workings of natural selection an instinct for order has been found superior to an impulse for disorder. If nature abhors a vacuum, it likewise abhors anarchy. The instinct of territory may benefit the muskrat in the spacing of his food supply; the field rodent in his protection from predatory birds; the baboon in his creation of a welded society: yet the rare marsh warbler, benefited little, will still hotly defend a territory.

Rank order of dominance similarly may insure in one society strong leadership, in another lack of social friction, in another the genetic virtue that only the best will breed: to a school of fish in Fairy Springs it will contribute no value other than decorative. But the hour of a particular species is a small thing in the time of all living beings. And what evolution has found wise in the past, wise in the generality, wise in all the ancient sortings, these things must we bear—whether we be lion or trout or cow or kob—in the particularity of our fleeting hour.

I may reach such a happy conclusion, neatly comprehensible, concerning a prejudice in favour of order that touches all living things. And there is at least a fair probability that I shall be right. But I have not explained such a natural prejudice; I have merely recorded it. And an uneasiness assails me. As the instinct for territory expresses some primal force which I may call animal nostalgia but cannot comprehend, so dominance may express some primal force for which I have neither hint nor name. I walk the high savannah and catch glimpses of stars that vanish when I bring my eyes to focus. Was the star perhaps a dark one? I walk the jungle path again—the wilderness not only of my long beginnings but of my own impenetrable nature—and images of dominance flit like bats through the void of my consciousness: the grinning face of a snaggle-toothed monarch; young lions dead; the drifting odour of a distant crematorium and of the roasting flesh of Jews; a defeated rooster, dethroned and unsexed; a humiliated guest departing early from a Westchester dinner party; a lizard bobbing his head four times in the presence of his master; a boasting schoolboy; a jackdaw fixing another jackdaw with a glittering stare; the trumpeting of a bull elephant in some nameless valley—or is it a sound of trumpets from hidden reaches of my own immemorial soul?

What in the primal nature of life has produced a force so pervasive, so agonizing, so precious? I do not know. I cannot guess. Somewhere in the dark wilderness of my ultimate beginnings lie moonlit pastures that I shall never see. But how precious is the force to life itself may be read in the death of individual creatures, as it may be read in the death of species.

Some years ago I came on an obscure but well-developed scientific paper called *Social Dominance in Mice*, by

Smith and Ross, in a journal called *Physiological Zoology*. So dehydrated was its scientific English that the paper was not only obscure; it was totally opaque, and I failed to understand it. But I made notes on it, and more than a year later going over my notes I beheld the lightning. And on my next opportunity to visit the British Museum I exhumed the paper.

The zoologists had taken thirty male mice and caged them in groups of three each. Within each group of three dominance was determined by such means as tail-biting and direct attack, and subordinance by squealing and submissive postures. Within three days the dominant male was recognizable in each of the ten cages, not only on the part of the zoologists but on the part of the dominated mice. Rank order having been established, on the fourth day all fighting ceased. The mice were now weighed and examined. All thirty were healthy. The dominant mice weighed slightly heavier on the average than the dominated, but not significantly so.

Now the essence of the experiment began. The mice were fed amply, but on a vitamin-deficient diet. The vitamin deprivation was such that the mice could not survive. In seventeen days all but two were dead. They had been given equal nourishment, and subjected to equal deprivation. Yet in every one of the ten cages the dominating mouse outlived his dominated fellows.

Dominance—beyond any comprehension—is related to the mystery of the fundamental life force.

A last haunting reference to the primal evaluation of dominance is being recorded today by that dying species, the mountain gorilla. How many individuals are left we do not know; some guess a thousand, some five thousand. All live in the general area where the Congo, Uganda, and Ruanda-Urundi meet. Above Walter Baumgartel's Travellers Rest on the high slopes of the Virunga chain of volcanoes there are bamboo forests at an altitude of about ten thousand feet. In these bamboo forests from which they gain their nourishment live a large share of all surviving mountain gorillas.

The forest ape, by and large, is an evolutionary failure. He became too specialized in his dependence on the forest both in his need for fruit and in his need for boughs. The ape's brachiating mode of getting about, swinging from limb to limb, resulted in anatomical specializations that confined him to forest environments. When five or ten million years ago he encountered a climatic crisis and diminishing forests (we shall go back to all this when we consider the emergence of man) his evolutionary road turned down. And his size became a crucial factor. The only one of the four great apes that can be said to thrive today even though in a limited area is the gibbon, the smallest. The chimpanzee, next largest, manages just to get by in restricted areas of Central Africa. The two largest, the orang and the gorilla, faced the same problem of huge bulk and diminished supply of forest food. The orang stayed in the trees and dies today, as it were, on the vine. But the gorilla came down from the trees on a more spectacular road to extinction.

The gorilla is today a stem-eater. And so we find the mountain species in that most limited environment, the high, inaccessible, cloud-infiltrated bamboo forests where by eternal tramping about he can just find sufficient shoots to maintain his oversize body. The farthest advanced of all the primates outside of the human line, he is a sorry paradox of architectural incongruities. Designed for life in the trees and for swinging from bough to bough, today he must scrounge for a living on the forest earth. His magnificent chest and majestic arms are approximately as meaningful to his present existence as an attic-full of memories to a bankrupt nobleman. Yet somehow, with his little, underdeveloped legs, the gorilla must scramble about on foggy mountain slopes in daily search for bamboo shoots or stems of the giant celery. The male rarely climbs a tree any more. George Schaller in a year of observation never saw one swing from a bough.

The gorilla is doomed by ancient crises beyond control or memory. Does a species know when it faces inalterable destiny and the black suction of extinction? The question is not quite so preposterous as it sounds. For there is evidence that in the way that an animal knows anything—in the balance of instincts governing its behaviour—gorilla instinct has responded to the hopelessness of a tragic situation.

When in 1942 C. R. Carpenter wrote that every primate society ever observed maintained and defended a territory, the gorilla had not yet been properly studied. Schaller's

observations of at least eleven societies will reveal that the gorilla is the lone exception. Whether the troop be of family size containing perhaps one male and three females, or whether it be so large and complex as to include many adult males and females, the society will defend no territory. A troop keeps itself apart, and there is social antagonism of a sort. If two wandering bands meet in the thickness of the forest a limited amount of chest-beating will ensue, but then the troops will separate and go their ways. The conflict is not territorial.

It is all but inconceivable that the gorilla alone among primates has no territorial history. Perhaps he left that history behind when he came down from the trees. Or perhaps it is a more recent loss. There is evidence at Travellers Rest that some kind of territorial conflict may yet be possible granted the presence of exceptionally vital males. In 1958 two such males fought on crumbling, gullied slopes high on Mt. Muhavura. Both were giants of quarter-ton bulk. Each was of a different troop. Through bamboo thickets and higher above into clumps of lichen-covered hypericum trees just below the volcano's crater they fought for twelve days until at last one was killed. Why had they fought? It had not been a sexual rivalry. The victor, who two years later died of gastroenteritis leaving a son and five widows, acquired none of his females from the vanquished. Neither can such prolonged and fatal conflict seem a reasonable consequence of simple contact between social groups. The fight was interpreted as a territorial debate since no other cause could be discerned.

There is fair reason to believe that vital discouragement in all but exceptional gorillas has weakened the territorial instinct. Other strange facets of behaviour, grotesque and profound, shadow the life of a tragic creature. The gorilla has no homeplace at the centre of his wanderings. Instead, wherever he finds himself at nightfall he builds himself a nest on the ground. The chimpanzee still does so in the trees, and perhaps the gorilla constructs his resting place out of arboreal nostalgias. In any event, he will not rise from his nest at night even to defecate. And so he must qualify as that rarest of animal beings, one who fouls his own sleeping-place.

But it is the weakness of the sexual instinct that throws the most significant shadow on the daily life of the doomed creature. He copulates seldom. Schaller followed a large troop containing six males and nine females, and had the opportunity of direct observation for forty-one hours spread over twenty-five days. Yet only twice did he observe copulation. In neither case did the dominant male take part although his females had intercourse with other males in his presence.

A tall, dignified, half-Watutsi named Reuben, who lives above Kisoro, must rank among the most famous animal guides in the world, and the young gorilla in the London zoo bears his name. For nineteen years Reuben's thin legs have taken him almost daily up the volcanoes to check the presence and movements of gorilla bands. Yet on only three occasions in all the nineteen years has Reuben witnessed copulation. The suggestion has been made to me that sexual activity may take place at night. A warden in the Kruger reserve with fifteen years of experience has never observed copulation between impala, so strictly do the males confine their activities to night hours. But the gorilla is a creature with after-dark habits all too plain. He takes to his single bed at sunset, and fails to rise from it until dawn for even the most elemental purposes.

The mountain gorilla moves through the twilight of a species' history. And in the way of the animal he knows his dark rendezvous. Vital instincts lose their hold. Primate compulsions universal in their incidence, frequently uproarious in their expression, fade like colour from the skin of the dying. Sex no longer beckons him; territory no longer commands his defensive energies; he no longer bothers even to keep his nest clean. But as the last long dusk encloses his future, and things that have mattered to ancestral species for seventy million years cease now to concern him, one last hold yet compels his life. The tragic figure sloping through the cloudy forests of mysterious African volcanoes still clings to the treasure of his dominance, and he will clutch that most precious of animal possessions even to his species' grave.

Chapter 5
Love's Antique Hand

It has been the fashion of this century to attribute to the animal the simplest possible pattern of instincts. First and most undeniable was his instinct to survive as an individual creature; his will to outlive circumstances of the most discouraging order and outwit enemies of the most discouraging appetites; his unyielding, unthinking, most fundamental vital purpose, in other words, to stave off death and to avoid to the best of his ability death's harbinger, pain. Other basic needs, for food, for sexual expression, for the welfare of the children, could be regarded if one were careless as subdivisions in one way or another of the survival urge.

To survive, one must eat. But the satisfaction of hunger can be accomplished at times only at risk of one's life. Too frequently in a world scrambling with creatures each equally involved with the pangs of hunger, an animal must play fast and loose with his life expectancy if he is to have any dinner expectancy at all. In that they may often conflict, the two instincts are distinct. And the demands of sex may likewise place before the animal a most embarrassing dilemma in relation to his natural impulse to live to a ripe old age. And should he be one of those creatures who takes an interest in the welfare of his young, then a fourth dimension is added to the sphere of inner instinctual conflict.

These few fundamental drives, however, seemed to careful observers the maximum number that the individual animal had to adjust in its daily life of resolving the opportun-

ities and hazards of habitat by means of the endowments
of his species: or so we used to believe. But the revolution that is proceeding these days in the natural sciences
threatens many a premise both scientific and philosophical
as it reduces to ruin our oversimplified view of animal behaviour. Three fundamental drives, for territory, for status
and for organized society become evident in the primates,
those creatures closest to ourselves. And behind all three
looms the vague outline of a fourth force, deep-set, un-
accountable, and perhaps unprovable: a mysterious need
for order. What more may be out there, we cannot yet
know.

None of these forces come to us as some special endowment of the human being. All have ancient springs in the
most remote foothills of our misty, animal past. Food, sex,
family, survival, property, sovereignty, rank, society—order, perhaps, itself—all or some must be reckoned as inter-
playing needs forming the personality and influencing the
conduct of any animal that lives. The complicated life
may have been raised to new heights by the human creature; we did not invent it.

No human urge better illustrates the complexity of life
than love. In the telling of the human story, men, women,
children and dramatists have alike been fascinated by the
inner conflicts and external travails that love may bring.
Love vs. duty, love vs. honour, love vs. God or ambition or
country; there is no end to the conflicts and complications
that sex can introduce to the least stormy of human lives.
And the animal, in his own way, has it no easier.

The demands of the loins must be satisfied. But in the
wild animal, as in civilized man, they must be satisfied in
conflict with many another demand. The lurid sex-life of
the domesticated cat has small counterpart in the African
bush; the lion is a family man. The amiable promiscuity
of the domesticated dog is a rare sort of thing in a state of
nature; the male wolf is responsible. We may gawk in secret, lascivious envy at the uninhibited sexual goings-on
of our animal friends in the zoo. But all have traded the
hard rules of nature for the more tolerant mastery of man.
In the wild, love—like life itself—has a passel of problems.

We shall now inspect the command to love as it exists
in the natural order. And the more deeply we look into
it, the more sharply we shall find revealed the multiplicity

of its rival instincts, and the means by which animals resolved their conflicting commands.

2

Len Howard lives alone in a Sussex cottage surrounded by birds, and signs such as NO VISITORS, and KEEP OUT, and THIS MEANS YOU. She is another of that peculiar breed, the British bird-watcher, but she bears no relationship to the illustrious Eliot. It has been Miss Len Howard's contention that if a bird in a natural state is to be observed as an individual, then the curtain of fear must be removed from his actions. He must regard the human observer, as Marais' baboons came to regard their observer in the Waterberg, as part of the natural scenery; only then is his behaviour unconditioned by the fear of man. Marais gave three years of his life to this end, in a Transvaal wilderness; Miss Howard has given a far larger portion of her life to the obliteration of self in the wilderness of an unvisited Sussex garden. Her compelling book, *Birds as Individuals*, tells many a life story gathered season by season from the fluttering world of her lone regard.

One of these biographies is the story of a great tit whom Miss Howard called Jane, and who lived about the place for some six years. Jane was a handsome, competent bird with a habit unique among great tits of singing during nesting time, and a fancy for large males as mates. The great tit is one of those birds that cherish monogamy, and mate for life. But Jane was widowed twice.

In her fourth year, Jane's mate died of injuries to a leg, so she took a second. This was a strong young fellow but he lacked something. Jane and her first mate had held a territory in the garden which the second was unable to hold. The two were driven down the road where they nested in a tree, while a more pugnacious pair took over the old place. In the tree down the road Jane fledged her new brood, but disaster struck again. The second husband died of an encounter with a cat. And the widow needed all her experience and competence to keep the fledglings alive by herself. Sometimes the pugnacious male who had ousted the pair from the garden would drop by and help out with a caterpillar. In one way or another, she managed.

The following year Jane took her third mate, again a young bird, a son of the pugnacious pair. He was also large and handsome, with a broad dark front. Events were to prove that if the second husband had lacked something, then this third lacked nothing at all. For very shortly another female entered the lives of Jane and her new mate. This female Miss Howard called Grey.

Grey was unmated. She was a shy, indecisive bird quite different from Jane. Grey first entered the Sussex cottage world when Jane encountered her in the orchard. The two fell into competition for a nesting box, but by early April both were bringing moss to it. Jane regularly threw out every last bit of Grey's moss. Never did Grey throw out Jane's. But some kind of rare accommodation must have been established between the two females. For soon Miss Howard found them both in the nesting box, making soft nesting sounds together.

In the meantime Jane's third husband was demonstrating all the pugnacity of his parents. Now and again he would glance in curiously at the nesting activities of the two females. For the most part, however, he so busied himself with the defence of his territory, the tree in the orchard, that he lost all his crown feathers in combat. From this time on he was known as Baldhead. Had he been an

older bird, he might perhaps have been more perturbed at what was going on in his own home; but since his wife was experienced, and Baldhead was enjoying his first mated year, he gave himself over to the glorious battles of the treetops.

Down below, meanwhile, the friendship of Jane and Grey proceeded. And so did the nest-building. Jane would sing, in her own special way, as she flew in with building materials. Grey, small and silent, would accompany her. Then, one day, Jane laid her first egg. That finished the friendship. Grey was barred from Jane's nest.

Now Grey, alone and distracted, turned hastily to building a nest of her own in a nearby tree. She brought moss. She stole fluffy, colourful wool from the cottage. So frantic was her hurry that Miss Howard had no heart to stop her. Rapidly the nest took form. It seemed a gay many-coloured altar on which a doomed spinster would lay nothing but hopes. Or so it seemed, at least, until Miss Howard saw Baldhead guarding both trees and the reason for Grey's hurry became evident. She had acquired a mate, Jane's husband. The energetic young Baldhead had thereby doubled his territory, doubled his responsibilities, and better than doubled—in the ordered, monogamous world of birds—opportunity for disaster.

Shortly Grey laid her first egg. Now Baldhead was the busiest young great tit in Sussex. He fed Grey. He fed Jane. He defended Grey's tree. He defended Jane's tree. When he fed Grey in her tree, Jane would spy from hers, and ruffle her feathers. But if something seemed not quite right to Jane, to Baldhead all things seemed in order. He was simply doing his enormous best for both of the females who had made nesting sounds together. His response to Jane's irritation was to feed her.

But now animal law slowly tightened. On May eighth of that year Jane's nestlings began to hatch. Promptly the world of the young husband became a far more complicated place. He saw the nestlings. He fed them. He fed his legal wife. But never once again did he feed Grey. She made sounds from her tree. He ignored her. She came out of her nest, fluttered her wings before him, made small cries. He avoided her. She came to the nest of her former friend, whimpering and fluttering; Jane and Baldhead together drove her away.

Now, on the eleventh of May, three days after Jane's, Grey's young began to hatch. The mother sat on her nest in the nearby tree making queer distressed sounds. Baldhead would not come near. Again and again she left her nest to follow him with quivering wings. His neglect was complete. Again and again she made brief, fluttering excursions to Jane's nest, and was beaten off. Half-heartedly Grey tried to feed her nestlings. It was not an impossible chore for a mateless female, as Jane had once proved when the cat consumed her second husband. But Jane's troubles had been limited to widowhood; Grey's problem was desertion. The final encounter between Grey and Baldhead occurred in a room in the Sussex cottage. The windows were always open. The cottage like the owner's person had no more special significance to birds than a sheltered place in the orchard. On this day Miss Howard had laid out food, and Grey had been among those who came. Then Baldhead appeared. Instantly Grey crouched before him, making little cries and quivering her wings. The young male, who had seemed equal to anything but whose first venture into family life had become so complicated, looked at her curiously. He tried to mount her. Angrily she drove him off and fled the cottage. To Miss Howard's knowledge neither looked at the other again.

Grey retired to her nest, and her nestlings. She seldom came out. And one afternoon she died. Grey's nestlings survived her by very few hours.

Jane's brood thrived. One cannot say that Jane and young Baldhead lived happily ever after. The handsome female with the curious habit of singing at nesting time lived to have another brood. She was growing old, however, and a little tired. Jane survived the bad winter of 1947, and died the following April.

3

Even the basic outline of Miss Howard's simple tale of the life and loves of three great tits in Sussex might once have been dismissed by scientific orthodoxy as the rankest sort of anthropomorphism But we should all know enough by now to understand that in the personal biography of any animal, such a story can be true. The sexual instinct, in its choice of objects, may become confused. Once embarked on a wrong course, however, the sexual attachment will encounter animal law in the form of conflicting commands, the multiplicity and subtleties of which we are only beginning to grasp.

How far an animal may go in its original confusion concerning a proper mate furnishes a long, pathetic theme in the world of animals. Birds are most unfortunately sub-

ject to getting mixed up, and of staying mixed up for a long time. There was a white peacock, for instance, at Schonnbrun Zoo in Vienna, whose inordinately misplaced affections made him an object of sympathy for many years. The peacock was the lone survivor of a brood that had died in a cold wave. A keeper succeeded in saving his life by placing him in the warmest building in the zoo, the reptile house. There the peacock grew up.

The reptile house at the Schonnbrun Zoo contained the usual assortment of snakes and lizards safely behind glass. These the white peacock ignored. But out in the open was a group of those giant tortoises like slow-moving boulders descended from some magical time when the very rocks held life. Their movements fascinated the innocent peacock. He followed them about. And when time came for such matters, the maturing white peacock fell in love with a tortoise. The bird refused to eat if removed from the reptile house. Neither would he give eye or least affection to the most attractive peahen the keeper could find. He had pledged his troth as birds will do, and monogamous instincts kept his heart unwavering. Through quite a long life the white peacock never left the reptile house, or ceased to follow his tortoise about.

Konrad Lorenz had a goose who grew up with chickens with no other geese about. She fell in love with a Rhode-Island red rooster and would not be separated from him. In a normal barnyard such an event would cause comment; in the barnyard of an eminent naturalist it spoke plainly and publicly of hidden disgraces which the naturalist must be planning for his animal friends. The embarrassed Lorenz took himself to market and bought the whitest, fattest, most hell-raising gander that the countryside could provide. The gander got nowhere; the goose repelled his most passionate advances. Her heart belonged to the big red rooster.

The sad tendency for birds to become fascinated by those with whom they are raised, regardless of species, brought Lorenz other difficulties. One of the male jackdaws whom he had raised from chickdom turned his sexual attentions on Lorenz. The general impracticality of the liaison approximated that of the peacock and the tortoise, and should have proved no greater inconvenience to the naturalist than it did to the Permian leftover. But the jackdaw, as we have seen, is a fellow of remarkable ways. And jackdaw love is expressed not merely by following someone about with a dejected, unrequited look. There is persistence, and there is ingenuity; there are even traditions.

The female expresses devotion to her mate by preening him. This is not a custom of the mating season but a year-around affair. She takes endless pleasure in sitting beside him gently poking his black feathers with her bill, giving special attention to the neck feathers, while with a pleasure just as endless he sits with eyes half-closed in a stupor of contentment. The male, on the other hand, expresses his devotion to the female by feeding her. This too is a matter not confined to the nesting season. Jackdaws begin their daily devotions when as immature birds they first pair, a year before mating.

Lorenz' jackdaw, being a male, most naturally expressed his affection for the naturalist by attempting to feed him. The attempt was rejected. But the jackdaw was not to be put off easily. He would drift about apparently absorbed by other things, while in fact keeping a sharp eye on the naturalist's movements. Lorenz had small interest in adopting a jackdaw diet, so he kept an equally sharp eye on the lovelorn bird. What had started as an affectionate gesture became a relentless pursuit. The jackdaw, of course, won. When the naturalist one afternoon sat absorbed by a book, he received in his mouth a full beakload of minced worm and jackdaw saliva.

The violence of Lorenz' rejection was now enough, one would think, to discourage the most smitten bird. It did, indeed, seem to convince the jackdaw that something had gone wrong; the mouth was the wrong place. From that time on the defensive problem became that of keeping the young jackdaw from sneaking up from behind to deposit a mushy warm tribute of love in Lorenz' ear.

Confusion concerning the object of sexual attention is a state of affairs far more likely to come about among domesticated or captive animals than among animals in the wild. But free or captive we who direct a portion of our behaviour through the associative powers of learning must expect now and then to become a little confused. Marais' young otter would probably have had as little difficulty in recognizing a female otter as he had in accepting the merits of water and fish. Marais' young baboon, however, needed teaching: teaching as to where he should go, what he should eat, even, to an appreciable extent, whom he should love. The adult male baboon has achieved a notorious and undeserved reputation for homosexuality simply because he so freely and joyfully mounts his fellow male. It is nothing but an error of observation on the baboon's part. Discovering his mistake, he immediately moves on until he mounts somebody who responds better. What was remarkable about the peacock and Lorenz' young jackdaw was not so much that they suffered sexual confusion, but that as males they persisted in their loving devotions despite the noteworthy unresponsiveness of tortoise and naturalist.

It is female responsiveness, as a rule, that guides and excites masculine attention. As the kingdom of the animal ascends, so likewise ascends the power of the female. She becomes a sexual specialist. Her ever-rising role rests on three developing masculine weaknesses; first his dependence on learning, which tends to produce a general woolly-mindedness concerning the proper object of sexual devotion; second a multiplication of instincts, resulting in a natural tendency to have things other than sex on his mind; and, third, among primates, the introduction of continual, periodic sexual activity which however it may broaden the pleasures of masculine life can only detract from the ardour of the annual, bellowing stampede.

Masculine woolly-mindedness has been a source of female power for a long way back. The wood frog is an amphibian, and so he is a fairly ancient creature. One can with extreme doubt ascribe to his conduct any great confusion caused by over-much learning. But the male wood frog will attempt copulation with almost anything that moves; another male, or even a bit of leaf floating past in his stream. If a female lies very quietly she will float through a group of male wood frogs with most disappointing results. All will ignore her. But let her give a wiggle. All, simultaneously, will get the idea.

Experiments have been performed on the usual mice, rats, and guinea pigs to determine what sense in the male most effectively rouses his sexual excitement. Remove his sense of smell: if he can see, he will respond; remove his sight: if he can feel, he will still respond. The movement of the female is what excites him, and what he must sense.

The specific conclusion of zoology regarding such experiments has been that it is not the mere presence of a female but her behaviour that is the determining factor in sexual discrimination. The conservative Zuckerman while giving full credit to the danger of sweeping generalizations has stated that "it is possible that in all lower animals the attitude of the female is, in some way or other, a necessary factor in eliciting the full sexual response of the male."

Whether we know it or not, such a statement juggles high-explosives as if they were Indian clubs. If it is the behaviour of the female towards a particular male that awakens his full sexual response, then we must conclude that the power of sexual choice rests largely with the female, and that sexual competition is not so much between males for the female of their choice, as between females for the male of theirs. And so the male becomes the sexual attraction, and the female in her response the sexual aggressor.

Cynics may on occasion have noted some such pattern in human affairs, but tradition and morality have assigned a far different role to the human female. The concept of the female as a passive sexual attraction for which competing, sexually aggressive males struggle has moulded our views for many centuries. And we have imposed that human preconception on our observation of animal affairs, despite full knowledge that it is the male who through all of the natural world bears the brilliant plumage, the fancy mane, the handsome markings, whereas the female is invariably drab. If that most all-powerful judge, natural selection, saw the female as the attracting force, then the decisions handed down from the natural bench for the last half billion years have for the most part been in singular error.

It is logical that even Darwin abstained from challenging the traditional view, although sometimes his failure is startling. Males of certain species, like the elephant, for example, show increased activity of musky scent glands during the rutting season. An increase of masculine scent can have only one function, to enhance the male's attractiveness in the nostrils of the female. Yet when such a case came to Darwin's attention, he rejected the interpretation. It violated the rule that the female, not the male, does the attracting. The case went into Darwin's file of enigmas.

We can understand Darwin's reluctance to grant a single exception to the law that the female attracts the male. Competition for status and territory was unknown in his day. For lack of any observed alternative, the father of the theory of natural selection was compelled to base its dynamics on the supposed competition between attracted males struggling for the favour of the female. But a century has passed since *Origin of Species*. And now we must note in example after example that the male seldom fights, in a state of nature, for the favour of the female. He fights for territory, or for status. The male with territory attracts the female. The male with status is assured of female favour. We may turn again to Zuckerman who states flatly that the notion of males fighting during rut for the possession of females is in almost all cases an anthropomorphic argument.

The idea that the male animal is obsessed by the sexual struggle for females has been a convenient explanation for the workings of natural selection; has fitted the moral preconceptions of our time; and has had the added advantage of flattering human egos, male and female alike. But it is not true. As George Gaylord Simpson has said, concerning the wandering ups and downs and ebbs and flows of evolution: straight lines do not exist in nature, only in the minds of naturalists. So the law of the sexes that females attract and males compete exists not in observations of nature but only in the nature of the observers.

Recall the chaffinch. The first stirrings of his springtime sexual cycle come upon him when February has not yet relaxed its winter's grip, when food is still short and predators still hungry. Now, as through all the winter, he shares his sheltering holly tree with male and female alike. Yet the sexual stirrings in the male at a time still untouched by spring cause him to desert the flock, to desert the females, and seek in competition with his rivals a place to make his own. Sex, to the male, means competition for property. Sex, to the female, means choice: the choice of a male from the ranks of the propertied. It is the male who attracts and the female who chooses.

Recall the jackdaw. It is the first order of business among maturing males to settle for all time their order of dominance. That transaction completed, and the males each carefully classified according to a catalogue of jackdaw virtue, the pairing can proceed. The male seems to choose among the females. But in fact it is his rank that is the criterion of choice, and choosing is the prerogative of the female. Number One may get the best; and jackdaw pomposity may be such that Number One will now solemnly congratulate himself on his discerning taste in females. Not he, however, but the most successful female has done the choosing. Had he found himself with another rank, he would have found himself with another mate.

C. R. Carpenter has stated that in primate societies it is the female, as a rule, who is the sexual aggressor. It is a truth of most unpleasant flavour for the more orthodox consumers of the romantic fallacy; yet it is a truth that like an unsentimental surgeon must some day be invited into the amphitheatre of modern thought. Natural selection has equipped the female far more than the male with an uninterrupted vista of sexual purpose. And no action excels adultery to furnish us with observation of what havoc can be wrought in the male's complex instinctual bundle by surrender to the simpler views of an aggressive female.

Adultery as we have seen happens seldom in bird-life. The case of the three great tits concluded with marriage triumphant. But Konrad Lorenz watched a story unfold with a somewhat different conclusion. It was the only case of a broken marriage that he ever witnessed among jackdaws; and we must add very quickly, out of deference to jackdaw integrity, that the incident took place not after mating but in the year-long period of betrothal. The affair, nevertheless, assumed the proportions of a considerable jackdaw scandal.

We may recall that upon his return the prodigal jackdaw immediately entered into a conflict for dominance with the original Number One in the flock. At the time there was a vacancy in the Number Two spot, a direct consequence of the scandal. The original Number Two in the rank order had been a good-looking bird with a character not too restless. He had his arguments at first with the old Number One, and fended off the belligerent claims of Number Three. Then he settled down to enjoy his Number Twoness; to enjoy with special contentment the bright young thing with whom he paired. He fed her according to best jackdaw tradition those brimming beak-loads of minced worm and jackdaw saliva which Lorenz had so perversely failed to enjoy. She preened him.

Number Two was a bird with an insatiable yearning for having his neck feathers poked. Through the long balmy hours of the ripening springtime his fiancée would stay close to his side, crouched just a little, poking gently and tenderly at her hero's fattening throat. He could not have enough of it. He would look, to begin with, straight ahead. Then his eyes would close. And Number Two would sink, like a happy whale, into a stupefying sea of self-satisfaction.

He was in such a condition one afternoon when the first tiny tickle of terrible events entered his tranquil life. The pairing was not yet completed in the colony, and a female lacking the ring had been keeping a sharp eye on Number Two and his romantic susceptibilities. For several days she had been lingering in the pair's vicinity, ignoring other males, and camouflaging her movements as best she could. Lorenz had wondered what was coming, and fortunately witnessed the first step.

Number Two's eyes were closed. His fiancée was crouched at his side, and all that penetrated his happy daze was adulation's tickle on the left side of his neck. Then a tickle began on his right. Number Two's peace remained unbroken; his eyes remained closed. That his fiancée to round out a happy hour should shift her affectionate attention to the right hand side of his neck offered nothing other than further evidence of her devoted character. So deep was Number Two's immersion in the slumber of the senses that it took quite a while for the truth to come home. He was being tickled on both sides at once.

Abruptly he opened his eyes. In alarm quite electric he glanced about and saw the strange female on his right poking at his neck feathers. Round-eyed he looked ahead again. It was a situation quite beyond jackdaw comprehension. No rattling cry on the part of society served to warn him that danger lay about. He waited, staring ahead, for something to happen. But nothing happened. His big body blocked from his fiancée's sight any view of the Other Female. She continued to preen him with accustomed fidelity, from the left, while her brazen rival, hardened by success, advanced her caresses from the right.

We must find in our hearts a compassion sufficient to forgive Number Two the craven course he now embraced. We must recall that like Miss Howard's temporary bigamist, Baldhead, he was young. He was inexperienced. He was newly engaged to a devoted female, but the marriage would not be consummated until the following year. Instinct must have apprised him of that stark fidelity demanded by jackdaw tradition. We must recall, however, that as a bird he was subject to all the confusion which learning brings to instinct; and that as a jackdaw he was peculiarly dependent on the counsel of a society that failed to warn him. What we may find most difficult to forgive is that such a cowardly step should have been taken by an aristocrat, by a Number Two, by a privileged bird who should have accepted his responsibilities to jackdaw society and set a better example. But, again, we must do all in our power to put ourselves in the position of a male jackdaw, difficult though the feat may be, and to comprehend how delicious it must have been to have one's neck feathers tickled from both sides at once.

In any event, Number Two waited, and nothing happened, and so he took the step of damnation across the jackdaw threshold into a world of no return. He accepted the double tickle, the double tribute, the deepened, ineffable sea of double self-satisfaction. He closed his eyes. It was not very long, of course, before Number Two's fiancée began to sense that something was wrong. She glanced under his black belly and saw the feet of the Other

Female. Battle was joined in a ruffle of wings. The rival fled. And Number Two's peace was over.

The struggle was long. The fiancée became more fiercely devoted than ever as fiercely she defended what was hers. But the sexual aggressor matched her in determination as she seized every opportunity, however short, to tickle Number Two's neck feathers. On countless occasions the fiancée must have felt final victory assured. But always the aggressor returned.

What are the progressive steps in the psyche of a fought-over jackdaw? What fresh and jackdaw-decadent pleasures are enlisted to replace the normal stupor induced by the attention of a faithful mate? What cross-roads of instinct did Number Two traverse? What inhibitions of monogamy, of hierarchical responsibility, of social propriety lay in the path of jackdaw-illicit love? Naturally, we do not know. We know only that Number Two got past all the cross-roads, since one day he treated his relentless admirer to a heady beakful of minced worms and saliva.

When Number Two closed his eyes and accepted the untrodden pastures of double jackdaw-pleasure, he sealed the letter of his fate. With the beakful of worms, he dropped it in the post. From that time on the fate of three jackdaws moved rapidly towards an address unknown. The fiancée still fought, but with flagging courage. The aggressor still fled her desperate charges, but now scarcely hesitated before returning. Number Two still basked in the sunshine of his own outsize attractiveness. But in the animal world you cannot have your cake and eat it. One last barrier of instinct lay yet ahead, a barrier too tall for even a high-ranking jackdaw of such proven qualities to surmount. That the aggressor had won the battle of the females, was evident. That Number Two, under the circumstances, had been thoroughly and irrevocably taken by a hussy, was equally evident. But while the finish of the drama might seem foreclosed, its actual climax could have been foreseen by only the most sophisticated observer of animal societies.

One morning they were gone. Number Two and the Other Female had fled the flock together. And they never returned.

Illicit love had conquered all. It had demanded and received the sacrifice of all those jackdaw instincts centred about the institution of marriage. It had undermined all those curious ways of aristocratic aloofness and responsibility which the high-ranking male instinctively assumes as a burden of his privileges. It had driven a determined female, in the first place, to flout conservative sexual patterns so valuable to female interests. And finally it had impelled a jackdaw male, complacent by nature and self-satisfied by association, to take the final radical jackdaw step.

Illicit love had conquered all—but not quite all. For the pair fled and by their flight they renounced the society of their fledgling destiny. They renounced that social instrument, the flock, which carries the wisdom of jackdaw experience. The troop may be the baboon's best friend; the flock, as we have seen, bears even a portion of jackdaw instinct, as in the recognition of natural enemies. Flight from their flock meant the surrender, in a sense of some segment of their jackdaw selves. And while they might, in time, be permitted to join another, their status would be low. It is highly unlikely that Number Two would ever be anything but Number Last in a society of strangers.

Why did they flee? What intolerable force interposed its instinctual dictation to say, Yes, but go! It could scarcely have been fear of social disapproval, for jackdaw society at no single point had warned Number Two of danger; nor had it expressed the least interest in his affairs, even in a situation so extraordinary. Yet the two fled. Out of the ancient depths of animal evaluation, sex had encountered a strange, vague figure, black and unlistening, and the figure had pointed to the dubious field beyond the lonely, unknowable river.

Why did they flee? What was the figure? We cannot guess.

4

We may say, with a decent measure of reserve, qualification, hesitation, and downright doubt, that instincts press all animals in one of two contrary directions. Hunger and individual survival extend an invitation to anarchy. So also does sex, if we view it as we must as a behaviour compulsion, and not with the hindsight of its biological consequences. Other instincts, however, immediately command order: care of the young, establishment and defence of territory, social survival, dominance. We may therefore speculate that at some early moment in the evolvement of living things, natural selection found in duality of purpose a superior endowment for the creatures in its charge. The individual creature must survive; but so must his group, his population, his race, his species. And so the anarchistic instincts favour the demands of the individual creature, the instincts of order the demands of his kind.

Human observers of animal conduct have recognized in the past only that range of instincts inviting anarchy. Care of the young has been the sole exception. What natural science has begun to recognize only in the course of its contemporary revolution has been the array of instincts inviting order: territory, status, the survival of society. It is as if we have regarded the conduct of animals with an eye for the tempest alone. We have recorded the battle, not the peace; we have smelled the jungle, not the neatness of clover-clad acres; we have looked to the history of clash and chaos, and not to the signing of animal treaties. Above all—whether through error of observation, through anthropomorphism, through anthropocentric illusion of plain human density—we have failed to see the conduct of animals as anything but the product of external conflicts. Only now, with the new recognition of the forces of natural order, can we begin to perceive the inward struggles that must arise from the duality of animal nature; the debate of the instincts, the apposition of interests, and the slow beginnings of evaluation.

It is a curious characteristic of the instincts of order that most are masculine. There are exceptions, but the species are few. The female phalarope is the territorial defender. The harem of the male Cuban lizard assumes responsibility for keeping not only territory in order, but the sexual adventures of its lord. One hesitates to compare that symbol of animal nobility, the African lion, to a Cuban lizard. But the male lion, despite overwhelming dominance, abdicates certain sexual prerogatives to the females of his harem.

Should a lioness widowed by a hunter's gun attempt to join the pride of a still-flourishing male, it will not be he who decides how many lionesses he can handle. It will be the members of his harem. They will look the applicant over, accept her, reject her, or fight a bloody battle with her. He, with regal calm, will observe all from a safe distance, and accept what he gets without protest.

Such examples of feminine command of the ramparts of order are infrequent. The female may share in the defence of territory. She may participate in the protection of society. She may and probably will gain status from the rank of her male. But the three natural battlements of the forces of animal order are as essentially male in their dominion as the fourth, the care of the young, is essentially female. That fourth force may be quite sufficient to prevent the female from becoming an animal anarchist, and keep her a safe advocate of a stable society and of such conservative institutions as propertied mates. But the powerful, anarchistic impulses of sex must in the female suffer fewer head-on collisions with other instincts than occur in the psyche of her more distracted mate.

In any dilemma of conduct the male animal must choose from a broader panorama of conflicting commands than must the female. Animal choice, of course, represents simply a giving way to the more fundamental of conflicting instincts. But time and again we have seen examples of male surrender to that instinct of order which protects not himself but his kind. The two male baboons in the Waterberg chose certain death to protect their society from the dusk-veiled leopard. It was a rare sort of action. The male baboon on Monkey Hill chose defence of his status to defence of his female. This was not a rare sort of action. The great tit called Baldhead came to a point in his bigamous career when some inner force dictated that he uphold the orderly monogamous way. The only rare thing here was that he had got into such a scrape in the first place. Eliot Howard's male reed bunting faced on three occasions the choice between defending his nest from a weasel, or his territory from another reed bunting, and made every time the shocking choice of repelling his fellow reed bunting. The choice was neither astonishing nor silly. He was simply answering a masculine instinct of order more funda-

mental to the preservation of his kind than even the defence of his young.

The commands of the kind lie mostly on the male. In the complex world of the upper primate those commands become most various and pressing. Howler or gibbon, rhesus or baboon, the male must lead the group in defence of the homeland. He must preserve the society which is his one most powerful instrument of protection. He must insure that through dominance there be a minimum of disruptive quarrels and a maximum of forceful leadership within the social mechanism. All must take precedence over the command to love.

In the daily life of the upper primate, the female becomes the sexual aggressor. She is free to pursue the sexual command less distracted than her mate. Someone must initiate the act of love. More often than not, she does. Someone's insatiable appetites must see to it that masculine resources be not entirely spent on larger affairs. The appetites are usually hers. Natural selection, eternal friend of mutation's inventions, has armed the sexual specialist in primate society with that bright new ever-ready tool of her trade, sexual periodicity. And as if this were not enough to insure that the individual female have sufficient resources to keep sex among the extant instincts, natural selection has even put numbers on her side. It has favoured among primates that institution of collective female sexual action which has come to be called polygamy.

The female of course has her own problems of conflicting instincts. She is the guardian of the young, although the primate male shares this chore, as a rule, to a surprising degree. Also, though, she must survive, she must eat. And sometimes she must satisfy such necessities in direct competition with the dominant male, whose instinctual objects of self-sacrifice seldom among primates include the female. And so she must scrounge for a living, and avoid bodily injury when incurring his displeasure. But these are female demands not necessarily in conflict with sex.

Forty years ago Kempf defined primate prostitution as "the giving of sexual favours in exchange for economic advantage or physical protection." The definition was widely criticized as too ideational. It conferred on the primate female too high a degree of foresight and capacity for evaluation to be probably at an animal level. But the giving of sexual favours for economic advantage or physical protection continued to be a thriving institution in ape and monkey communities, and was finally explained as a response to the status system. The female, of inferior status in any primate rank order, has discovered that sex and survival are instincts which may be allied.

A female monkey will scramble for a bit of fruit, seize it, then discover bearing down on her the outraged dominant male to whom the food by all monkey law belongs. She will promptly present her behind to him in an effort to keep him otherwise occupied, or at least distracted, while she devours the fruit.

A female baboon, one member of a harem, may take it into her head to lead the family towards food, towards water, towards plunder or adventure, or simply towards a change of scene. Such leadership is the prerogative of the overlord. He may acquiesce. On the other hand, he may take mortal offence at such an exhibition of arrogance on the part of his female inferior, and descend on her punishment-bent. Hopefully she will present.

Promiscuity is something in which the primate female indulges only when custom or circumstances warrant. Such circumstances seldom exist in zoos. Her overlord, afflicted by the boredom of unemployment, may find a chief source of exercise in his exertions as a policeman, a condition promoting her most unswerving fidelity. But when the captive primate female falls off the wagon of virtue, she does so with a bang.

Such a fall took place among the hamadryas baboons on Monkey Hill, and its proportions were not less than spectacular. Among them was a properly wed female who developed, for reasons known only to herself, a wandering eye. This deviation from zoo orthodoxy kept her overlord a busy male. She could not have been unaware, as events turned out, either of his potentialities as a heavy-handed policeman, or of the fact that the law was on his side. But still the eye would wander.

The eye, naturally, attracted the lascivious attention of the Hill's horde of frustrated bachelors. But the overlord was a baboon of great dominance, one not to be seriously challenged. Just the same there came a day when without warning the fun broke out. In a way the fault lay with the overlord since he committed a grave tactical error. Chasing away bachelors had become his normal activity. On this occasion he chased a bachelor too far—chased him, in fact, to a point where he could no longer observe the behaviour of his female. He was out of sight for precisely forty seconds. In that forty seconds, which we must assume she had been anticipating for a very long time, the female somehow managed successful copulation with two different bachelors.

Now the overlord, heavy with suspicion and raging with cuckold fury, returned. The female saw punishment coming. She cringed, flattened herself on the ground, made piteous gestures to indicate that it all had been the fault of the bachelors, and as the unappeased overlord closed in on her, prayerfully presented.

The debate of the instincts in that sexual specialist, the primate female, need not be of too long duration.

5

One ranges through time-buried, jungle-hidden vistas of animal behaviour that may or may not have contributed to the way of the human primate. One touches on a species that tempts speculation, but about which little is known. One touches on another well enough known, but from observations made under captive conditions. Doubts, maybes, reservations, perhapses pile up. The keeper of the accounts of a revolution yet in progress recalls with sinking confidence that straight lines exist not in nature, but only in the minds of naturalists. Surrounding all conclusions like a morning mist must linger—perhaps not only for now but for always—that devious mystery of infinite variation in which natural selection cloaks its stratagems.

Nevertheless, moving figures appear on the stages we behold. They are the shadows of forces that we cannot directly observe, but again and again they appear in sharp outline playing now on this scene and now on that. We come to recognize them. We give them names: dominance, territory, social survival. Some we have never recognized before. The shadow we call sex seems not quite what we thought it. And there are shadows for which we can give no names at all, so fleeting is our glimpse of their comings and their goings. Yet slowly we must realize that these are the shadows of life itself; that they touch us, whether we will it or not; and that their presence on every stage we watch gives unity to the drama of living things.

One ranges through the vistas. One samples the savannah. One visits the tree-tops, the desert, the sea shore. And at last a single conviction takes form, an unshakeable conclusion beyond challenge, and in relief one exhibits it like a trophy.

For sheer originality in dealing with the shadows, one species stands quite alone. None other can rival him in his sorting out of instincts, turning each to his shining advantage. No creature can touch him at turning loss to profit, pain to pleasure, risk to certainty, or wasting struggle to unique satisfaction. Nor can one attribute his soaring triumphs simply to the ascendant primate brain. Others have been so blessed, and many other has fallen. This creature, and this alone, has received in his nature some ingredient of ingenuity beyond present identification. He creates. He pioneers solutions. He negotiates such treaties amongst the instincts that for daring and cunning they will last through the ages. I refer, of course, to the uninhibited, unprincipled, invincible howling monkey.

The howler will stoop to anything. No demands of honour, modesty, reticence, or conformity serve to dilute the effectiveness of his solutions. If he chooses to repel an intruder by defecating on his head, then he will defecate on his head. And by the ingenuity of his defence, he repels not only the particular invader but all potential invaders who may hear about what happened. His sweeping indifference to preserving his good name gives him freedom of defensive action equalled only by the skunk.

Neither does the howler allow his institutions to be undermined by rampant ego, ruthless ambition, or an over-opinionated nature. His passion is for the practical. He is the master of the half-decision and the total solution. If border warfare is decreed as the way of living things, the howler accepts the command and fulfils his obligation with verve and dedication—but not to a point that passes beyond pleasure. His creative contribution to the problems of war and peace must stand, as we have seen, as a model without duplicate. He has embraced all that is satisfying; he has abjured all that is dangerous.

It is to the explosive battlefield of love, however, that the howler has made his most astounding contribution. He has approached the sexual instinct with the same fine flair for the optimum with which he has approached the territorial drive. He has applied the same creative principle to embrace all that is satisfying, to abjure all that is dangerous. And he has evolved his solution with just and practical regard for all factors involved: the masculine urge more flamboyant than enduring; the feminine resources rarely glimpsed in full splendour; the general effect of sex on society; even the providing of children with the greatest possible number of devoted parents. I can think of no species of living beings which has met the anarchistic sexual impulse with quite such a far-reaching programme of order.

Rotating mateship is the term applied by science to the howling monkey's answer. What the term does not quite convey is that in a given howler society all females exert their affectionate demands on all males, that no male competes with another but rather looks on his fellow as a friend in time of need, that sexual frustration becomes something as obsolete as Jurassic reptile eggs, that masculine solidarity takes on the invulnerable overtones of a London club, and that a profound, tightly-woven democracy extends its amiable pattern through the whole society. Every adult gets all the affection that he or she can handle, and every child gets a full complement of fathers.

This appalling condition of fully-employed happiness has been achieved by the howler's customary shameless-ness. The female, as coy approximately as a mountain loco-motive, has surrendered all primate pretence of feminine passivity and has taken full charge of sexual affairs in her own relentless interest. The male has responded in the great tradition of the howling monkey by abandoning any effort to defend his good name. With such luggage forsaken as excess, it has been possible for him to concede that love's delicate contest finds himself sadly wanting, and so he invites in his friends. The Babylonian events that fol-low have been shielded from man's envious eye by the scientific term, rotating mateship.

We have seen that a group of howling monkeys contains on the average three males and seven or so females. The female has a menstrual cycle of twenty-eight days. That period is divided into the time of menstruation, when fortunately her affections are immobilized; a period pre-ceeding and succeeding menstruation when she cannot be considered a sexual predator; and the time of oestrus, or heat, about one-third of the whole cycle, when the full prowl is on. Such a limited period of overwhelming affec-tion may not seem excessive. But one must remember that from the point of view of the three male howlers, there is a fair likelihood that on any given date two females will be in oestrus simultaneously.

The female howler has a way of signalling her readiness for love by a series of tongue movements. The male has other things to think about, such as destroying the morn-ing peace with his howling, leading the troop in its search for food, defending the arboreal territory with a vocal war, or perhaps picking up infants dropped from trees. But being a male, he of course responds to the signalling tongue, and the day progresses. In due time, however, his interest will flag. While he recovers his enthusiasm the female will shift her signals to a second male. The day will continue its progress. A time will come, naturally, when the second male will start longing for somebody to drop an infant from a tree. But by now love in the tree-tops is becoming a bit complicated. The first male, well recup-erated, is not available for the relief of the second, for the third male has long since taken to headlong flight from the second female's undiminished affections, and the first male has gone to his rescue. The second male must make out as best as he can till the third has had his grapebreak. When he can hold out no longer and becomes a fugitive, then the grand design of true primate love begins to take form. Shameless, heedless of traditional pretences, undisguised by any efforts on behalf of public relations, howler love sways the treetops with a gay pattern of happy, purposeful females chasing males who by now have but one consuming goal, the concealing cloak of night.

No such rescue however is as a rule necessary. By late afternoon peace will descend on the female heart. Her affections amply fulfilled she too will turn to the simpler values, to the chatter of society or the dozy warmth of the setting sun. Should love's ample resources still stir her feminine fancy to one last mildly-seeking prowl, companionship may be difficult to find. By now the three males will have hidden themselves in some vine-concealed nook, deep in the territory's fastness, where side by side in contented solidarity they enjoy the fruit, the sunshine, and themselves; and the happy, secluded outcome of a happy, busy day.

By his realistic appraisal of upper primate instincts, the howling monkey has produced a society in which male rivalry is non-existent and female frustration is forever over; in which rank order of dominance extends only mildly to leadership and feeding, and comes closer to equalitarianism than in any other primate society; in which paternity, as a collective action, becomes a collective responsibility so that at the cry "Infant dropped from tree!" every male dutifully responds; in which the birthrate is fulsomely assured; and in which both social friction and waste of social energy have been reduced very nearly to absolute zero.

The howler's has been a handsome achievement made possible by his indifference to glory, on the one hand, and to orthodoxy on the other. But it has been made possible, also, by a way of life relatively free of enemies in a habitat bursting with food. It is more than doubtful that the beleaguered baboon on his unfriendly earth could ever have afforded such total commitment to the luxurious estimates of love.

The howler dwells in a happy valley on the far horizons of animal behaviour. Evolution nods to his achievement, but darkly passes him by. New forces gather in the primate world. New combinations of instinct take the evolutionary gamble, marshalling their genetic regiments. The monkey has had his try, and succeeded in his limited way. The ape has had his day, and largely failed. The experiment of the enlarged brain and the generalized body teeters on the edge of life's discard. Natural selection searches the Amazonian jungles, the Himalayan highlands, the hot, reaching, yellowing African savannahs.

Chapter 6

The Romantic Fallacy

During the last years of the nineteen-thirties and the first years of the Second World War, the United States of America had an attack of originality. My native land is subject to such seizures, much as a cat has fits. While such a spell is on, loose ideas float about like toy balloons at a crowded carnival, and a visit to New York is worth even the hotel bill. Our most recent convulsion may be recalled by the theatre-goer as the time of Thornton Wilder's *Our Town,* and *The Skin of Our Teeth.* The reader may think of William Saroyan. There are those who may recall the atom bomb. Anything may come out of such a time of American trance, even the Illusion of Central Position.

Who was the author of this brief theory of human growth, I do not know. It was released in my presence at a New York dinner party by a famous attorney who had heard about it somewhere. Like a bright balloon in the summer air it bobbed above our heads for a while and then drifted out of a window. I never saw it again. Perhaps as a theory it leaked. Perhaps as an American idea it lacked the properly enchanting mixture of poppycock and pragmatism. Certainly it was not so much original as striking, not so much definitive as illuminating. But as we pause in this chapter to inspect that uniquely human institution, the romantic fallacy, our digression will be simplified if first we consider the theory that floated away through a New York window while the world sat down to war.

The Illusion of Central Position, so the theory goes, is the birthright of every human baby. He enters an unknown world. He lies in a basket, or a cradle, or a clutch of straw. His eyesight is vague. Bright objects appear for his amusement, bottles and breasts for his comfort. His groping consciousness finds no reason at all to doubt the world's consecration to his needs and purposes. His Illusion of Central Position is perfect.

Time and growth, however, unfold experience, and most experiences disillusionment. The baby wakes in the midst of the impenetrable night and his wails command companionship. But weary parents sleep unheeding. The baby has encountered neglect. Or in the bright, cheerful, morning sun the inexplicable cat may scratch him. The baby has encountered hostility. Or most dreadful experience of all, in a year or so a baby sister may arrive. Now the laughter and breasts and bright objects are showered on another, and shout of the world's deceit.

Self-awareness is a human attribute; and central position, so the theory states, is its primary assumption. But every human being throughout his entire life-span faces an unending series of experiences each of which is a disillusionment affecting the primary assumption. We may accept the blow, reintegrate our personality to include it, and proceed with our Illusion of Central Position slightly dented; in that case we mature. Or we may by one fanciful means or another reject the experience, escape the disillusionment, and proceed with our primary assumption intact. In this case, of course, we fail to mature.

Human resource is a mine of great richness; and coins of many metals may ransom our illusion. We may as far as possible renounce the challenge of experience and retire at early age behind the sheltering skirts of a co-operative mother. Or, renouncing even her, we may find our refuge in mood and masturbation. Or we may take a quite contrary course and accept all blows, even seek them, while we interpret every unpleasant experience as evidence of some grand conspiracy magnificently arranged against us. By this cunning means we not only preserve intact the Illusion of Central Position; we exalt it, and see the world in its acute hostility as confirming our peculiar station.

Convictions of moral superiority; obsession with moral degradation; the necessity to run faster, climb higher, swim farther, or suffer more severely than any other human being; all may, on occasion, be means of gaining public proof for our most private illusion. And many a human institution, the theory indicates, would wither away were it not for adult dedication to the infantile assumption. The exaltation of drunkenness; belief in a personal God who hears one's prayers and will assume an answer in the next world if not in this; national lotteries, horse races, and all those forms of profitable entertainment resting on somebody's conviction that he is about to be lucky.

In our investigation of the animal sources of human behaviour we need not, fortunately, give critical attention to such of our qualities as seem exclusively human. The Illusion of Central Position, if it exists, may perhaps be one of these. But before we pass on to a concept more appropriate to our investigations, one paradoxical footnote should be added to the brief little story of man's grand illusion. The theory states that maturity is achieved by the acceptance of reality and the capacity to absorb each disillusionment and still keep going. Nonetheless the theory grants that should a man ever attain a state of total maturity—ever come to see himself, in other words, in perfect mathematical relationship to the two and one-half billion members of his species, and that species in perfect mathematical relationship to the tide of tumultuous life which has risen upon the earth and in which we represent but a single swell; and furthermore come to see our earth as but one opportunity for life among uncounted millions in our galaxy alone, and our galaxy as but one statistical improbability, nothing more, in the silent mathematics of all things—should a man, in sum, ever achieve the final, total, truthful Disillusionment of Central Position, then in all likelihood he would no longer keep going but would simply lie down, wherever he happened to be, and with a long-drawn sigh return to the oblivion from which he came.

2

The romantic fallacy stands in relation to the entire human species as the conviction of central position stands in relation to the individual human being. Both in their most naked aspects rest on assumptions of special creation, of special blessedness, of unique destiny and innate sovereignty; and both are false. But whereas a certain illusion concerning one's central position may be a primary and perhaps essential mechanism of individual existence, an energy source which we cannot wholly do without, the romantic fallacy is quite something else. It is a contrivance of human thought approximately contemporary with the steam engine and the flush toilet and like both still in widespread use. But neither the steam engine nor the flush toilet—be it recorded to their everlasting glory—has produced such varying sources of anxiety as the neurotic woman, the Communist state, or despair of civilization.

As we experience it today, the romantic fallacy is a transparent curtain of ingenious weave with a warp of rationality and a woof of sensation that hangs between ourselves and reality. So transparent is its quality that we cannot perceive its presence. So bright in outline do men and affairs appear beyond the curtain that we cannot doubt but that reality is what we observe. Yet in truth every colour has been distorted. And rare is the conclusion based on such observations that would not bear re-inspection if the curtain were lifted.

The romantic fallacy may be defined as the central conviction of modern thought that all human behaviour, with certain clearly stated exceptions, results from causes lying within the human experience. We have been generally agreed that the will to survive and the compulsions of sex are forces larger than ourselves; and most of us would include the ties of family. But having granted these exceptions, we have proceeded to a logical conclusion that since the origins of our behaviour lie within the human experience, then human behaviour itself lies within the general jurisdiction of enlightened man.

Contemporary thought may diverge wildly in its prescriptions for human salvation; but it stands firmly united in its systematic error. Whether we look to the elimination of the class struggle for the elimination of injustice, or to the abolition of nations for the abolition of war; whether we see in mother rejection the cause for human creativity, or in protein deficiency the cause for cannibals; whether we expect from poverty an explanation for crime, from lack of love an explanation for young delinquents, from city life a flowering of wickedness or from primitive simplicity a garden of goodness, the rational mind in any case views the human scene through the romantic fallacy's transparent curtain and prepares prescriptions which though quite possibly fatal to the patient may be delivered with confidence, with logic, and with the cleanest of hands.

Even though our investigations of the contemporary revolution in the natural sciences have not yet taken us to the emergence of the human stock on the African highland, to the adoption of the carnivorous way by our terrestrial primate ancestors, to the probable acquisition of the weapon as a vital necessity in the life of a predatory primate unarmed by nature, or to the final development of the big brain only half a million years ago, in the midst of the changeful African Pleistocene; still it should be apparent that the materials thus far presented place in an embarrassing light the central assumption of rational thought. Human behaviour in its broad patterns cannot with any assurance be attributed to causes lying within the human experience.

To conclude that human obsession with the acquisition of social status and material possessions is unrelated to the animal instincts for dominance and territory would be to press notions of special creation to the breaking point. To conclude that the loyalties or animosities of tribes or nations are other than the human expression of the profound territorial instinct would be to push reason over the cliff. To conclude that feminine attraction for wealth and rank, and masculine preoccupation with fortune and power and fame are human aberrations arising from sexual insecurity, hidden physical defects, childhood guilts, environmental deficiencies, the class struggle, or the cumulative moral erosions of advancing civilization, would in the light of our new knowledge of animal behaviour be to return man's gift of reason to its Pleistocene sources, unopened.

"God made all things good," wrote Jean-Jacques Rousseau. "Man meddles with them and they become evil." In a single sentence Rousseau compressed a metaphysical assumption into a rational context and fathered the romantic fallacy. Stated so baldly, the Illusion of Original Goodness may bring a shudder to the contemporary spirit. But from Rousseau's proposition a host of conclusions, all logical, all magical, came into being: that babies are born good; that in innocence resides virtue; that primitive people retain a morality which civilized people tend to lose; that a man's moral worth declines in rough proportion to his distance from the soil; that civilization must be held accountable for man's noteworthy catalogue of vices; and that human fault must therefore have its origin in human institutions, relationships, and environments. The farther one moves from the sentimental premise, the more thoroughly one forgets that a premise ever existed.

When Jean-Jacques Rousseau arrived in Paris in 1742, his image of nature had been gained from the gentle, cultivated hillsides above his native Lake of Geneva. His image of primitive people, I assume, had been formed by the ways of wild Swiss villagers in the formidable Juras. Yet curiously enough, the philosophy erected on such a foundation has long outlived the reputation of its author. Rousseau is dismissed as a muddled thinker today, even by those who most firmly hold to his muddled tenets. His noble savage is regarded as a good-natured myth by sophisticated minds whose entire intellectual scaffolding would collapse but for the props of the good-natured myth. As we shall inspect at some length, the burden of the romantic fallacy has been carried by later and more respected thinkers whom fashion has scarcely discarded.

Among all the brilliant founders of the American republic, Thomas Jefferson's name is the most adored today. Yet Jefferson dedicated much of his adult thought to the dubious proposition that the man of the soil possesses a soul degrees purer than the man of the city, and that a nation to remain uncorrupted must found its strength on rural rather than urban society. Whatever political forces may have shaped Jefferson's thinking, the proposition philosophically was sheer Rousseau. Out of it evolved the American myth of the honest, barefoot farmer boy; of the rugged, straight-talking backwoodsman; of cowboy innocence. Heartwarming images become part of the American memory: of Abraham Lincoln splitting rails, and Gary Cooper, infinitives. The farm became the symbol of national virtue. To this day a presidential candidate who cannot find some touch of the cowbarn to lean upon risks the solid distrust of the electorate.

Sir Grafton Elliot Smith is a name rather less well known than Thomas Jefferson. But he too possessed a giant intellect entirely capable of bending before the Rousseau magic. And since Elliot Smith was one of the greatest anthropologists of the last generation his authority on the original nature of man carries influence in circles where Rousseau himself would be smiled off.

It was Elliot Smith who provided the romantic fallacy with its most respectable scientific rationale. Like his contemporary, Dr. W. J. Perry, he asserted that man's original nature could be studied if one observed those primitive peoples who by physical isolation or manner of life were most thoroughly cut off from all influence of civilization. The Eskimo, living on the frigid periphery of human existence, became a favourite object of such studies. The Yahgans of Tierra del Fuego became another such favourite, for the remoteness and hostility of the Yahgan environment could scarcely be rivalled anywhere on earth. The African Bushman was and still is pursued by anthropologists in his Kalahari desert refuge. These and other peoples in tropical hideaways of central New Guinea, of Malaya, of Borneo, all revealed natures much the same—gentle, shy, extremely timid and entirely non-aggressive. Rousseau's thesis of original goodness seemed to stand confirmed. "It is important to recognize," wrote Smith, "that instead of bringing enlightenment and appeasement, civilization is responsible for most cruelties and barbarities."

The conclusion appears inarguable. His method was irreproachable, his evidence overwhelming. His error however was total, for like most scientific error it lay in the premise. The assumption that people living under remote conditions untouched by civilization will reveal like walking museum pieces the original nature of man, is quite false. The conclusion that the shy, timid, amiable, non-aggressive nature of pristine man has been revealed by the character of these people is a logical sequitur simply to a false premise. What has been revealed is nothing more than that people living where nobody else wants to live may quite possibly suffer from non-aggressive dispositions.

Who disputes with the Eskimo his blubber, his long night, his home built of ice cubes? No one. By adapting himself to a way of life superbly unattractive to Sioux or Apache, a shy creature has insured his survival in perfect confidence that he will escape the notice of all but romantic anthropologists. Similarly the timid Yahgan, though he had to retreat down the howling length of the two Americas, found at last that stronghold of desolation, the barren castle of rock and storm, that territory beyond argument, Tierra del Fuego. So has it been, concluded Sir Arthur Keith, with all the escapist peoples studied so assiduously for revelations concerning our original nature. Civilization may or may not be responsible for modern man's less ingratiating modes of behaviour. Early man may or may not have shared in the amiable disposition of the Eskimo. All that has been actually demonstrated by this loosely disciplined but immensely popular raid into the outposts of man's nature has been that timid people tend to live at unfashionable addresses.

More has, in fact, been demonstrated by the aberrations of a Thomas Jefferson and the dedications of an Elliot Smith: the powerful will to believe in man's essential purity and conditioned corruption. Despite political exposure and scientific disillusionment, despite experience and history and plain horse sense, the romantic fallacy carries on. But it proceeds in a form not unmodified by the doubts of thoughtful men. The Illusion of Original Goodness, like those remarkable illusions concerning central position, has the power to survive contradictory experience, to make certain curtsies to the inevitable, to absorb self-doubt and high levels of rationalization, and still to emerge with its natal absurdity as gloriously unbroken as a soft-boiled egg.

Jean-Jacques Rousseau's sentimental excursion into the reality of things must be more than forgiven; it must be admired. Set against its mid-eighteenth-century landscape it endures as an unforgettable camping ground marked by man's revolutionary armies: We came this way. If Rousseau knew little of nature beyond his ordered homeland—well, then, who at the time knew more? If he knew nothing at all about the primitive man whom he apotheosized, then we must recollect that the Age of Discovery had most recently closed, and that reports on the ways of distant, savage lands were not yet quite ready to be engraved on stone. Rousseau's was a transitional philosophy of incalculable revolutionary magnitude, a half-digestion of half-knowledge combined with total intuition as to what men needed.

Man's emotional dedications, in Rousseau's day, had become as a consequence of the Enlightenment of a barren order. From the time of the earliest witch and the first

taboo, divine forces had seemed to order our daily lives.
Even such humanists as the Greeks had retained the concept of hubris, that a man must not lift his head too high or
the gods, challenged, would destroy him. More immediate
to the background of modern thought had been the doc-
trinal epoch of the middle ages, equating the power of God
with the power of the state, demanding submission and
condemning doubt whether mundane or divine. With the
Enlightenment of which Rousseau was a contemporary
came man's declaration of rational independence from
the tyranny of the supernatural. The Enlightenment wrought
havoc with a certain human, emotional posture that had
been with us for a fairly long time. Windows might be
thrown open to astonishing vistas of the political and intellectual future; but the cold crept in.

Before man could acquire his first spiritual frostbite,
however, Jean-Jacques Rousseau arrived with his heart-
warming message. The gods might be dead: long live man!
For a religion of the Supernatural Being he substituted a
religion of the Natural Man. For the starving, shivering
nouveau pauvre he arrived like a Christmas delivery boy
bearing that half-baked duck, *La Nouvelle Héloise*.

How else can one explain—except as a substitute for
old religious cravings—the immoderate influence on the
rational mind of the doctrine of innate goodness? Rousseau
cannot be blamed for the defective nature of the duck;
a duck was demanded, and his was the best he could
produce at the time. Less admirable is the length of stay
that this sorry source of philosophical indigestion has made
at the table of modern thought.

That any Rousseau-derived philosophy is irrational and
contradictory is unimportant; all religions are that. But
that it is pretty on the outside and ugly within; that it
poses as scientific truth while being a metaphysical assumption; that it is fraudulent, self-pitying, debilitating,
corrosive, a down-grade view of an admirable animal:
these are other matters. The pretty assumption of man's
pristine nobility—flattering, appealing, self-inflating, solid
box-office—commands the uninspiring corollary that man's
post-creation struggles have done nothing but work him
downhill. As a source of energy and courage it makes a
very poor religion.

The poverty of the modern religion goes not unrecognized by informed men. It asks too much of the political realist to believe that the European peasant or American farmer possesses by the grace of his rural environment some quality of goodness superior to that of his urban fellow. It asks too much of the present-day observer of African affairs to believe that future African republics, responsible to an electorate conspicuously deficient in civilization, will be relatively free of such political institutions as demagogues and corruption, power rivalry and corpses on the border.

Man's propensity for evil has long troubled both secular philosophy and advanced religious thought. A century ago Cardinal Newman wrote in his *Apologia Pro Vita Sua:* "If there be a God, since there is a God, the human race is implicated in some terrible aboriginal calamity. It is out of joint with the purposes of its Creator." With pioneer courage a modern Catholic scholar may state: "We do not start with a neutral disposition but with a definite bias towards evil contracted quite apart from any sins of our own." And the modern Protestant may give more and more uneasy attention to the hot, misty outlines of Original Sin. But it is not the Christian thinker, frankly dedicated to a metaphysical premise, who has suffered from the odious demands of the romantic fallacy. It is the secular thinker, pretending to rational premises, who has woven the transparent curtain half of sentiment and half of reason to distort our vision wherever we may look. And what must be regarded as a calamity scarcely aboriginal is the simple truth that the three giant influences on contemporary thought—Charles Darwin, Sigmund Freud, and Karl Marx —left almost no mark at all on the nostalgic assumption of man's innate innocence.

As we proceed in this chapter to investigate certain animal attitudes in relation to human attitudes and institutions, we shall encounter again and again the romantic fallacy as the chief obstacle to man's more profound understanding of man. In proper context we shall consider the neutrality of Darwin, the compromise of Freud, and the unconditional surrender of Marx, as each faced the nostalgic temptations of the Illusion of Original Goodness.

When Pope Pius XII, in 1952, issued the encyclical, *Humani Generis,* he stated: "The teaching of the Church leaves the doctrine of Evolution as an open question—as long as it confines its speculations to the development of the human body." But if the statement is to be regarded as the Church's dogmatic defence of the uniqueness of the human soul against rational attack, then the defence is unnecessary. No such attack exists. The transparent curtain, with its warp of reason and its woof of sentiment, guarantees that man will continue his half-blind groping for rational conclusions uncontaminated by reasonable assumptions.

The contemporary revolution in the natural sciences points inexorably to the proposition that man's soul is not unique. Man's nature, like his body, is the product of evolution. If he is special as a species, then so is every other species special; so too are those bats who must sleep hanging upside down, or those remarkable fish who to breed must return to the place where they were hatched. Man's nature must be regarded, like his body, as the sum total of all that has come before plus those modifications which are the hallmark of his kind. And if those modifications have presented him with a potential beyond any other species of livingkind, then he may thank his lucky stars but not some patient Maker who has been sitting it out for billions of years waiting to devote His exclusive attention to that moment that is Man.

An Archbishop of Canterbury, William Temple, once said of evolution that he preferred a God who once and for all impressed his Will upon creation to one who continually busied about modifying what he had already done. What was said about man's body may with equal justice be said about man's soul. It partakes either of all living things, all that has come before and all that will ever come after, all that exists on this particle, Earth, and all that exists in the most speculative pastures of unknowable space beyond the last red shift: either that, or it partakes of man's estate and span alone, which read on any mathematical scale must come very near absolute zero, and we are minor beings bowing before gods as appropriately insignificant as our own imagination; we are a transitional species, nature's first brief local experiment with self-awareness, a head above the ancestral ape and a head below whatever must come next; we are evolutionary failures, trapped between earth and a glimpse of heaven, prevented by our sure capacity for self-delusion from achieving any triumph more noteworthy than our own sure self-destruction.

3

"Private property," wrote Pierre Joseph Proudhon, "is theft." "If you follow the chain of our vices," wrote Mably, "you will find the first link fastened to inequality of wealth." Diderot believed that it was a waste of human energy to work for a good government or a good society until the privacy of property had been once and for all destroyed. François Babeuf, guillotined at the age of thirty-seven by the evolving forces of that same French Revolution of which he had been a creative force, believed that nature had decreed the equal sharing of work and goods; and that man's institution of private property, flying in the face of nature, was responsible for all human vice. For such sentiments, whether eighteenth century or mid-twentieth, cannot be traced back to Jean-Jacques Rousseau's *Discourse on Inequality* in which the logical sequence of the theme was first displayed: Man is naturally good. Any evil in his nature must originate in his social institutions. Private property and the state are the twin institutional demons which man has invented. The first produced not only inequality but the necessity for the second to perpetuate the inequality. Private property and the state have combined to insure man's ruin.

Edmund Wilson has pointed out that the atmosphere of the early nineteenth century was so saturated by the thoughts of Rousseau that a man had only to breathe to imbibe them. Out of this atmosphere condensed the sparkling dew of equalitarian socialism and a thousand utopian communities in the United States alone. Science in the nineteenth century was becoming a tool of increasing usefulness in the kit of human self-delusion, and with its aid a man could arrive at false conclusions by more and more systematic means. And so Robert Owen believed that given the proper environment man could be rendered "with mathematical precision" universally happy and good.

We need not linger over the fate of the utopian communities since they no longer adorn our maps. But the assumption of early nineteenth-century romanticism that man is a product of his social environment, that the less praiseworthy manifestations of human behaviour are consequences of defects in that environment, and that society, an institution of human invention in the first place, may therefore be redesigned "with mathematical precision" to return man to his original state of grace and happiness, was a dream that lingered. Empowered by a later conviction that to achieve an end so exalted any means are justifiable, the dream became a principal figure in the following century's catalogue of nightmares.

Few men in modern times have possessed intellects to rival those of Karl Marx and Friedrich Engels. Yet they embraced the Illusion of Original Goodness with a breathtaking enthusiasm that might well have brought consternation to Rousseau himself. Like Robert Owen, Engels drew his observation of the human condition from the misery of mill-trodden Manchester, in England. Like Owen—and like so many interpreters of the Great Depression almost a century later—he drew the conclusion that human fault finds its source in the human environment. Then along came Marx with his rationale for that environment, the philosophy of economic determinism. And the game was on.

Man's original nature is peaceable and good. His social environment must therefore be the cause of hostility and vice. The nature of man's society is determined by the ownership of land and the means of production. The nature of man himself is therefore determined by the ownership of capital. So long as ownership remains in private hands, humankind will remain divided between the exploiters and the exploited, and states will exist to protect the exploiters. All history, in consequence, must be interpreted in terms of the struggle between the two classes; all wars in terms solely of the exploiting class's efforts to gain or defend economic advantage. But if the exploited can gain control of the state, then private ownership will be ended. The exploiting class will be ended. The class struggle will be ended. War, misery, vice, hostility, and at last the need for the state itself will be ended, since man is naturally peaceable and good.

Marxian socialism represents the most stunning and cataclysmic triumph of the romantic fallacy over the minds of rational men. Viewed through the transparent curtain,

the single metaphysical thread all but vanishes in the vast fabric of unassailable logic. And an observer of the animal role in human affairs can only suggest that much of what we have experienced in the last terrifying half-century has been simply what happens, no more and no less, when human energies become preoccupied with the building of social institutions upon false assumptions concerning man's inner nature.

That unparalleled brutalities were required to suppress in the partners of the new society an instinct as old as the fish; that an unrivalled tyranny was demanded to administer an institution truly of human invention, the social territory on a national scale; the nationalist emotions unimagined by Marx or the howling monkey became pressing necessities for human beings denied other outlet for territorial expression; that the state declined to wither: none should surprise us.

A logic larger than the Marxian pursued its own inexorable way in all those societies subjected to full socialist doctrine. In a state of nature a society founded solely on the social territory must have territorial isolation; the Communist society got it. The iron curtain became a feature of socialist geography, the iron hand a weight on socialist communication, the iron jug too frequently the chief educational adornment of the enlarging brains of socialist youth. But a society so isolated must still be welded, and so ancient territorial noises came to enliven the new social scene. Threats of war, display of might, creation of incidents, alarms of aggression, all the paranoiac paraphernalia of the primate's perpetual territorial hostility became permanent features of socialism's external relations. The masters of private property might with some likelihood turn a profit from an atmosphere of peace; for the inheritors of Marx's logic, the likelihood was less.

The final application of natural law to Marxian doctrine came with the emergence of the new ruling class. Any student of evolution might have apprehended the development, since nature abhors the unclassified. But the rigours and manners of socialism's hierarchy can be explained only by one of the subtler revelations of science's contemporary revolution.

We have seen how classical biology, from Darwin down, saw natural selection in terms of male competition for the female. But we have witnessed evidence that it is the females who compete for the male, and that the true competition between males is for territory or status. Such a fine distinction in evolutionary law would seem of peripheral importance to the aftermath of the Russian revolution; yet in every likelihood it was a major determinant. With the abolition of private territories the new societies unwittingly installed competition for dominance as the sole means of natural selection.

Whom shall I fear? Who must fear me? A straightline, barnyard pecking order of the most extravagant dimensions became a permanent feature of socialism's internal relations. Even those curious, abstract territories which had commanded status in a hierarchy of private ownership— the artist's name, the hero's fame, the wise man's sayings— became a demonetized coinage in hierarchical struggles based only on dominance and submission. And so the final irony of a logic proceeding from a false assumption may be read in total socialism's more stressful times when a man who trusts the next man's goodness has nothing to lose but his life.

Marxism today is the opium of the masses. History has tattered its transparent curtain, and the magic is not what it was. But the toll of the Marxian disaster cannot alone be measured by a divided world, or by the potential fate of all those peoples who exercising the franchise of their ignorance may not yet embrace the smoky dream. The true measure of the contemporary calamity must be calculated in terms of the social energy, in a time of technological change, wasted on an attractive doctrine itself nullified by a false assumption.

The social waste has been as varied as it has been vast. There has been the wasted energy of those who embraced socialism outright, fought, won, and lived to see the dream's collapse. There has been the wasted energy of those who embracing socialism outright fought outmoded social institutions in the name of a doomed one, and lost for want of a better weapon. But as important as any has been the untellable waste of energy on the part of those who rejecting socialism still failed to perceive its false assumption, and accepting portions of the logic lodged their dreams and their dedications in the half-way houses of Marxism: that man is a product of society, or that economic motives determine his nature.

It is the superb paradox of our time that in a single century we have proceeded from the first iron-clad warship to the first hydrogen bomb, and from the first telegraphic communication to the beginnings of the conquest of space; yet in the understanding of our own natures, we have proceeded almost nowhere. It is an ignorance that has become institutionalized, universalized, and sanctified. It is an ignorance that transcends national or racial boundaries, and leaps happily over iron curtains as if they did not exist. Were a brotherhood of man to be formed today, then its only possible common bond would be ignorance of what man is.

The idealistic American is an environmentalist who accepts the doctrine of man's innate nobility and looks chiefly to economic causes for the source of human woe. And so now, at the peak of the American triumph over that ancient enemy, want, he finds himself harassed by racial conflict of increasing bitterness, harrowed by juvenile delinquency probing championship heights. But the practical Scandinavian is no better off. He must brood over his small, stable societies which have achieved a most perfect balance of political freedom and economic justice, together with some of the most impressive records of alcoholism, mental breakdown, suicide and abortion so far gathered in the modern world. And the Russian administrator—granted that the Soviet pecking order tolerates his enterprise—must consider the lunatic splendours of the

Hungarian uprising, unanticipated by even his own secret police, and conclude that he has no notion at all as to what his subject people are thinking about. Societies everywhere—whether government be the servant of the people or people the servants of the government—whether their compulsory aspirations be the enhancement of freedom or the reduction of freedom, the pursuit of justice or the avoidance of justice, the gaining of what they haven't or the maintenance of what they have—face approximately the same dilemma: the society must solve maximum problems with a minimum understanding of its own members.

Any animal with a capacity for learning must in part be a product of his environment. Any animal with a capacity for hunger must in part be dominated by economic motives. But to believe that the fascination with war and weapons, or the imagined accomplishment of a perfect crime, or unyielding temptation to lord it over somebody or everlasting drives to acquire someone else's wealth; to believe that such as these find their source in human society and may be exorcized forever by environmental manipulation is to make of a man a most modest blackboard on which any other may write his name.

Somewhere above a vast oak tree beside some English field two cuckoos fight for exclusive domain. Neither will homestead his territory, for the cuckoo is parasitical and builds no nest. Neither will use his conquest towards romantic ends, for the cuckoo is polyandrous, and these embattled males when the fighting is done and the real estate properly apportioned will amicably share their lovelorn bride. They compete, simply, because they must. They compete for reasons of ancient law, stern and abiding, forgotten by men and cuckoos.

In low, flat osier beds beside some sluggish stream the rare marsh warbler takes his stand, stakes his claim, patrols his boundaries, and sings his marvellous song. Embattled, pugnacious, he cocks his feathers at the breeze. Why does he bother? The female, unimpressed, still wings her migrant way from reedy southern places. So alone is he in his scattered marsh-warbler world that it cannot be said that he competes for anything: for glory, for food supply, for freehold, or for wing-tip room. But in an economy of marsh-warbler abundance he must still play the role of the propertied competitor, fulfilling oldtime laws natural to a world of crowded species if inappropriate to a world of marsh warblers.

If man is a part of the natural world, then he possesses as do all other species a genetic inheritance from an ancestry as long as life itself. The territorial urge, as part of that inheritance, may in the human species be wrong or right, bad or good, destructive or constructive, wasting or conservative. But if man is a part of the natural world then his competitive drive cannot be erased by the elimination of private property, an institution itself derived from his animal ancestry; the drive can only be shifted—as happens in those social animals holding territory in common—from an expression of individuality through control of material objects to an expression of individuality through dominance over his fellow beings.

4

In 1920, the same year that Eliot Howard published *Territory in Bird Life,* Sigmund Freud published *Beyond the Pleasure Principle.* In this work the death wish was first advance as an explanation for human aggression. Freud had long been troubled by the inconclusiveness of any explanation for the observable human tendency towards hostility. The Marxist answer—private property and the class struggle—seemed to Freud superficial and fallacious. With the death wish he found an answer which whatever its fallaciousness can scarcely be called superficial.

In every organism, Freud reasoned, two opposing forces are continually at work. There is a vital instinct, the will to live, and there is a darker instinct, the wish to die. In human kind the vital force presses man to preserve life and to develop himself and his social units; the antithesis seeks to dissolve such units and to return the human being to inorganic death. This death wish turned outwards towards society becomes aggression or destruction. Anything obstructing the outflow turns the death wish inwards towards neurosis and self-destruction.

Unlike Marx, Freud recognized aggression as a characteristic of human behaviour. But he saw it entirely as a human manifestation of the death wish turned outwards. Later Freud wrote in *Civilization and Its Discontents* that never did he have such a sense of discussing things that were common knowledge as when he wrote of aggression as a simple instinct. "For this reason," he said, "if it should appear that the recognition of a special independent instinct of aggression would entail a modification of the psychoanalytical theory of instincts, I should be glad to seize on the idea." Freud could not, however, even as late as 1930, find any scientific evidence to justify his recognition of aggression as a special, independent instinct. And such recognition seemed to him now unnecessary, since his explanation of aggression in terms of a presumed death force satisfied him.

Freud was far too shrewd an observer of man's nature to waste time on Rousseau's sentimentality. A genius of Karl Marx's order could become a total victim of the romantic fallacy for reasons that we can only guess: his Germanic nature, his impregnable vanity, his unimpeachable record of minimum human experience. Freud's genius, however, was of a different sort. One gains always the impression that had the present day revelations of the natural sciences been available in the last century, a Freud would have greeted them with a sigh of relief, a Marx with his last drop of blood.

It was Sigmund Freud's misfortune that he lived too soon. He had nothing to draw on but the observations of a generation of zoo watchers. But it is the world's misfortune that the science of psychiatry which he so influenced —a unicorn science, half fable, half horse-sense—has ever since been chained in dogmatic stocks discarded by advanced zoology for a generation.

That the maintenance and defence of territory is the

chief characteristic of primate society was an observation unknown in Freud's day. That territorial proprietors, whether group or individual, live in universal hostility towards their neighbours was a scientific conclusion unavailable to Freud in his puzzlement over human misbehaviour. That no successful primate, with the exception of the gibbon, maintains a society limited to the family unit; that every primate society so far observed maintains within its ranks a system of dominance; and that both territory and status may be compulsions more powerful than sex: none of this information was available to Freud, or is for that matter much more available to the doctor who today must tinker with the subtler compulsions of one's oedipus complex.

The romantic fallacy demands that any fall from graciousness on the part of man must be caused by his environment. Rejecting economic determinism, Freud turned to emotional determinism for causes and cures. Science forbade him genetic necessities other than hunger and sex and the family. The pattern of psychoanalysis was thereby determined: two innate forces in human behaviour, the family and sex, must somehow be made to account for phenomena produced by an instinctual endowment in fact far richer. Freud's genius was forced into channels of mere ingenuity.

The relation of a son to his father, for example, became within the constraints of such science fiction the astounding melodrama of contemporary literature. Freud could only assume from the assertions of science that the earliest human society was limited to the family. The tyrant of such a society must logically be the father. But he has sons, and the sons mature, and their awakening sexual drive finds as its object the mother. (The family, of course, exists in a geographical vacuum with no other mature females for miles about.) Any physical desire for the mother, however, must be inhibited by the towering figure of the father. The sons, in their jealousy, come naturally to hate him.

In his *Totem and Tabu* Freud sketches the consequences of this disagreeable family arrangement. When the brothers mature their first object must of course be the disposal of the father. This they do with murderous finality. But the revolt of the brothers leaves the little family band without a tyrant to hold things together. And so as a substitute for the father's will appears the totemic stage of culture. Laws are born, and a sense of right and wrong takes the place of submission to the father's domination. Freud notes that the first accomplishment of culture was that a band of humans could be made to live together.

So vast has become the literature of the oedipus complex that no contemporary author can approach the sacred cow with other than shaking hands. I must nevertheless suggest that no shred of evidence exists to lend substance to Freud's analysis of the innate relationship of son to father. The baboon—that terrestrial primate whose way of life most resembles the human—lives in multi-family societies averaging a hundred members. The Australian aborigine when first encountered, according to Keith, lived in tribes numbering almost exactly that of the baboon troop. That parents and sons could have at any pristine moment in the history of the human species suffered the social confinement which is a necessary premise to Freud's thesis becomes a matter of extreme improbability.

Furthermore, despite all anecdotes to the contrary, dominance in primate groups as observed in a state of nature is the exercise of a hierarchy, rarely that of a lone tyrant. "Control of the entire group," writes Carpenter, "is not the exclusive prerogative of a single individual in any kinds of primates that have been systematically observed in the field. Control is distributed among the individuals and classes of individuals in direct proportion to the prestige statuses of the individual or classes." The normal successful primate society, in other words, does not present the maturing male with the tyranny of a dominant father; rather, the class of maturing males faces a hierarchy, the class of dominant fathers. Should by chance one elder by abnormal dominance establish anything resembling a tyranny, he becomes not a personal problem to his sons but a political problem to his contemporaries.

In any animal society dominance, as we have seen, is a lasting and all but unchallengeable attribute of the male whose superior status has been once established. Among Carpenter's rhesus monkeys on Santiago Island a high-ranking male, to discourage competition, had only to signal his status by posture or carriage or upward-flexed tail. Among gibbons, the only primates possessing a family-limited society resembling that postulated by Freud, the

tyranny of the father is indeed such as to emblazon a psychiatrist's dream. Unfortunately for the modern myth, however, the dominance of the gibbon father is so profound that as by natural law it guarantees the exit of the maturing male from the family circle to seek mate and fortune in the outside world. Unlikely it is that human society could ever have resembled that of the arboreal gibbon; unlikelier still is it that human sons, granted such a society, would have behaved in a manner strikingly different from that of the maturing gibbon.

One final comment must be made on the happy ending of Freud's murderous proposition. If in consequence of the brothers' revolt law was substituted for tyranny and the first achievement of human culture became the capacity to create a society, then such creation must have come about at a most unreasonable expenditure of animal experience. The earliest vertebrate inhabitants of long-forgotten Devonian seas established their fishy societies with far less trouble than did we.

As one views human nature through psychiatry's transparent curtain, the ruddy hues of sex colour all behaviour. If fathers and sons are at times in conflict, then sex must be at the bottom of it. If the human being views the snake with terrified fascination, then the snake must represent a phallic symbol. If man has the capacity to love friends and family, then somewhere beneath it all must lurk an aim-inhibited eroticism. If the human being, markedly different from animal beings, dislikes public exhibition of his genitals, then it is a natural consequence of sexual preoccupation brought about when man assumed his erect posture and exposed them. That man's primate ancestors started standing erect perhaps ten million years before man came along; that a capacity for devotion between members of a group is an imperative in the defence of social territory; that the bird views snakes with equal terror and fascination, yet possesses no penis; that systems of dominance are characteristic of all animal societies, insuring order, and of all animal families, insuring the dispersal of the young: these are considerations denying that uniqueness of man's soul which psychiatry in its essence defends.

The contemporary revolution in the natural sciences has not yet unfolded to a point where any general reappraisal of psychoanalysis becomes possible. The advanced American practitioner for example, less impressed by his successes than his failures, must yearn for the moment every time a new woman patient comes into his office. What ails her? According to every American ideal—and every tenet of the romantic fallacy—she lives in a feminine Utopia. She is educated. She has been freed of the dustmop cage. No social privilege is denied her. She has the vote, the bank account, and her entire family's destiny gripped in her beautifully manicured hands. Yet she is the unhappiest female that the primate world has ever seen, and the most treasured objective in her heart of hearts is the psychological castration of husband and sons.

The emancipated woman of whatever nationality is the product of seventy million years of evolution within the primate channel in which status, territory, and society are invariably masculine instincts, in which care of children has been a female preserve, and in which social complexity has demanded of the female the role of sexual specialist. Yet she must somehow struggle along in a human society which idealizes in her behaviour every masculine expression for which she possesses no instinctual equipment, downgrades the care of children as insufficient focus for feminine activity, and from earliest girlhood teaches her that a rowdy approach to the boudoir will bring her nothing but ruin. Should she attain the analyst's couch walking on her hands, it would be little wonder, for she lives in an upside-down world.

Our studies of the female in primate societies have not yet reached a definitive level. And until they do, the weary analyst must continue to grope through the trivialities of his patient's past for the sources of problems of timeless dimension; and we must continue to speak only of tendencies, and hazard only guesses, and regard our feminine companions with no more than a newly speculative eye. But more important, any true reappraisal of psychiatry must wait until the looming probability that man is an innate killer has definitely been affirmed or denied.

The remaining chapters of this account will be devoted to the human emergence in Africa; to a detailed consideration of that remarkable killer, *Australopithecus africanus,* the last animal before man; to the evidence that the extinct creature was our last direct ancestor in the animal world; to the significance of such a final, critical contribution to the animal sources of our nature; and to the stupefying task which confronts modern thought if it should finally be accepted that man is a predator with an instinct to kill and a genetic cultural affinity for the weapon. Assumption upon assumption will lie like dead men in the road; the Illusion of Original Goodness; more lately-conceived notions that environment must be held responsible for human aggression; and finally, deader than a herring, buried in the dust of ignominy, forgotten we may hope until the end of time, the most suffocating sequitur of the romantic fallacy, that civilization is the enemy of man.

I shall assemble in these pages, to be judged for the first time by scientist and layman alike, certain lines of proof that the systematic use of weapons preceded man on earth. But until such time as natural science affirms or denies, with equal definition, the existence of the weapons fixation as a cultural instinct in the human being, then psychiatrist and statesman, educator and judge must alike wait on one foot. Whatever suspense, however, may be attached to the verdict of science on man's propensity and facility for killing, other human drives remain in less doubt. The roles of territory, of dominance, and of society in the play of our ancestral animal instincts exist without question, and by their existence cast extraordinary doubt on the most precious premises of a post-Freudian, post-Marxian world.

5

In his *Descent of Man* Charles Darwin argued with utmost caution that man's intellectual and spiritual qualities may have been derived from animal sources by the force of natural selection. While this seems an inevitable conclusion to the theory of physical evolution, Darwin never quite entertained it. Whether Darwin could not bring himself to dispute the uniqueness of man's soul; whether accepting the philosophical war into which physical evolution had plunged him he rejected the temptation to enlarge it; or whether as a hard scientific mind he refused to precipitate debates which in his time could only have been speculative: what precisely was the nature of Darwin's reluctance, we cannot know. Perhaps a notation in his *Life* provides a clue commensurate with the size of his intellect. "With me the horrid doubt always arises," he wrote in 1881, "as to whether the convictions of man's mind, which has been developed from the lower animals, are of any value or are at all trustworthy."

Darwin's doubt was a horrid one, indeed. David Lack, in his *Evolutionary Theory and Christian Ethics*, illuminates the horror which may have inhibited even the inquiring spirit of a Darwin. If man's mind is no more than a product of natural selection, then how can any of its convictions of truth be trusted, even its conviction of the truth of natural selection? Out of the magnificence of Darwin's intuitions he may have guessed that without some final illusion concerning human central position, man dies.

We have been looking most briefly at the relationship of the three giants of modern thought to the central prop-

osition of the romantic fallacy. We have seen how Karl
Marx embraced with joy its most preposterous sentiments,
and with overwhelming gusto wove from it a transparent
curtain to deceive the most astute. We have seen how
Sigmund Freud rejected the Illusion of Original Goodness
but accepted what might be called a Bias of Original
Blandness: an assumption that man is created in all ways
bland, except in those where you can prove he isn't. The
romantic fallacy, in the hands of Freud and his followers,
remains splendidly intact. But it is a very great question that
this would be so had Charles Darwin not chosen to remain a neutral.

To a fair extent, Darwin was himself a victim of false
assumptions. He never questioned, for example, the assumption that sex is the single driving instinct forcing
competition between males. With the authority of Darwin
behind the sexual principle, one must forgive Freud his
reluctance to embark on voyages of more remote discovery.

To a limited extent, however, Darwin was a victim not
so much of false assumptions as false interpretations. It
was not he but Spencer who gave to the world an image
of evolution as a jungle battle, jowl to jugular, in which the
victor invariably received his crown while standing on the
head of his lamented opponent. Darwin saw his theory as
a far less melodramatic process: the quiet tendency of
those individuals with superior genetic endowment to breed
in greater number than their less successful contemporaries.
But in another and even more significant area of fundamental principle, Darwin's convictions were further distorted by his most eloquent prophet, Thomas Huxley. And
it is the Huxley distortion which may explain why the
theory of evolution failed to challenge the romantic fallacy.

Huxley interpreted the evolutionary contest existing in
the time of human dawn as one between individuals, not
groups. Like Spencer he could not, perhaps, in his passionate advocacy of the theory of evolution, forgo the
dramatic appeal of cave-man contest, a shadowy prize-
fight, club against skull, with a shrinking woman in the dim
cavern's reaches clutching a wailing babe. The Huxley distortion of individual conflict set back progress in evolutionary thought for sixty or seventy years; together with
the Spencer jungle distortion condemned evolution to the
milieu of a bar-room brawl in which nice people do not

indulge; and so totally blacked out Darwin's true convictions that to this date the observer of human affairs, impressed by man's real capacity for mercy, for charity, and for altruism, can find no principle in the evolutionary process adequately to explain them.

Not for a moment did Darwin interpret the early human contest as one between individuals. In his *Descent of Man* he saw early man as definitely a social being, and any contest in such primal times as one between communities. He saw the tribe as a "corporate body" entrusted by nature with a set of genes differing from that of any other tribe; and natural selection as a contest between such tribes, each of which by evolutionary necessity must maintain its integrity through an infinity of generations. In his *Letters* he wrote: "The struggle for existence between tribe and tribe depends on an advance in the moral and intellectual quality of its members." Again, in the *Descent of Man*, he wrote: "No tribe could hold together if murder, robbery, or treachery were common." A tribe "superior in patriotism, fidelity, obedience, courage, sympathy, mutual aid, and readiness to sacrifice for the common good," will be naturally selected over that tribe poorer in these qualities.

In Charles Darwin's observations of primitive man he found the answer to the question of how the various facets of goodness can be of evolutionary value. If the contest exists between individuals only, then qualities of mercy and altruism will contribute nothing to a competitor's fortune. But if the contest is between societies, then the member of a successful society must develop two sets of emotional responses: the many facets of friendship and cooperation reserved for members of his own society, and the many facets of hostility and enmity for members of the opposing society. Natural selection may be trusted to weed from its human garden those social groups deficient in either set of responses.

Unfortunately for the history of modern thought, Darwin was writing about tribes, not troops, about the human species and not about its primate ancestors. And philosophy, puzzling over the dual nature of man, could therefore reach no more sensible conclusion than that it was a unique and remarkable characteristic of the human species, acquired from sources unknown. The romantic fallacy went unchallenged.

When in 1892, in his old age, Herbert Spencer published *The Principles of Ethics* he analyzed brilliantly the paradox of man's dual nature: "Rude tribes and civilized societies have had continually to carry on an external self-defence and internal cooperation, external antagonism and internal friendship. Hence their members have acquired two different sets of sentiments and ideas adjusted to these two kinds of activity. . . . As the ethics of enmity and the ethics of amity arise in connection with external and internal conditions respectively, and have to be simultaneously entertained, there is formed an assemblage of utterly inconsistent sentiments and ideas." But Spencer was himself a victim of Rousseau's doctrine of human innocence. He regarded tribes, societies, and the consequent paradox of human behaviour as of fairly recent origin, a graft on man's inherent nature. And so he was confident that by one means or another the code of enmity could be made to die out, leaving the code of amity in sole charge of man's conduct. It need hardly be mentioned that as is so frequently true of conclusions premised on the romantic fallacy, Spencer's ethical principles made small contribution, in 1892, to any estimate of human conduct in the following sixty or seventy years.

Spencer's amity-enmity complex was the most spectacular characteristic of the German nation, the activities of which lent such barbaric splendour to various interludes of the post-Spencerian world. But nationalism as such is no more than a human expression of the animal drive to maintain and defend a territory. It differs from the social terri-

toriality of the primate only to the degree of man's capacity
to form coalitions. The Germanic tribes of the fourth
millenium, B.C., numbered probably between 150 and 200.
In response to varying pressures their number throughout
history reduced or expanded. But so far as the amity-
enmity complex is concerned, the mentality of the single
Germanic tribe under Hitler differed in no way from that
of early man or late baboon.

It is a law of nature that territorial animals—whether
individual or social—live in eternal hostility with their territorial neighbours. If civilized man on occasion demonstrates for his territorial neighbours a tolerance somewhat
greater than that of the rhesus monkey, then one need
only reflect on what a miraculous transformation is brought
to the nature of this same civilized man when aggression
threatens his territory. It seems probable that the demands
of civilization, not the yearnings of an inherently genial
nature, account for any temporary lapses in human bellig-
erence.

In 1942, Dr. C. R. Carpenter told the New York
Academy of Science: "Those activities which are ethically
accepted—such as altruism, strong emotional affection, and
co-operation—are attributed to man's higher intellectual
processes if not to superhuman origins. The naturalistic
approach to the study of human behaviour, competitive
and co-operative, egoistic and antagonistic, recognizes roots
at a pre-human level. . . . Defensive actions may involve
the close co-ordination of all group members in a concerted attack. In these attacks, individuals are killed, but
this is incidental to the fact that the group survives and
the species is perpetuated."

The dual nature of man differs in no respect from the
dual nature of any primate living in a state of nature.
When Darwin observed that a tribe of men endowed with
superior capacities for patriotism, courage, sympathy, and
mutual aid will be naturally selected over a tribe poorer in
these qualities, he could have written the same words in
application to the howler, the baboon, the chimpanzee, or
the si mang. We have only to recall the evolutionary worth
of Marais' two heroic chacma baboons in that terrifying
African dusk when they gave their lives to still the leopard;
of Zuckerman's hamadryas baboons who despite the anarchy of Monkey Hill nonetheless defended their dead

from the hands of the keepers; of Kohler's chimpanzees at Tenerife whose capacity for group reprisal became dangerous if one of their group was punished; of Carpenter's Central American howling monkeys who in manic concert repelled all invasions and in concert quite equal if more sublime responded to the wailing cry "Infant dropped from tree!" In every case we observe the triumph of social amity over individual anarchistic instincts, and the evolutionary worth of an animal society harbouring a superior capacity for patriotism, courage, sympathy, and mutual aid.

The territorial drive, as one ancient, animal foundation for that form of human misconduct known as war, is so obvious as to demand small attention. When Sir Arthur Keith found himself too old for any active contribution to the Second World War, his broodings produced the marvellous volume, *Essays on Human Evolution,* and the conclusion: "We have to recognize that the conditions that give rise to war—the separation of animals into social groups, the 'right' of each group to its own area, and the evolution of an enmity complex to defend such areas—were on earth long before man made his appearance." Such an observation of a human instinct probably more compulsive than sex throws into pale context the more wistful conclusions of the romantic fallacy: that wars are a product of munitions makers, or of struggles for markets, or of the class struggle; or that human hostility arises in unhappy family relationships, or in the metaphysical reaches of some organic death force.

But the drive to maintain and defend a territory can be regarded not as a cause but only as a condition of human war. One can recognize its workings in the fury of a Finland attacked by a monstrous large enemy; in the madness of Hungarians attempting to reassert their land's integrity; or in the lonely, irrational heroism of the Battle of Britain, when never did so many owe so much to so few. These were defensive social actions taken in strict accordance with territorial law and deriving from profound instinct the unbelievable magnitude of their energy. But in every case territory was the *condition* of war, not its cause. Human warfare comes about only when the defensive instinct of a determined territorial proprietor is challenged by the predatory compulsions of an equally determined territorial neighbour.

We observed in Dr. Carpenter's studies the extraordinary effect of a super-dominant male on an essentially non-aggressive society of rhesus monkeys. The dominance of a specially endowed individual communicated a capacity for domination to an entire society and resulted in aggression. We observed in the lions of the Kruger reserve the coalescing of prides into super-prides for predatory purposes passing natural balance. But the world of contemporary animals offers few hints as to the conditions or causes for aggressive human warfare. And when Dr. W. C. Allee with all his intimate knowledge of animal societies still clung in 1939 to a conviction that war of conquest must be an acquired characteristic of the human species, he was temporarily correct. He was correct, that is to say, in 1939 when man's fossil ancestry had yet to announce its qualities.

Any reflections on the causes of human warfare as an expression of instincts acquired from our genetic inheritance must wait for the end of this account and final exploration of our total evolutionary heritage. For the moment we may rest on Keith's summation that the territorial drive brings about the *conditions*—not the motives—that give rise to war: the separation of men into groups, the alliance of men and territory, and the latent capacity for the enmity code to dominate the most civilized man in his relation to a hostile neighbour.

But it is the other side of the territorial coin that may provide the foundations for a philosophical revolution. It is the hidden, unread, animal cipher stamped on the metal of our nature that may resolve the dilemma of a Spencer, the doubts of a Darwin, or the despairs of contemporary man. *The command to love is as deeply buried in our nature as the command to hate.*

Amity—as Darwin guessed but did not explore—is as much a product of evolutionary forces as contest and enmity. In the evolution of any social species including the human, natural selection places as heavy a penalty on failure in peace as failure in battle. The territorial instinct, so ancient in its origin that we cannot mark its beginnings, demands *of all social animals*, with equal force, the capacities for co-operation as well as competition.

In our groping understanding we repeat the phrase: *of all social animals*. It was society that produced in our most remote beginnings the amity imperative. Strip man of his social instincts and we will be left with Huxley's jungle law, with no higher authority than dog eat dog, and no way of existence beyond screams in the night. It is our innate necessity for society as a means of primate survival that has demanded of man those capacities which we regard as ethical.

The dual nature of man is the supreme product of the social territory. It has evolved, like stereoscopic vision, along the hidden paths of primate ascendancy. No uniqueness of the human soul, nor intervention of local gods summoned like spirits from some vasty deep of human self-delusion, need be called forth to explain the virtues of human behaviour. The virtues are innate, compulsive, antique and abiding, rather more ingrained in our animal inheritance than that recent compulsion to kill our own kind.

Chapter 7
A Roomful of Bones

For the 1955 report of the Smithsonian Institution, published in Washington the following year, Raymond Dart was requested to submit his case for the southern ape. The article was called *The Cultural Status of the South African Man-Apes,* and with its publication Dart's creature emerged from the shadowy underground of specialized scientific publications to become a recurrent figure in the world press. In the course of that article he recalled:

"The South African 'missing link' story goes back to 1924 when the late Miss Josephine Salmons, then a young science student in anatomy, brought me a fossil baboon skull that she had found on the mantelpiece of a friend she had visited the previous Sunday evening. It had come from the Northern Lime Company's works at Buxton, and was the first intimation that any fossil primate had been found in Africa south of Egypt. So we became very excited, and after interviewing the professor of geology, Dr. R. B. Young, learned to our satisfaction that he was going to Buxton the following week.

"Arriving at Buxton, Professor Young learned that in the previous week a miner, M. de Bruyn, had brought in a number of fossil-laden rocks blasted out the week before. When they came to Johannesburg I found the virtually complete cast of the interior of a skull among them. This brain cast was as big as that of a large gorilla; and fortunately it fitted at the front end on to another rock, from which in due course there emerged the complete facial skeleton of an infant only about five or six years old, which looked amazingly human. It was the first time that anyone had been privileged to see the complete face and to reconstruct accurately the entire head of one of man's extinct ape-like relatives. The brain was so large and the face was so human that I was confident that here indeed was one of our early progenitors that had lived on the African continent; and as it had chosen the southern part of Africa for its homeland I called it *Australopithecus africanus,* i.e., the South African ape."

In such an off-hand, homey, accidental fashion was one of the most significant of human adventures initiated. Buxton is a village on the fringe of the Kalahari desert near a railway station the name of which was then spelled Taungs. Dart's discovery became known as the Taungs skull. The fossil-laden rocks had come not from the deposit itself but from a cave formed within the oldest of four mantles of lime. Geologic evidence combined with the nature of the associated fossils to indicate that the infant man-ape had lived in the early part of the Pleistocene, towards a million years ago. The arid nature of the site discouraged any interpretation of the creature as a type of advanced arboreal ape. The ape is a forest creature, but forests could not have existed there in his day any more than they do in our own.

Dart had nothing but this single immature skull as companion for his meditations. But on the basis of tooth development he could assay the creature's age at five or six years. From the position of the *foramen magnum*——a little opening in the skull through which the spine connects with the brain——the young anatomist could tell that the creature walked upright. Quadruped monkeys and brachiating apes hold their heads forward on their bodies. Only a true biped can hold his head squarely on top. The southern ape walked erect or very nearly so.

On the basis of many an anatomical diagnosis Dart projected the adult creature as being four feet tall and weighing ninety pounds, with a brain about as large as that of a gorilla. He concluded that his infant's baby canine teeth would be replaced by mature canine teeth no larger than human. Out of his total anatomical diagnosis emerged a simple definition that still fits all of the hundred-odd individual australopithecines known today: They were creatures lacking the fighting teeth of apes who combined man's erect carriage with the ape's small brain.

To his anatomical description Dart added his conclusion that *Australopithecus africanus* had been a carnivore. Evidence for his revolutionary conclusion was of three sorts. First, in the arid environment of the Taungs site there could have been no sufficient source of nourishment for a fruit-eating, vegetarian ape. And secondly, there was the matter of the associated fossils. The deposit resembled that of a kitchen midden such as is left behind by primitive man. If the fossilized bones were not the remains of animals brought to the cave as food, then how had they got there?

But it was Dart's third line of evidence that concerns us most deeply as a clue to our human ancestry. The teeth of *Australopithecus africanus* are all but indistinguishable from our own. They are small. The enamel is not very thick. The shape and arrangement are like ours. And the crowns like our own are totally inadequate for the endless grinding and munching of a vegetarian creature who must gain from low-calorie foodstuffs sufficient daily nourishment to support a fair-sized body. All evidence combined to indicate that Dart's little infant found in a lime deposit on the edge of an African desert had once been a member of a meat-eating family of primates.

Dart's claims were crushed by northern science, as I indicated in the opening chapter, until the old zoologist, Robert Broom, attracted by the controversy came out of retirement and found fossil after fossil to confirm Dart's predictions. Broom was seventy when he began the work. In the course of a great career in zoology he had succeeded in demonstrating the emergence of the mammal from the reptilian background. Now in 1936 he turned to the emergence of man from the mammalian background.

As I have already described him, Robert Broom was a tiny man who dressed even in the midst of the bush in black hat, black tie, and stiff white collar; and I question that a more zestful figure has ever hustled through a Permian landscape. Broom was a doctor as well as a zoologist, and an accumulator besides. He collected everything: fossils, Rembrandt etchings, postage stamps, susceptible girls. In one of Broom's obituaries there appears a touching note concerning the breadth of the little man's activities. At one stage of his career, it seems, he quarrelled with the South African government over the free use of passes on the railways, and retired in sullen obscurity to a Rand town named Springs. Obscurity, however, was a condition continually eluding the doctor. Within three months, the obituary notes, he had become medical officer to two gold mines, president of the chess club, president of the revolver club, and mayor of the town.

When Robert Broom at the age of seventy turned his attention to the australopithecines, he was already known from zoology as one of the most distinguished living scientists. And so his discovery of an adult man-ape in the cave called Sterkfontein, near Johannesburg, captured the immediate attention of science. But although he made his first discovery after just eight days' search, it was a year before he made his second. And then fairly shortly World War II broke out, and the digging stopped at Sterkfontein. Through all the long war years Robert Broom—whose nature could never have been described as patient—had to wait.

Not till 1946 could Broom get back to work at Sterkfontein. The scientific world shuddered when it heard that blasting operations had begun among Sterkfontein's precious fossils; but Broom was eighty now, and there was little time. And the fossils piled up by the scores. By the late 1940's few northern authorities could still persist in the view that Dart's southern ape was merely an aberrant chimpanzee. And when Sir Arthur Keith, the leader of English anthropology, retracted his long-held opposition to Dart's claims, the case was about closed. But there still remained the Asia-firsters.

Many a European scientist had invested his thoughts and his life in *Pithecanthropus erectus* and Pekin Man, and could not part easily with the proposition that mankind had arisen in Asia. But then a great French Jesuit philosopher and anthropologist emerged on the African scene. Père Teilhard de Chardin had done most of his work in the Far East, and when he returned as a frail old man he insisted on visiting South Africa and viewing all the australopithecine sites. And in 1952 he gave a definitive report to the New York Academy of Science. He placed the era

of the australopithecines as the Villafranchian, that is, between five hundred thousand and a million years ago. He
regarded them as an autonomous zoological group, neither
ape nor man, that to a large extent formed a bridge between the two. And he concluded: "Their late Tertiary occurrence in Africa offers an additional argument that this
continent was the main birthplace of the human group."

The Asia case was closed by one of its principal ad-
herents, and a new case was opened, that of the australopithecine ancestry of man. The southern ape had become
not only respectable. It had become significant. But its case
had also become sadly mixed up. The South African veld
is a long, expensive journey from northern museums and
universities. Few scientists besides Chardin had had the
opportunity to observe the sites. And the wild men of the
south had done a masterful job of planting confusion on
their distant acres.

Many scientists in the field have an enthusiastic way of
giving new scientific names to their discoveries, whether
justified or not. It is a pity that when in 1936 Robert Broom
discovered an adult specimen of Dart's creature he could
not have contented himself with Dart's name for it. What
Broom found was simply *Australopithecus africanus*, but
the old zoologist in the stiff white collar found it necessary
to create not only a new species, but a new genus. And
so he called it *Plesianthropus*. Dart was not to be outdone,
however. When after the war he himself began to find a
wealth of examples of his own Taungs discovery at a new
site in the northern Transvaal, he created a new species.
Under the impression that the Makapan valley citizen had
used fire, he called him *Australopithecus prometheus*; and
although no important evidence has ever been found to
support the claim, Dart clings to the name to this day.

African anthropology has been the work of wild men,
and one must simply hold one's breath; for had there been
no wild men, there would be no African science of man,
and the world would be the loser. But one must have a
certain sympathy for the northern scientist struggling to
make sense of rapidly accumulating discoveries at the other
end of the world. The scientific papers to which he must
turn ascribe to three different species in two distinct genera an extinct creature who varies no more than Nor-

wegians, Swedes, and Danes. And the sorriest product of the confusion was that when Robert Broom found something truly different, the meat got lost in the stew.

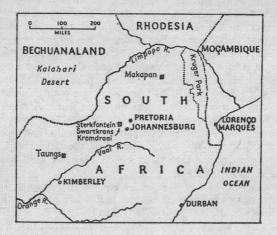

Taungs lies two hundred miles to the west of Johannesburg, and Makapan, Dart's second site, two hundred miles to the north. Robert Broom initiated his discoveries at Sterkfontein cave a little to the north west of the city, and then in 1948 began work at another cave less than a mile from Sterkfontein. The new site was called Swartkrans. And here he found an utterly different creature. He promptly created a new generic name for it, *Paranthropus,* but since he had already created a new genus for the Sterkfontein creature, his discovery failed to receive the attention it deserved.

Early in a play a dramatist will allow his audience to know that there is a gun in a drawer; and the audience will be alerted to watch for lethal things to come. I cannot fail at this moment to exhibit a gun in the drawer. The significance of *Paranthropus,* lost on science in a litter of scientific names, must not be lost on us.

Broom's new site was loaded with fossils. In 1950 the great accumulator gave a breezy report in the *American Journal of Physical Anthropology:* "We have found the de-

posit at Swartkrans to be very rich. In thirteen months'
work we have discovered of the large man-ape 5 lower
jaws and 4 faces with palate. We have a couple of adult
skulls . . . the skull of a child of about seven years, . . .
and over 150 teeth, many in superb condition. We have
also a few bones of the hand and arm." He was eighty-four
then, and the next year he was dead. His able young assistant, Dr. John Robinson, carried on his work at Sterkfontein, Swartkrans, and at another site, Kromdraai. But
Broom died too soon to know the ultimate significance of
his later discoveries.

The Swartkrans man-ape was an australopithecine without doubt, for he combined the small brain with reduced
canine teeth and erect posture. But in much else he differed.
A. africanus was small, light-boned, evidently agile; *Paranthropus* was big, heavy-boned, thick-skulled, and his body
spoke of clumsiness. Dart's *africanus* had a fairly full
forehead, a smooth cranium, and teeth like our own.
Broom's *Paranthropus* had a sloping forehead, a crest on
his skull like a gorilla's, and square, heavy grinding molars that any lay observer could distinguish from human.

Every evidence indicated the most striking difference
between the two: that whereas little *africanus* had been
basically a carnivore, big *Paranthropus* had been basically
a vegetarian. The heavy molars, the thick jaw-bone, the
crested skull, all comparable to those of the forest ape,
are the marks of dental and muscular development necessary for a life of eternal chewing. And John Robinson's
microscopic studies of australopithecine teeth confirm the
difference. *Paranthropus'* tooth enamel shows pitting from
sand that could have entered the diet of none but a habitual
root-eater. The teeth of *africanus* are as smooth as a leopard's.

Paranthropus created the first of a series of African riddles. Dart's creature resembled man to an astounding degree. Given a single advance, a doubling of brain-size
accompanied by a consequent flattening of face, and he
would become a true man in anatomical features. He *preceded,* however, Broom's creature in point of time. The
two were not contemporary. By the time of the brutalized
southern ape, his refined cousin had vanished from the
veld. And for *Paranthropus* to have evolved into man—

if such evolution could have been possible at all—would have required mutations by the dozen.

We shall close the drawer on the mystery for the moment as a dramatist closes the drawer on the gun. *Paranthropus* will provide the clue to a larger mystery, when the time comes, more closely allied to the human fate. But for the purposes of this narrative we shall cut through the wilderness of scientific names that has confused science and can only confuse the reader. One genus and two species are all that the South African discoveries should allow. And so from this point on we shall revert to a classification once suggested by Oakley and speak of *Australopithecus africanus,* the small man-ape who was a carnivore, and *Australopithecus robustus,* the large man-ape who was not. That is all we need remember. And since for a long period we shall neglect Broom's specialized *robustus,* any reference to the southern ape, or to australopithecus, may be understood to refer only to Dart's little *africanus.*

One more discovery must be mentioned, however, before we leave this description of our lost southern friends. Just before Broom died, John Robinson made the most enigmatic of all the South African discoveries. In the midst of the Swartkrans breccia, which has yielded some eighty fossilized fragments of long-dead gorilla-crested creatures, Robinson found five fragments of two individuals quite unlike their heavy fellows. Their bones had the delicacy and their teeth the form of an advanced *africanus.* They seemed almost surely to be carnivores. A fragment of an upper jaw showed evidence of a flattening face and a true nasal spine. Robinson called his discovery *Telanthropus.* But were they australopithecines? Or were they true men? And what were they doing in the Swartkrans cave, five hundred thousand years ago?

If the mysterious strangers in the Swartkrans cave were indeed true men, then no earlier are today known anywhere on earth. But we have too few fragments to effect positive identification, and no more are likely to be found for a while. Shortly after the discovery, Robinson went off on his annual leave and a toothpaste manufacturer invaded the cave. The tooth-paste manufacturer was in search of lime, and when Robinson returned the cave was a ruin. No one has ever had the money to put it together again.

2

By the sheerest of accidents was australopithecus first discovered on the edge of the Kalahari desert, and by a less happy accident was the discovery of what may have been the first true man prevented in a cave on the high, windy veld.

The role of accident in human affairs carries bottomless humiliation for many a mind. Perhaps determination by accident subverts the Illusion of Central Position in spirits both haughty and logical. Bernard Shaw despised the theory of evolution not because it was godless, or materialistic, but because it was accidental, and condemned it as "Darwin's chapter of accidents." One suspects that from Shaw's point of view evolution's most odious feature was that it denied him centre stage.

Raymond Dart, however, has never demonstrated a spirit so devoted to stage centre as to deny the force that brought him there. In the introduction to his *Cultural Status*, he makes no effort to minimize the role of accident as it determined the career of our most courageous challenger of the romantic fallacy. The young Australian anatomist who had accepted reluctantly the job of administering an anatomy department in a South African medical school was almost immediately and by the most humble of accidents handed the limey remains of an extinct baboon found on somebody's mantelpiece. In consequence, for thirty years thereafter, we find him challenging the uniqueness of man's soul.

Such are the accidents that point our paths. And since sooner or later an American dramatist who has become engaged with howling monkeys, Villafranchian fauna, predatory man-apes and basement rooms in scattered museums, must in one way or another produce an *Apologia Pro Vita Sua*, the time might as well be now. For it was by accident considerably more opaque than Dart's, and by all odds less dignified, that I blundered into his life brandishing ignorance like a coat of arms, and through a miraculous compilation of mis-statements, distortions, exaggerations and unwarranted speculations made possible, at a critical moment, his authoritative Smithsonian report.

When accident entered my life, it came not in the form of a woman student bearing an unidentified baboon but in the form of a very tall professor bearing an unpronounceable rumour. The event occurred in January, 1955. I lived in California in those days, and I was at home recovering from a Broadway calamity, an event which in the life of a dramatist must be regarded as more normal than accidental. To promote my recuperation I had agreed with Mr. Max Ascoli, publisher of *The Reporter,* to retire to Africa for a few months to write a series of pieces for his magazine. Visions of the Mau-Mau, then flourishing, and of large, unfriendly animals with overdeveloped canine teeth struck me as a refreshing contrast to memories of a first-night New York audience. And had my old friend, the very tall professor, chosen to postpone for but a few days his investigation of certain ancient saline deposits in the Mojave desert, I should have been on my way with none but the routine objectives of a correspondent in Africa. He appeared however when he did, and I entertained him for the night. And in consequence I, like Dart, am now challenging the uniqueness of the human soul.

I can neither blame nor credit Dr. Richard Foster Flint, chairman of the geology department at Yale University, for the major interruption that he brought to my life. I cannot hold him responsible, in any way, for the validity of observations or the soundness of conclusions put forward in this account. But the man did come into my home carrying like a trombone a rumour of deafening potential: that a South African scientist was about to explode a philosophical bomb, a positive demonstration that the first recognizably human assertion had been the capacity for murder.

It was the first time, to my best recollection, that I had ever heard of australopithecus. I struggled to pronounce it to the rhythm of those-who-do-not-seek-us. I struggled with the preposterous adjective, australopithecine, for which one must master a different rhythm, pass-me-the-pickle-brine. Flint supervised my struggles with cheer and hailed my African journey as providential, since neither museums nor universities supply budgets for the running down of rumours in the southern hemisphere. And so to my expected itinerary covering gold mines, apartheid, lions, and contemporary massacre, I added australopithecus. And the very tall professor, after bumping my children's heads against the ceiling as was his custom, resumed his journey to the Mojave desert; while I, bumped on the head by accident, proceeded in the general direction of the African continent.

It is one thing to be enthusiastic, another to be informed. My background in the natural sciences was not too sadly wanting, but had been acquired as a member of the Class of 1930 before the southern ape had achieved scientific standing. On my way to Africa I spoke with Père Teilhard de Chardin in New York, but I gained from the forest of his French accent few clearings other than further enthusiasm. And when in London I surrendered myself to the tutelage of the British Museum's Dr. Kenneth P. Oakley, I encountered a scientific mind so subtle, so complex, so sceptical, and so diabolically detached that my enthusiasm was left floundering like a porpoise in a newly drained swimming pool.

Through the unanticipated years of commuting between London and South Africa I would come to know Oakley as the scientific antithesis of the intuitive, emotional, conclusion-jumping Raymond Dart. In his office in the basement of the Kensington Museum, Kenneth Oakley sat as a sort of one-man Supreme Court on all matters pertaining to African anthropology. And if he tended to look tolerantly on most African anthropologists as a collection of over-age juvenile delinquents, I would come in time to accept it as a becoming posture; for Oakley was a judge. And if Raymond Dart, six thousand miles away, directing inspired forays into the African bush from his formaldehyde-scented GHQ in Johannesburg, tended on occasion to regard Kenneth Oakley as an intellectual prison warden with a heart frozen since the penultimate glaciation, then I would come to regard this too as a becoming posture; for Dart was a genius. Out of the play of judge and genius truth sometimes comes about.

In the northern winter of 1955, however, my interest was less in lasting truths than in a few quick facts about the southern ape. But Dr. Oakley, most unfortunately, had the kind of mind difficult to contain within nutshells. Together with Dr. J. S. Weiner, also of the Museum, he had questioned Piltdown Man and through his famous fluorine tests had proven it a hoax; with equal ease he could question one's most confident interpretation of the time of day. And so, when I headed south, I carried as part of my luggage a sheaf of scientific papers too specialized to be intelligible; a sense of discouragement concerning my own capacity to judge anything; an intense regret that the tall professor had not gone looking for saline deposits in somebody else's direction; and a profound conviction that I could never write for a magazine as authoritative as *The Reporter* a responsible story on Dart and his works. But East Africa and the Mau-Mau happily came first.

I lost myself among the lions, and encountered the loneliness of Tanganyika's hills. I sampled in the terror-brightened streets of Nairobi the primal dreads of a primal continent. I learned to fear for my life in a thousand ways, and in a thousand moments to yearn for the mortal security of civilization. And if by the time I at last reached South Africa I had added nothing to my knowledge of the southern ape, I had at least added something to my knowledge of myself: Africa scared me. If this continent had indeed been the cradle of humankind, and had I been the first man, then I should have been born in fear.

Johannesburg brooded on its golden reef in the golden, southern autumn. A last rare storm of the rainy season darkened Dart's upper-floor office at the Medical School. My mood of discouragement returned. Fossil bones of extinct animals piled up before me. Unfamiliar Latin names assailed my ear-drums. Despite all the best efforts of this sandy, smiling, persuasive, indiarubber man, I could gain no brainhold on concepts so fearfully specialized. Then I found in my hands what seemed a human jaw.

I mentioned in passing, in the introductory chapter of this account, the jaw of a twelve-year-old southern ape which Raymond Dart showed me on our first meeting. This was that jaw. And as I held it for the first time—staring into its headless, disconnected history as into the darkness surrounding Cardinal Newman's aboriginal calamity—my discouragement fell away. My sense of incompetence vanished. One needed nothing but the lay common sense of a juryman to return a verdict that at some terrible moment in most ancient times, murder had been done.

The jaw was heavy. Three-quarters of a million years of residence on the floor of a dolomite cave had turned its bone and dentine to stone. The jaw seemed human. The cusped pattern of the teeth would have been familiar to any dentist. And the jaw seemed young. Several of the permanent molars were only partially erupted. One canine tooth had not yet come in at all, though I could see its point hovering in the tooth canal. But the jaw while both young and heavy with antiquity was not human; for had the skull been attached, it would have revealed a braincase little larger than that of a chimpanzee.

What I held in my hand was the last remains of an adolescent australopithecine whose life had been brought short by a heavy blow. The four front teeth were missing. Just below was a cracked, abraded area where the blow had fallen partially splitting the jawbone on the left side and breaking it quite through on the right. The injury could scarcely have occurred as some post-mortem indignity of nature afflicted on an old jaw lying about the cave, for in that case the fragments would have been scattered about. Flesh must have held the fragments together to be fossilized as a single whole. Nor could the blow—or other simultaneous blows—have resulted in anything but death. There was no least sign of knitting along the lines of the fracture.

My mind struggled to recapture the situation. Could the injury have been acquired accidentally? By a fall, for instance? It seemed unlikely. When falling, one inclines to land on almost any sector of one's anatomy other than the point of the jaw. I thought of the cave in which the mandible had been found. Could a rock jarred loose from the cave roof have been the instrument of accidental injury? But to provide such a target for a falling fragment, one would have to visualize the youthful man-ape as sleeping on the cave floor with his jaw directed neatly to heaven, and even this unlikely situation brought difficulties. The scar on the jawbone, rough and abraded, had an area of less than a square inch. No falling rock so small as to leave a scar of this dimension could conceivably be heavy enough to produce the damage.

I dismissed accident as the mother of injury. The youthful creature had died of purposeful assault.

I considered the means by which death might have been administered. Could a fist have done it? Yes, a human fist to a human child. But the jawbone of the southern ape, lacking a chin eminence, is more heavily constructed than is ours. This child's jaw had the thickness of bone that one would find in a man. The aggressor, on the other hand, could have swung no such power as an adult human male. *A. robustus* is not found at Makapan. And *A. africanus,* we recall, stood four feet tall and weighed, at the outside, ninety pounds. To visualize a fist causing such injury one would have to see a ninety-pound human boy with a single swing knock out his father's four front teeth and break the jaw in two places.

A fist seemed unlikely. I inspected the point of impact where the blow had landed. It was a rough place, very slightly flattened. Would a piece of stone, grasped up impetuously from the cave floor and driven or thrown against the jaw leave a scar of this order? It was possible, but it was not probable. A jagged, sharp-cornered, uneroded rock fragment such as one finds in caves, to have achieved fractures of the jaw on both sides, would almost surely at its point of impact have left a more decisive mark. As compared with the likelihood of a purposeful bludgeon of some sort—a bone or wooden club which would have left a flattened, roughened mark precisely like that beneath my thumb—the use of an expedient stone shrank into moderate improbability.

The afternoon darkened with a fleeting thunderstorm. A window rattled with the earth movement of a collapsing tunnel in the gold reef a mile below us. I had put the jaw on Dart's desk, just before me, and it jiggled. Dart stood at the window looking out at the storm while I contemplated the remnant of antique assassination. Evidence for murder lay clearly before me, but the mere question of murder shrank rapidly in significance. A spectre far and away more grisly entered the dark periphery of my consciousness. Long before the time of man, had this creature surrendered his life to a weapon?

I asked Dart when the jawbone had been found and under what circumstances. I was told that Mr. Alun Hughes, one of Dart's assistants in the anatomy department, had found it in 1948 in the earliest horizon of a cave deposit at Makapan. I asked if in Dart's opinion death had resulted from the intentional use of a weapon. He suggested that I read his paper on baboon injuries which had been published the following year. I had read the paper in the British Musuem and failed to understand it. I asked to see it again.

While Dart went on about his appointments, I studied the paper. It had been published in the *American Journal of Physical Anthropology* under the awe-inspiring title: *The Predatory Implemental Technique of Australopithecus*. As far back as 1934, when the only known remains of the southern ape had been the single infant skull from Taungs, Dart had pointed out that fossil baboons found in the same deposit showed evidence of fractured skulls. By 1946 Robert Broom's discoveries at Sterkfontein swelled immensely the reservoir of australopithecine material and revealed more damaged baboons. In the southern summer of that year the famous anatomist of Oxford University, Sir Wilfrid Le Gros Clark, visited the various australopithecine sites in South Africa and expressed the opinion that not enough attention had been paid to the baboons. He suggested that all baboon material distributed through various museums and collections be assembled and examined for statistical evidence of intentional violence.

This was the background for Dart's baboon study. He enlisted the aid of a local authority on contemporary violence, Professor R. H. Mackintosh, head of the department of forensic medicine at the University of the Witwatersrand. It is difficult to imagine an expert on head injuries so happily situated as Professor Mackintosh, who throughout his career had been confronted on the one hand by the rich reapings of Johannesburg's murder rate, and on the other by the harvest of gold-mine tunnels collapsing continually on native heads. What had happened to various extinct baboons was quite, one might say, down the professor's dark alley.

Dart brought together fifty-eight baboon skulls from three sites, two hundred miles apart. All three sites were caves which through the action of dripping, evaporating water had been solidly filled with lime deposits better than half a million years ago. In these lime deposits had been preserved and fossilized those creatures, including the southern ape, who whether through choice or necessity had made the caves their last resting places. Among these creatures had been found the baboons. Of the 58 specimens, after setting aside those sixteen too fragmentary for study, there still remained 42 skulls, a significant number. And every one of the 42 showed damage to the skull or muzzle.

While in such a study of fossil remains wide room for error must be granted, still even after the most cautious discount the evidence for intentional violence seemed overwhelming. Adding to the intentional nature of the violence was Dr. Mackintosh's diagnosis of the direction of the blows causing the damage, for the direction had not been random. Among 42 assaulted baboons, 27 had definitely received blows from the front; only six definitely from the rear. Of the remaining nine struck from the side, seven had been struck on the left side—that is, from the attacker's right. Only two had been struck from the attacker's left.

Throughout the course of this account we have paid considerable attention to the contemporary baboon. The adult is an animal dangerous even to man. Yet well over half of Dart's baboons had been adult. Also, we have noted the tendency of the whole baboon troop to defend an individual, and we have no reason to believe that extinct species differed from contemporary species in social action. Yet if these dangerous, troop-defended animals were killed by the southern ape, then they were killed by a creature who weighed ninety pounds or less, and who had fingernails and canine teeth no more lethal than our own.

Could any being other than the southern ape have been responsible for the broken baboon heads? Could man himself have been responsible? Certainly not in South Africa, at the time of Makapan, was there the least evidence that man was yet around. Could then some other agency than attack have accounted for the fractured craniums? Could by some statistical miracle falling rocks from cave roofs have scored bull's eyes on 42 out of 42 baboon heads. The proposition was absurd.

To my layman's judgment there seemed no way out.

The baboons had been the victims of nothing other than the assault of the southern ape. But how could such assaults have succeeded, had australopithecus not been armed?

It was at this point in the paper, of course, that Dart launched forth into a speculation that brought down on his head from affronted northern science an assault as severe as any which *Parapapio izodi* ever received from the hands of *Australopithecus africanus*. It was an assault which, from the date of the publication of the paper in March, 1949, to this date in March, 1955, consigned Dart to the scientific outback reserved with peculiar care for those scientists who may in careless moments suffer attacks of pure inspiration.

One might puzzle now as Dart had once puzzled over certain reports from his baboon morgue. Specimen One, from Taungs, contained within its clinical description: "A powerful downward, forward, and inward blow, delivered from the rear upon the right parietal bone by a double-headed object." Having digested the fate of Specimen One, Taungs, the puzzler could turn to the mortal rendezvous kept by Specimen Six, also from Taungs: "The V-shaped island of bone left standing above the obvious depression of the cranium shows that the implement used to smash it was double-headed . . . having vertical internal borders or sharp margins, and measuring approximately 30 mm between the two heads."

What had been the double-headed weapon? Not many of these early victims of violence, subjected to autopsy so long delayed, retained with such crystalline clarity the dimensions of their fate. Some had been battered by too many blows; some had been partially defaced by post-fossilization injury. Still, of the 42 showing skull damage, seven indicated clearly an assault by a double-headed instrument, and four more showed the probability. Better than a quarter of the victims retained the mark of the same lethal instrument. What had been that instrument? To follow the line of Dart's deduction, we must turn to the character of the most famous australopithecine site.

Limeworks Cave, in the wild valley of Makapan two hundred miles north of Johannesburg, was long ago a vast empty cavern extending many hundreds of feet back into the ancient dolomite of the region. For many millions of years through the geologic era called the Pliocene, Africa had been dry. No deposits formed in the cavern. Then, with the opening of Africa's rainy Pleistocene a million years ago, water saturated with lime dissolved from the dolomite began seeping into the cave. Here it evaporated, leaving layer upon layer of white, shining lime, until the cave was entirely filled. So it remained, a solid deposit of lime, until shortly after the First World War. Then spurred by war-created shortages, South African prospectors discovered the deposit and mining operations began. But the miners encountered an odd—and to them worthless—characteristic of the deposit. At several stages in the pure lime occurred layers of breccia—a kind of rocky consolidation of whatever had lain on the cave floor at the particular period when the breccia was formed. Most of this breccia was a mixture of consolidating lime, cave dust, and rocky fragments dropped from the cave roof. But frequently it contained bone—animal bones in unimaginable quantity—fossilized and turned to limestone throughout the unimaginable years.

The bones were largely those of extinct Villafranchian fauna, found exclusively in the first half-million years of our era. But the breccia was of no value to the miners. And so, as they excavated the lime for the pressing demands of the building trade, they dumped the riches of man's Villafranchian origins on the sunny slopes beneath the cavern's mouth. And it is from this discarded treasury that Raymond Dart and his students, for the last fifteen years, have been extracting the limestone story of australopithecus and his animal world.

When in 1949 Raymond Dart was confronted by the puzzle of the double-headed instrument which seemed to have caused such an abnormal death-rate among Villafranchian baboons, he turned to his Makapan treasury with the hope of discovering an answer. And he published that answer. The humerus bone—the upper foreleg bone —of the common antelope had been the southern ape's favourite weapon. Its heavy double-knobbed knuckle fitted perfectly the double depression in the baboon skulls.

A somnolent juryman, dreaming his way through a highly technical murder trial, would probably at this point come abruptly awake, fix the shrinking defendant with a convinced eye, and under his breath mutter, "Hang him." Any horror-drenched *aficionado* of the modern detective story, combating his insomnia with the deductive super-powers of his favourite private-eye, would probably at this point shrug, "That does it," and close his book and go to sleep. But deductions no matter how logical do not constitute scientific proof. And the jeers of northern science had been the answer to Dart's claim.

I put aside the paper. I found myself alone with the normal complement of ventilated skeletons and grinning, eyeless skulls that must adorn any anatomy department. On Dart's desk still lay the remains of the violated youth discovered in Makapan's most ancient breccia. The rain no longer afflicted the windows. From the elevation of Hospital Hill one could look out at the vast, serried, African sky now ranged in stripes of blue and frowning grey like a mutated zebra or somebody's flag.

I cursed my all-around incompetence. I knew that when Dart returned from his appointments he would show me whatever new evidence had been gathered to prove the thesis of his baboon paper written six years before. I knew that the existence of such evidence constituted the substance for the rumour that had reached men like Flint and Chardin and Oakley. I had gathered from Dart that the luck of my arrival at this particular time meant that I was to be the first observer from the northern hemisphere to see the evidence. I thought of Rousseau. I thought of Marx. I thought of Freud. I recognized the philosophical stakes involved if Dart should successfully demonstrate that the systematic use of weapons had been part of our inheritance from the animal world.

But I did not know humerus from tibia. Terms like epicondylar and bregmatic, mandible and maxillary, were sounds that fled past my ears like unidentified objects. My inadequacies for the job at hand loomed about me like leering jailers. Dart returned, beaming with enthusiasm. Was I ready? I was as ready as I was likely ever to be.

The Medical School of the University of the Witwatersrand is a large, U-shaped building, fairly ugly, fairly old, with the approximate aesthetic appeal of much of Johannesburg itself. On the bulletin board one finds announcements for picnics and sing-songs. In the basement one finds dissecting rooms, white-robed students, and the overflow population of Johannesburg's morgue. We passed through a small room decorated by South Africa's contemporary dead to enter a large room littered with the remains of the veld's most ancient citizens.

It was a roomful of bones. The bones stood on tables, on shelves, in cases, in drawers, in open packing boxes. I had never seen so many bones; and none in fact were bones since all were limestone.

For six years Dart and his students had been patiently removing from the breccia at Makapan the fossilized animal bones that once had lain on the old cave floor. From five thousand tons of rock, dumped as worthless by the limeworkers, they had sorted out some twenty tons bearing animal remains. From a sample of this bone-bearing breccia, in the course of six years, they had removed every single bone. To develop a fossil requires the chipping away with a steel tool of all its surrounding limestone matrix. In this room in the basement of the Medical School were 7,159 fossils so developed. Many flakes and scraps had been too fragmentary to identify. But 4,560 bones or portions of bones or loose teeth had been sorted, identified as to genus, and anatomically described. It had been a considerable exercise in rock lifting, limestone pulverizing, and comparative anatomy.

One wandered about in a layman's stupor through the stony graveyard. Here before one was the lost world of australopithecus. Antelope and wild pig, rhinoceros and leopard had contributed portions of their carcasses to the floor of his underground establishment. Extinct giraffes, monkeys, horses, porcupines; hares, guinea fowl, tortoises, vultures; jackals, hyenas, baboons, hippopotami: it was a fossilized zoo. Dart had claimed from the days of the discovery at Taungs that the abundant animal remains found always in association with the southern ape constituted the bones of his prey. The kitchen midden from Makapan testified eloquently to the varied tastes of that creature standing halfway between ape and man.

As I travelled about through the roomful of bones, however, I began to recognize that if Dart was attempting to prove with his bone pile that the southern ape had gone armed, then again he would fail in the eyes of science. Common sense would grant that the creature could scarcely have killed such animals as these bare-handed. But there was nothing to say that he had not been a scavenger. The bones could represent the remains of carcasses dragged back to the cave from the half-eaten kills of lion and leopard. But my travels were caught short by a chilling sight.

On a case stood the entire skull of a hyena. From the animal's mouth protruded the end of an antelope leg bone. It had been forced into the hyena's mouth with such thrust as to break the palate and damage the skull at the rear of the throat. The entire fossil memento of violence stood before me precisely as it had been chipped from its limestone matrix formed three-quarters of a million years ago, a quarter of a million years before the time of man. For all eternity the dead hyena would stare eyeless into space, gagging on its lethal bone and swearing unhappy testimony to revolutionary forms of sudden death being encountered in his unhappy time.

I felt myself stiffening. Still I could apprehend that a single piece of evidence could bring scientific objections which I should be incompetent to answer. But the short, sandy, cheerful man with the rubbery nature was getting out a chart. It was a statistical distribution of the 4,560 identifiable bones found in the sample of breccia. And my incompetence vanished.

One never knows what absurd ability acquired in some absurd corner of one's experience may not come into critical play at some unknown future date. When in 1930 I had come out of the University of Chicago I encountered the Great Depression and the naked streets of my native city. For a good many years I did anything for money. Although no one in Chicago played the piano quite so badly as I, still I managed three dollars a night playing with dance orchestras. Although I had never been south of New Orleans, still for two years I earned twenty dollars a week in the Maya exhibition at Chicago's World Fair giving authoritative lectures on the pre-Columbian American Indian. Certain of my activities, I must now recall, while not quite punishable in a criminal court could scarcely be held up as an example for honest young men. And one was my career as a statistician.

At an early date in Chicago's struggle for existence, there was revealed to me a salient truth glimpsed by few others of the unemployed: that to declare oneself a statistician was the safest sort of lie. Statistics in the early 1930's formed a new trade. Few were about who had been properly trained in its labyrinthine complexities; and so, even in periods of the most drastic unemployment, there was always a demand for statisticians. To become gainfully employed, one had only to declare oneself a member of this secret fraternal order. That I knew next to nothing about statistics was a matter of no importance; the man hiring me, it was safe to predict, knew nothing at all.

A time came when awareness of this chink in the armour of American business presented me with my margin of survival (and ironically, at a much later date, with a similar margin of survival in a roomful of bones). I wanted to write, for reasons which I cannot now recall, a novel about Cro-Magnon man. I had to eat. The depression had hit bottom. Praying that the end would justify the ignoble means, I answered, "Yes," to the first employer who inquired if I were a statistician. For the next year and a half I prowled night-times the valleys of Magdalenian man; and day-times, at forty cents an hour, the coefficient of correlation. And when the work was all done, only ruin lay about me. I had written a novel so bad that no friends —let alone publishers—could read it. And I had become a first-rate, eagle-eyed, professional statistician.

Over twenty years had elapsed since playwriting saved me from the calculating machine. But as I leaned over Dart's chart—a statistical distribution according to genus and anatomical part of all the identified bones—old forgotten images scampered before my eyes. I might not know *Chalicotheriidae* from *Cercopithecidae*, or a metacarpal from a metatarsal—but I knew a normal distribution when I saw one. And this was not a normal distribution.

Of the 4,560 bones—a sample fairly acquired, wholly processed, and of such size that probable error could not be significant—518 were antelope humerus bones. Of all the bones remaining from what had once been the lively bodies of at least 433 individual animals, better than eleven per cent were specimens of the bone which Dart, six years before, had deduced to be the southern ape's favourite weapon.

Could the startling figure be explained in terms of food preference? If this were simply a kitchen midden, could it be that the upper part of the foreleg represented nothing other than the favourite food of the southern ape? But the hind quarter of the antelope, as of other ungulates, gives the solidest meat. And of femurs there were only 101, less than one-fifth the number of humeri. It made no sense that a carnivore would have dragged back from kills in the field five times as many forequarters as hindquarters.

What if one assumed, to explain the disproportion, that the southern ape had not been a killer but a scavenger? In this case the hindquarters might have been devoured by the original killer, and the less desirable forequarters left to the scavenger. Such a situation would account for a prevalence of humerus bones in the scavenger's cave. But following this line of reasoning only led one into another statistical astonisher.

Dart, in his classification of antelope species, had made four categorical divisions: Large, such as the huge, modern kudu; Medium, such as the waterbuck; Small, such as the impala; and Very Small, such as the modern duiker. It was a classification devised by H. B. S. Cooke, South African geologist, for dealing with extinct species. Referring back to the baboon head injuries, one found that it was the humerus bone of the Medium that best fitted the double-depressed fractures. And now one encountered in Dart's chart a salient incongruity. While the Medium category contributed only 30% of the individual animals to the antelope total, it contributed 60% of the humerus bone fragments.

Could this abnormal distribution of antelope humeri be accepted as accidental? Provisionally, one might so accept it. But it was the distribution of fragments that now provided the true statistical astonisher. Rarely did a bone appear whole in the fossil collection, and Dart had subdivided each category of humeri into three, according to which portion of the bone appeared among the fossils. There was a middle portion, which included no joint; there was a distal end which included the knee joint; and there was a proximal end, which included the shoulder. The shoulder joint was useless as a weapon. It was the distal end which fitted so precisely the double-depressed fractures in the skulls of the baboons.

Two hundred and thirty-eight examples of the distal end of the humerus bone of the medium-sized antelope appeared in the collection; seven of the proximal end.

To my mind, no wildest improbabilities of chance could account for such a statistical distribution. Dart had made the claim that the Villafranchian baboons were killed by weapons, and that the antelope humerus bone was the most common weapon. In the southern ape's rubbish pile, he had found eleven per cent of all bones to be the bone predicted. Among types of antelope, he had found that sixty per cent of all humerus bones fell in the most useful size. And in the category of the most useful size, that portion of the bone which could be used as a weapon outnumbered by over thirty times that portion of the bone which could not.

The evidence was overwhelming that some sort of systematic, intelligent selection towards premeditated ends had determined which bones should be brought into the cave, and which should not. And the evidence was not confined to the spectacular confirmation of Dart's prediction concerning humerus bones. Other unanticipated categories in the chart struck one's eye, for the southern ape had not confined his armoury to antelope upper forelegs.

So that the reader may enjoy—inconceivable though the possibility may seem—the drama of statistics that confronted me in a roomful of bones, let us record here a few numbers: 3, 2, 0, 0, 10, 0, 0, 21. Precisely what they refer to is of no great importance, although we are reading from the anatomical distribution of bones belonging to the category of the small antelope. We conclude the series: 36, 0, 53, 51, 34, 13, 2, 6, 40, 6, 7, 0, 8, 11, 8, 10, 44, 12, 7, 9, 10, 21, 15, 10, 4, 58, 66, 191.

Is it possible to look at such figures without demanding what the 191 represents? In answer to my demand, Dart led me to a set of drawers and boxes. The figure 191 represented the portions of mandibles—or lower jaws—of the small antelope. Before me lay the specimens, mostly half-jaws with sharp teeth all in a row. Whether they had been used as slashing implements lay beyond proof. But that they *could* have been used for such a purpose lay beyond denial. Few throats could have resisted the saw-tooth edge. And the weapon rested easily in the hand.

I consulted the distribution, which resembled not at all that of the heavier medium antelope. From the carcasses of some hundred small antelopes butchered in the field, the collector had brought back few portions of trunk, and more but not many portions of the limbs, too light for use. What he had brought in significant quantity were heads. But even in the bringing of heads there had been intelligent selection. Had he brought back the whole head, then the number of skull fragments would have mounted to the hundreds. There were instead only 58. He had brought back only those parts of the head for which he had use in his predatory life: horns—sharply pointed—78; and the 191 slashing sections of mandibles. The upper jaw, in contrast, was of less apparent utility. And only 66, a third as many, appeared among the fossils. Had the collector not, in the field, on many occasions cut the lower jaw from the head, it would be difficult to imagine how three times as many lower jaws as upper could appear in the sample.

Purposeful, intelligent, systematic selection—how else could one explain such figures? Now Dart called my attention to a drawer full of tiny jaw-bones. Almost all were halves off the original V-shaped mandibles, each a straight segment mounted with its compact line of extremely sharp

teeth. It seemed as close to a knife as the animal world was ever likely to produce. We referred to the chart. It was the mandible of the Very Small antelope category corresponding to the modern duiker, or to Thompson's gazelle. The anatomical distribution was all but blank. Not a neck bone, trunk bone, or limb bone had ever been found—not a single bone back of the head. But 53 examples of what I held in my hand, and accepted as a knife, had turned up among the fossils.

I was dizzy with bones, and totally convinced. Significant evidence for the systematic use of weapons at a prehuman level of evolution existed in this roomful of bones. If the concept of the weapon had been part of our animal legacy, then our devotion to the weapon must be reckoned as a probable animal instinct. And politics and philosophy, education and psychiatry must alike grapple with the speculative consequences.

Dart and I were gripped by a fury of excitement. We retired to his upper-floor office, that lonely outpost of nonconformity at the wrong end of the world. We discussed plans. This was March, and my article for *The Reporter* would be published sometime during the northern spring. The schedule fitted well with Dart's, since in July the Pan-African Congress in Prehistory would meet at Livingstone, in Northern Rhodesia. It was a quadrennial meeting to which some hundred anthropologists would be coming from four continents and towards which Dart had been shaping his study for the past two years. The packing boxes which I had observed in the roomful of bones were being prepared already with the specimens to be shipped to Livingstone. The chart which I had studied was the statistical evidence which he would submit to the Congress. The little, wild-west, Northern Rhodesian town, only a few miles from Victoria Falls, would witness one of the most sensational events in modern anthropology.

By May I was back in the United States and my article had been published in *The Reporter*. Despite my compelling ignorance of the African Pleistocene, of Villafranchian fauna, of the vagaries of ancient dating, and of anatomy other than my own, there emerged with fair clarity the basic proof of Raymond Dart's thesis. The article was a success, and in succeeding months was reprinted in several digests. I was confident that nothing remained now but inevitable acceptance at the Livingstone meeting. I returned to my normal life which involved throughout that particular summer getting thoroughly lost in Europe. I did not return again to the United States until September. And there awaiting me was a letter in Dart's formidable hand. The ink was blue; it should rather have been blood.

The Congress had lasted for five days. Dart had been allotted twenty minutes. He had presented his vast subject as well as he could in the time. There had been two or three questions, no more. Some of the eminent visitors had taken a look at his carefully arranged exhibit of specimens; the majority had not. The general reaction had been that hyenas, not the southern ape, had collected the bones. The Chairman, concluding the brief discussion, had commented that one must be very cautious of conclusions drawn from cave deposits.

Raymond Dart is a robust man. The Livingstone Congress had swept his six-year study back into the unreported darkness of the African limbo. But the letter described other developments. The Smithsonian Institution had read my *Reporter* piece and had requested a full account for its annual report. And a wealthy manufacturer of machine tools had appeared at the Livingstone meeting with Dr. George Barbour of the University of Cincinnati. Barbour had been one of the very few impressed by Dart's evidence. And the manufacturer, Mr. Leighton Wilkie, had been so infuriated by the treatment accorded Dart's work that then and there he had drawn a cheque for three thousand dollars so that Dart might continue his analysis of the Makapan breccia.

Incredible though it may seem, it was a happy sort of letter.

3

There are seasons distinguished by ghosts. The season that followed was for me such a time, when a lugubrious Villafranchian skeleton danced nightly in every imprisoning clothes closet. I received optimistic letters from Raymond Dart, each with its quota of enthusiastic exclamation marks. I replied as cheerfully as I could. But murder had been done not at Makapan but at Livingstone. And the ghosts danced on.

What kept the ghosts dancing in my mind, however, was not an act of injustice in the back bush of Rhodesia. Injustice is not a flavour so rare in one's diet. Neither was it the situation of a brave pioneer, past sixty years old, whose first excursion into scientific unorthodoxy had taken twenty-five years to receive affirmation and who now seemed about to recapitulate that experience, but perhaps a little late in life. One's sympathy went out to Raymond Dart; but more poems grace the world than live poets.

What kept the ghost dancing was one's daily life. Why did children play with guns? Why did boys scarcely out of their diapers cock their fingers and go bang-bang? Was it frustration? Had they all been rejected by their parents? Had they all been broken to the toilet too young? Or was it by genetic impulse?

We have already discussed that truism of zoology, the capacity of a species to include in its genetic make-up cultural attitudes just as fixed and complex as the shape of wings. My broodings introduced me to the history of the Rhône beavers and their return to the building of dams

after centuries of interruption. They introduced me also
to the ways of the weaver bird, and to the forgotten writings of Eugène Marais.

It was Marais who performed an experiment with a cultural instinct that can hardly be rivalled for classic simplicity. The weaver bird is an African sort of finch that one
finds all over the highlands from the eastern Congo to the
South African bushveld. It is a tiny, colonial creature
who plaits a tight, globular nest of grass or other flexible
fibres. The nest is remarkably large for such a small bird,
but the weaver fastens it to a branch with animal hair, tied
in a distinctive knot. In a much later season I was to have
a colony of weavers near me in Uganda, and the round
nests glittering in the high, equatorial sun decorated a tree
as if they were Christmas ornaments.

Marais' experiment was as rigorous as it was simple. He
took first a pair of weaver birds and hatched their eggs
under canaries. The new generation of weaver birds was
denied access to grass or any substitute material which
might be used for building, but was induced to breed.
These eggs, too, were hatched under canaries. For four
generations Marais' weaver birds were denied the care of

their kind, as well as any possible contact with normal
weaver-bird environment. They were even fed on a synthetic diet. Then the fourth generation, when nesting time
came, was given access to natural materials. Vigorously
they set about plaiting nests indistinguishable from the
nests in the bushveld. And fastening each to its branch was
a horse-hair strand, tied in the distinctive knot.

We know from such experiments as that of Marais
with the baby baboon and the baby otter that the higher

the animal, the weaker is the grip of instinct. It is doubtful that any cultural instinct in man could approximate the hold of those on the weaver bird or otter or beaver. Learned responses, such as a baboon receives from its mother or a jackdaw from its society, can play almost as powerful a role in the conduct of the higher animal as instinct itself. But there is a difference between the learned response and the cultural instinct. The one must be taught and retaught to every individual in every generation; the other, like a desert river, may disappear underground through parching years of drought, but will and must reappear without bidding when times are right.

One observed one's own growing children through all the trying time which any honest parent must describe very simply as that of civilizing the beast. One recollected the ease with which Adolf Hitler had brought about in a generation of German youth his education for death. Had he in truth induced a learned response? Or had he simply released an instinct? Which was the genetic cultural affinity that like a desert river could vanish for season after season, then in a flick of a thunderstorm come ripping and raging out of the inscrutable earth? Was it man's adoration of books and bridges? Or his adoration of things that go bang?

Throughout that year when the ghosts of Makapan haunted my daily life, I was writing in Hollywood. A dramatist writes for a more primitive being than does the novelist or poet. He writes—whether through images on a screen or through actors on a stage—for an audience reduced by darkness and anonymity and a kind of hypnosis to a group of reacting organisms in whom ethical, moral, virtuous, or thoughtful considerations play a limited part. It cannot be said that he writes for primitive man. What he writes for, rather, is contemporary man in a most stripped-down, uninhibited, unselfconscious moment of his nature. If a play like Miller's *Death of a Salesman* runs for two years before Broadway audiences in which men, not women, contribute the maximum gallonage of tears, then a fair statement may be made: the American business community feels far deeper self-doubt than it will express at the next Kiwanis' Club meeting. And if that pulsing, peripatetic monument to self-pity, the late James Dean, becomes overnight a hero to an age-group so international in character that shops even in Switzerland can profitably sell James Dean pillows on which to cry oneself to sleep, then another fair statement may be made: a considerable number of young people in the most unexpected corners of the world must feel very, very sorry for themselves.

Salesmen may come, however, and put-upon adolescents may go, but the western film goes on forever. Why? Because people enjoy the sight of horses? Because the vaster vistas of the American West serve as soothing syrup for city-pent souls? Neither is unimportant. But suggest to an experienced film-maker a story in which all the standard western ingredients come into play, with one exception, that not a character goes about armed. I submit that you will receive a glacial response unrivalled in the entire million years of the Pleistocene.

The film-maker knows: it is the blazing six-shooter that the audience must see. The film-maker knows: violence, not sex, is the essence of box-office. Whether the audience be New Yorkers or New Guineans, Latins or Londoners, white or yellow or deepest Bantu brown, whether it be gathered in a Broadway, Leicester Square, Champs Elysées, or Kurfürstendamm cinema palace, or around the tailboards of an aspirin truck in the heart of the Amazon: whatever be the qualities or circumstances of that hypnotized, anonymous cinema community, its stripped-down, uninhibited, unselfconscious members may be cheated of the seduction scene, of the banquet orgy, or of the speech delivered from the monument; but they will not be cheated of that moment when the six-shooter blazes or the cannon speaks or the bomb, long-awaited, goes off. Hollywood knows more about the inner nature of *Homo sapiens,* viewed as a species, than any political, philosophical, or scientific school on earth. Hollywood is Hollywood, scorned and envied, feared and censored, because it has made minimum use of the romantic fallacy in its negotiations with mankind.

Man takes deeper delight in his weapons than in his women. He will pledge a treasury to the one; a pittance to the other. From handaxe to hydrogen bomb his best efforts have been spent on the weapon's perfection. Nor have the failures of nations or the descents of civilizations ever slowed the weapon in its even advance. It is the hallmark of human culture. Mayas and Egyptians may have left behind their pyramids, the Greeks their temples, the Americans their skyscrapers, the Magdalenians their cave paintings, the Romans their forums, the Easter Islanders their monoliths, the Winnebago Indians, temporarily, their birch-bark canoes. All have left weapons. Yet nowhere in his *Civilization and Its Discontents* does Sigmund Freud include the weapon as a part of human culture. The transparent curtain forbids.

It is sometimes necessary to define a species by a cultural attribute. Two genera of Old World warblers, *Sylvia* and *Phylloscopus*, are difficult to separate on any morphological basis. Yet *Sylvia* builds cup-shaped nests well away

from the ground, while *Phylloscopus* builds dome-shaped nests on or near the ground. And so they are defined. In recent years there has been a tendency in anthropology similarly to define man by what has seemed his chief cultural attribute. Benjamin Franklin first spoke of man as the tool-making animal. Now the British Museum publishes Kenneth Oakley's authoritative handbook on anthropology, *Man the Tool-Maker,* in which that definition is accepted. Any inspection of Oakley's handbook, however, should reveal that the continuity of development in man's cultural efforts is not truly that of the tool; it is that of the weapon.

Yet we dare not say so. To suggest that we find in the competition of weapons the most exhilarating human experience is to speak a blasphemy. For the British Museum to publish a handbook entitled *Man the Weapon-Maker* would be to provoke in the House of Commons a question period of heroic proportions. And for a hundred responsible anthropologists gathered in a Rhodesian town to admit the scientific possibility that australopithecus had systematically used weapons, would be to invite a cultural definition of man as the creature who systematically makes them.

I recollected, in my season of ghosts, that first conversation with Dart in his office on Hospital Hill when we spoke of responsibility. In a moment of history when science reveals animal instincts evermore evidently as the basis for behaviour regarded until now as exclusively human; when we witness daily the disastrous failure to explain and solve human problems—such as crime and race and neurosis and nations—by a frame of reference no broader than the human experience; when looming above all towers that giant mushroom, the problem of nuclear weapons and global, nuclear catastrophe: dare one, at such a moment, suggest that the weapon is mankind's primary cultural affinity, genetic in nature, the criterion of his species? And that what we are witnessing is in fact the consummation of that species' most distinctive drive? I recalled Dart's answer: that we had tried everything else, so perhaps we should at last try the truth.

Yet if such was the responsible course, then what could one do now? The truth—if it were the truth—lay buried at Livingstone beneath the alibi of northern science that the hyena, not the southern ape, had accumulated the Makapan bones.

In February, 1956, Raymond Dart published his answer. It was a paper entitled *The Myth of the Bone-Accumulating Hyena,* and it was published in the *American Anthropologist,* and it was totally unsatisfactory. Dart did not choose to make a limited demonstration that his particular bones deposited at a particular site in a remote but particular time could scarcely have been accumulated by hyenas. Instead, he chose to put forward the broad claim that no hyena anywhere, at any time, of whatever species extinct or extant, had ever under any conditions accumulated bones in caves. He accepted a battleground of science's choosing, allowed the argument to shift from his roomful of bones to the ways of the hyena, took a position where he commanded no authority, and fashioned a defence that could be penetrated by a single demonstration that somewhere sometime a lonely hyena had once consoled its neuroses by accumulating bones in a cave. The greatest of playwrights must write his bad plays, and the greatest of scientists his bad papers. But Dart's had come at a most unfortunate hour.

Later in the spring Kenneth Oakley visited me in California for a brief rest between fossil beds and university lectures. I question that any traveller has succeeded in cheating American Airlines of quite so much excess luggage. When he got off his plane, I took his raincoat and promptly dropped it. The innocent garment cloaked a rock pile. For several happy days we devoted ourselves to such closely allied subjects as movie stars and ancient dating, the Labour Party and the last days of australopithecus.

Oakley had been to the Livingstone meeting the previous year. He agreed with the general verdict of science in the sense that he regarded Dart's case as unproven. Slowly I came to apprehend the mighty difference between courts of law and courts of science. In the one, a man is prejudiced innocent until the body of proof leaves no alternative other than to declare him guilty. In the other, a proposition is prejudged false until a body of proof leaves no alternative other than to declare it true. Before a rigorous scientist would accept the thesis that Dart's Makapan bones had been systematically collected to be used as weapons, every logical support for the hyena alibi, no matter how preposterous, would have to be demolished.

I began to perceive further arguments that would have to be met, and something inside me sank like a descending elevator through floor after floor of helplessness. What in fact had been man's relationship to the southern ape? Who really knew? Raymond Dart or any other investigator would have to meet not only the hyena alibi, but also the entire question of man's origin. The acquisition of an instinct for weapons, if it existed, was simply an incident in the long story of human beginnings. But even this was not enough, for there was the romantic fallacy to be overcome. No inquiry could content itself with the source of a single animal inheritance, for the doctrine of human uniqueness would resist any such limited attack. Nothing less than a revelation of the entire animal legacy implicit in our African beginnings would place the predatory inheritance in its proper perspective.

Slowly I came to apprehend, through the talks with Oakley, the terrifying panorama of subjects in which the scientific detective would have to acquire at least modest competence before any responsible judgement could be passed. Problems of geology competed with problems of genetics, techniques of zoology with techniques of ancient dating.

Who would ever have the time, the freedom, the resources, and the inclination to choose to take on such an investigation? And suddenly, with considerable horror, I realized that Oakley hoped I would.

Almost a year later I found myself in the Athens airport waiting for a southbound plane. By now my notebook had become my most treasured possession. As I waited with some tension to pick up my African commitment, I recognized approaching me like an attenuated Nemesis a very tall figure in the crowd. It was my friend, the professor. I had not seen him since that night in California when by accident he had plunged me into a dramatist's delirium; by incredible accident we now met again. He was off for Africa to make the first comprehensive study of ancient African climates, and we talked with excitement but had little time. His plane for Uganda left in five minutes, mine for Kenya in thirty. Africa is a large, magnificent continent in a large, magnificent world, and accident, unhappily, has presented us with no further encounters.

Chapter 8
Time Was

The evolution of man—little different from the evolution of butterflies or the Pleiades or the Allegheny Mountains—has taken place in an obscure corridor without known beginning or known end, and we pace it off by a single dimension: time. Most human considerations yield to measurements of human relevance. Evolution does not. We may consider the farmer's life in terms of bushels or acres, the athlete's in goals or home runs. But time is not so easy. We may journey to Rome and there through relevant monuments and fountains and churches and aqueducts trace generation by generation our long way back to Christ and Augustus, and gain through things we can touch a vague perception of our civilization's prime dimension. Two thousand years, however, is about as long as the human imagination can stretch without snapping. And most regrettably the simple unit of time which we must apply to our own evolution—the single pace which we must take walking back along the corridor of our coming—is not two thousand years but a million.

I suspect that the first and last difficulty afflicting the student of pre-human affairs is the length of the yard-stick which he must carry about with him. If a million years were as easy to grasp as a breakfast tray, then much of our history would be as digestible as orange juice. It is the yard-stick, not evolution, that sticks in our throats; and with very good reason, since for a creature whose life span is three score and ten, any real comprehension of a million years is a bit too much to ask. But if we cannot truly understand the term, then we may at least gain a certain respect for it.

The task is not too difficult, since it is more one of the spirit than of the mind. What is demanded is humility, not mathematics. And so let us as an exercise in humility place ourselves on a California beach to the west of Santa Barbara where the foggy mountains slope down into a blue-green sea. Here the beach is narrow. The coast runs east and west, and we are facing directly south. It is a lonely sort of place. Nothing lies behind us but uninhabited mountain slopes, brown and forbidding. Nothing lies before us, to the horizon, but empty sea. Could we bend our eyesight to the curve of the earth we should still discover nothing but the silent Pacific, on and on, eight thousand miles to Antarctica.

Now let us make two assumptions. The first, not difficult, is that the visible horizon is just ten miles away. And secondly, we must assume that our sea is death, and that it is rising. This is not too difficult an assumption, either, thanks to the lonely beach with the muted cries of a few distant gulls, and no other living thing. It is a sea of death that we face, stretching beyond the visible horizon to the other end of the once-living world. The death-sea rises, slowly and eternally as it has always been rising, covering all things that it touches. It laps now quietly at our narrow beach, the present.

Where the little waves fall back not twenty feet across the shining sand, we see revealed the rotting, moss-grown, Spanish hulks of the Great Armada. A bit farther out there is a glint beneath the water of the Field of the Cloth of Gold. Kings and barons are alike gone. A gentle trough between two incoming swells reveals for an instant not a hundred feet from where we stand a cross. It stands near the Mount of Olives. We could splash the cross quite easily with a pebble.

Just beyond the Mount of Olives the sun catches briefly the white marble of the Erechtheum, standing high upon the Acropolis. And a little beyond, whether we can see them or not, we may imagine the topless towers of Troy. Hammurabi's Babylon is lost beneath the water amidst shifting sands. We cannot see it, for the sea has risen too high. Eighty yards from our little beach, however, what seem to be three rocks break the incoming swells and make white water. They are, of course, the pyramids at Giza.

Nothing breaks the surface of time's ocean beyond the pyramids. The only feature that we may note is a brownish tinge in the water. Had we the courage to wade out into this sea of no return, and to swim but a few strokes, we should find a sandbar just below the surface. These are the fields and pastures of those Middle Eastern peoples, nameless and forgotten, who domesticated wheat and barley and cattle and sheep, and made possible farming and a surplus food supply. All that we call civilization stands between the sandbar and the shore.

Just beyond, only a few yards beyond the protective sandbar, the water turns sharply and mysteriously blue and deep. That blue marks the last rotting ice of the final glaciation, eleven thousand years ago. From where we stand on our narrow beach we can see the blue water precisely five hundred feet from shore. We are now permitted to raise our eyes to the horizon a million years away.

The beach we stand on is the precarious present. It will be swallowed before long as other beaches have been swallowed, and a new one will form just behind us. And so, while opportunity permits, we are invited to look out at that vast seascape, the time of our kind. Beneath these waters lie, where we shall lie, all manner of creatures that may be called men. Beyond the horizon, we know, are none. At our feet is the shallow rim of water containing all that we may call civilization. Time and death have taken ten thousand years to engulf it. Beneath the horizon's waters, a million years away, lie only the near-men, the not-yet-men. Somewhere between, hidden by the sea that shines before our eyes, rest our first truly human ancestors.

Geologists call this million-year pace the Pleistocene. Hidden at the bottom of the broad blue bowl of death are the scars and the hillocks of successive glaciers and the rubble and sediments of equatorial rains. The Pleistocene was a wild time, like no other known time on earth, and we shall look into its mysteries later. But now we need only regard the flat blue sea a million years across, which for a few more moments we shall yet survive. Beneath it are all those beings, human and near-human, who did not: species that failed, species that prevailed, random experiments that came to nothing, and accidents that came down to us. Even Cro-Magnon man, towering, handsome, creative, the last of the cave men and the first great *Homo sapiens*, rests close to shore. His luminous paintings in the Lascaux cave, fifteen thousand years old, lie hidden not three hundred yards to sea. Were our beach his, then Cro-Magnon man would be looking back on an ancestral sea with virtually the same perspective as do we. Fifteen thousand years is that short; a million years that long.

The swells of the past break on the pyramids and agitate our beach. A sea-bird cries. Half a mile from shore lie the last European remains of pathetic Neanderthal, the end of a line that once thrived in Asia but could come no farther. His patiently-chipped handaxes litter the sandy bottom. Did he die of discouragement, or of Cro-Magnon's more imaginative weapons? Some think, discouragement. Beyond him the sea and the mystery deepen. Scattered weapons lie about, but few are the remains of their makers. It is a vast sea to search and what all may be out there we shall never know. One truth however would seem to be emerging from the soundless depths with clearer and clearer definition. The remains of true men, whether found in the submerged gravels of the Thames valley or in the flooded caves of ancient China, come all from that half of the seascape closer to the shore. Half-way to the horizon about five hundred thousand years ago, the sea turns greenish. Beyond that line is what geologists call the Villafranchian era, the earlier half of the Pleistocene. And in these depths we have so far found significant remains of only the African australopithecines.

We stand before the time of man. At the limit of our eye-sight rests the millionth year where not-yet-men arrive from beyond the horizon. Could we now take our single pace and stand on that horizon we should find unfolded before our eyes, of course, another horizon and another million years. Thus leaving our California beach we could pace our way south across all the past's drowned world. And for pace after pace we should find no hint of man's forgotten trail. But then, twenty horizons from our narrow beach a surprise would await us. We should find ourselves standing above the fossilized remains of those terrestrial, East African apes who resembled ourselves far more closely than does the gorilla or any living primate. How long is a million years? How long is twenty?

Fifty horizons still farther south we pass the eariest of our primate ancestors, tiny, squirrel-like, fallen from their trees into green oblivion. We pass the first birds and the first shy mammals, and trespass upon the watery grave-yard of the great dinosaurian reptiles. But soon two hundred horizons will have opened before us. The million-year time of man, that seemed so vast, is a memory now difficult to recapture. The wave-washed towers of civilization linger only as a notion and the precarious beach as a fragment of some hurried dream.

Yet, could we make such a journey down the length of the Pacific stillness, we should not yet have reached the earth's equator. We press on south, slow pace upon pace. The gigantic reptiles have shrunken. We pass the first snake, the first turtle, the first ancestral crocodile. Huge primitive forests that someday will be coal are inhabited only by insects and worms. Somewhere south of the equator we come on the earliest amphibia emerging from the Devonian waters of their birth.

The land forests shrink, and in the seas fish thin in number. The first with a true backbone leaves his skeleton on the ocean floor. Those most ancient of spectres, the shark and the ray, still lurk in the ancient seas. Then these are gone, and the lampreys. The continents and islands are barren of vegetation. We are in a world of antique clams, of ancestral oysters and shrimps and their landgoing relatives, the horny-coated insects.

South and farther south we travel. We are four thousand miles from our California beach, four hundred million years across the sea of engulfing death. Twenty more horizons each the length of the Pleistocene, thirty, forty, fifty. Change is slow now. Molluscs still contribute their shells and soft bodies to time's old graveyard. Seaweed still leaves its print on the ocean floor. Lesser life still flourishes in these remote Cambrian seas—sponges and coral, starfish and sea-lilies, plankton in the depths, algae on the green-scummed surface. But then there is a sudden change.

We have passed the five hundredth horizon. And all in a few paces we leave behind us the first of the grandfather clams, the crabs, the shrimps. The algae scum remains, the protozoa, and the teeming microscopic life. But now unexpectedly there are no more sponges, no more starfish, no more remains of what was once living coral. In a space only a few lengths longer than the time of man we have passed the beginning of all significant forms of complex animal life. A more shocking change, however, is coming about. The sea is changing colour. It is shallowing.

Should we make this journey, then one more pace will take us to our last horizon. And before us will loom a coast. We have come to the end of the sea. Uncharted, unguessed, and unbelievable, the unknown coast of life-without-out-death stands before us. Death, nature's most startling invention, starts here.

We can make such a journey only in our minds. Mortal beings, our bodies are chained to the little beach to the west of Santa Barbara. Gulls wing above the cliffs and cry to the fog-bound mountains. The sea rises, imperceptibly. It will prepare a new beach soon, behind us. A trough between the gentle swells rolling in from ages past reveals the marble glint of the Erechtheum. A stone's throw out white water breaks on Cheops' pointed tomb. Nothing else meets the eye but that blue-green fragment of eternity, the Pleistocene, the time of man.

2

Death is a term that we all use loosely. We speak of dead seas, dead fires, dead teeth, dead hopes. But death in its strict sense can mean only one thing, the state of non-being that a living entity which has emerged from non-being struggles ceaselessly and intuitively to avoid. And such death was an invention of life.

Before a certain moment in the history of living things, death did not exist, even as it does not exist in the inorganic world. Then through one of those accidents known to science as mutation, death became a character in the vital drama. All things became possible. Mussels and trilobites, crayfish and starfish, sponges and coral, crabs and spiders could adorn a world that was now on its way. It would seem to me a very great question whether, had death not intervened, we should not all of us still be lost in some remote, pre-Cambrian slime. And if life is to be regarded as in its essence good, then death must be reverenced as its foremost angel.

We can be more precise. As we look back into the ultimate origins of the force that would one day be man, we come to a breaking point some five hundred million years ago. Earlier, very few and only the simplest of the major possibilities of life (which biologists call phyla) are in existence. Then in very short order, as evolutionary time goes, the rest quite suddenly appear. Almost all of the first examples of the infinitely varied, infinitely complex animal life that we know today occur in Cambrian beds and not earlier. Why? What happened, five hundred million years ago, to create the beginnings of a vital, varied world?

We might surmise, of course, that life itself had come into existence only shortly before. But the surmise would not be true. We do not yet know the age of our planet, although an order of four or five billion years is as good a guess as any. And as we do not know our planet's age, we do not know the time or circumstances when life began. Whether the first amalgam of inorganic matter into vital being took place by accident or by imperative, because it simply did or because it simply had to; whether it came about by the process of chemistry, of radioactivity, or of divine absentmindedness: all these are points debatable. But of one thing we can be fairly sure, that a half billion years before the Cambrian's sudden complexities, there are traces of what had once been life in oldtime rocks. And it is reasonable to suppose that the beginnings of life took place not less than a billion years before its emergence into varied and complex forms.

To comprehend evolution, I have said, we must gain at least respect for the immensity of time. When we have acquired some shuddering comprehension of that abyss called a million years, then we can understand how a chinless, small-brained, but man-like creature, the last of the animals, could plunge into that abyss with all his capacities to run and throw and hunt and kill and all his primate-inherited instincts for sexual and social relationships, for property and status, for enemies and friends; and how we could emerge from the abyss without very much added but a chin and a bigger brain. Similarly, when we have faced that incomprehensible void, five hundred spans each the length of the time of man, we can at least bow before the probability that evolution could produce from a slim world of oysters and cockles, crayfish and spiders, the panorama of life that is ours. But now we must reverse our incredulities, and turn our incomprehension inside out. If nature, in half a billion years, could produce the living world we know, then why, in the preceding billion years, could it produce little more than the scum on a farmer's pond?

The answer, of course, is quite simple. Death in Pre-Cambrian times was unknown. Life existed, but not death. The world of the algae, the amoebas, and the primitive worms is a life of continuous existence. The organism may grow at one end and slough off at the other. Death is no more involved than in the cutting of fingernails. The organism may sprout a branch that flourishes, withers, and falls away. But death, as we think of death, has occurred no more than in the windy fluttering of scarlet maple leaves on a New England autumn afternoon, or in the pulling of a tooth.

Throughout these first billion years of the time of life, reproduction had not yet come into vogue. Division was the fashion. The amoeba, as we know, bears no young. It simply swells and divides. Where once was one amoeba, there now are two; then four, and eight, and sixteen. At no point does the original amoeba cease to exist, for it retains existence in all its derivative members. Should one perish, we can scarcely speak of death. The organism has preserved its identity in the remainder of the clan. From the viewpoint of the original amoeba—if we may ascribe to an amoeba such an improbable capacity—life continues undisturbed so long as one surviving amoeba remains.

Pre-Cambrian life was, I suppose, a Utopia of a sort. Non-disturbance was the motto carved on its walls. Time passed, and did not pass. Separate organisms existed, and did not exist. Lacking individuality, there was little conflict. Lacking mortality, there was no fear. Peace, that supposed desideratum of the human condition, here reigned like a fat old queen. Neither competition nor the crying of children, war nor the terror of the predator, pain nor sorrow for the dear departed, neither cruelty nor injustice nor enmity for one's fellow served to break the calm of Pre-Cambrian days. Life was good. For all those who speak persuasively concerning the collective soul, or for those who yearn wistfully for life everlasting, I can only recommend the immortal slime.

And immortal, very nearly, it remained. There seems no striking reason why a condition that prevailed for two-thirds of life's span could not have hung on for just a little longer. But accident, as I have emphasized in another context, is a factor never to be ignored in the reality of vital processes. There is the accident of variation, that the two halves of the amoeba may not quite resemble each other. Darwin attempted to account for the differentiation of species on this basis alone, and his failure very nearly resulted in the foundering of the entire theory. But there is another form of natural accident unrecognized in Darwin's time. That is mutation: a sudden, unguessed, unpredictable, more-or-less radical differentiation of an organism from its parent or partners. A tail may grow where no tail grew before. Four toes may fringe a foot where five have been the decoration of the ages. An accidental change or accumulation has afflicted the genetic determinants of an organism. And the total change is inheritable.

What drowsy occupants of the late Pre-Cambrian slimes were afflicted by a series of accidents that combined to deprive them of their immortal ways? We do not know. The rocky record of these soft-bodied creatures is entirely too poor. But a remarkable series of mutations—made statistically probable, I presume, as something that could or must happen in the course of a billion years—brought about in some family of forgotten organisms the capacity to reproduce themselves.

The individual became possible. Reproduction, rather than division, became the means whereby life could perpetuate life. The hen need no longer split herself in two. She could lay an egg.

An oversimplification of a sort is made by my recording that life invented death. What life invented was the individual. It was a new sort of being with the capacity to reproduce itself and its kind, a living entity separate and distinct from all other living entities with separate history, purposes, passions, and fate. But what goes up must come down, and what acknowledges a beginning must acknowledge an end. The individual being, life's most significant invention, came wrapped in a cloak of many potential colours: loneliness, insecurity, ambition, greed, animosity, sacrifice, hatred, love. None had been possible before, and none for a while might become apparent. But what did appear, imperatively and immediately, was individuality's husband, death.

Life-without-death had left its billion-year record in the mediocrity and changeless monotony of the tranquil, primordial, undifferentiated slime. Then individuality and her relentless husband appeared in a geologic overnight. And they left their record in cockleshells and ruined castles, in dinosaur bones and buried cities, in sabre teeth and suits of armour and paintings on old cave walls.

Individuality meant infinite variation; death, infinite selection. Individuality meant the birth of a fresh, bright hope with the coming of every new living being. Death meant division, the false from the true. Individuality might plant a garden with over-generous hand. Death, old reliable, would take care of the weeding. Individuals might compete for living space, nourishment, dominance, or the right to reproduce. Death, ever-watchful, kept his tallies in the judge's stand.

The advent of the individual half a billion years ago meant that life need no longer be confined to a single stillwater and expressed in a few simple forms. Creativity and change became possible. New environments might be explored, new spheres of existence made available. Accidental modifications in the structure of an organism, if favourable, could be retained in its descendants and made the basis for new species, new forms, new promises.

Death, very simply, meant evaluation. Life without death had been life with few values. Now success could be rewarded, failure punished, promise encouraged, debility eliminated. A creature afflicted by that natural accident, a mutation, met instantly his judgement day. Did the change bring about a new being better qualified to gain nourishment, repel enemies, thrive in an accustomed environment or adjust to a new one? Then death held back, and the creature was permitted to reproduce his kind complete with the added, inheritable fortune. But what if the gift from the stars were a dark one—as in all likelihood it would prove to be—and it produced a creature of diminished value? Then predators ate him, parents neglected him, disease wasted him, competition overwhelmed him. Rarely would he live to pass on to descendants his unfortunate legacy. Death closed his books.

Evaluation of accidental change was the supreme gift that death brought to life. Accidents had befallen the inhabitants of Pre-Cambrian algae beds. But means of evaluation had been rare and slow, and since most mutations are for the worse, mediocrity and stagnation became the colour of our beginnings. With the advent of death, paradoxically, came all that we think of as life. It was as if the streets were swept nightly, the rubbish burned daily, the books balanced regularly. Now the cockle could find his rocky ledge, and jawless fishes their deep blue sea; crabs could explore the tidal inlets, and spiders the sandy shore. At the risk of death, all could be free of immortality's slimy prison. A world was born.

It was Charles Darwin's genius that earlier than any other man he grasped two of evolution's three main principles. He saw the role of time in the long haul. He saw the significance of death as the editor of nature's follies. Only the mechanics of variation eluded him.

The meaningfulness of time's immensity was the intellectual achievement on Darwin's part that freed him from the error of earlier scientific thought. Half a century before him, Lamarck had given the world the essential theory of evolution, that all species of life have evolved one from another, the special from the general, the complex from the simple. But to the question of how they had evolved, Lamarck could give only his famous answer, that acquired characteristics are inherited. A giraffe, competing with other giraffes for browsing space, develops a longer neck with which to reach higher leaves. His off-spring inherit that longer neck, and reaching still higher develop necks still longer.

The inheritance of acquired characteristics was the

theory of a man in a hurry. Darwin crushed it. His observations convinced him that a characteristic acquired during the lifetime of an organism, whether neck-length in a giraffe or wing-spread in an eagle or waist-line in a beauty, could not be passed on to a descendant. But Darwin, unlike Lamarck, saw time as it was. He saw time in its leisure, time in its grandeur, time indifferent to the fate of men. And on those monstrous marches between now and time that was, Darwin found all the spaciousness that spacious life demanded. Here accident had time for error, and purposelessness time to wait. Where ten thousand years was a moment, death alone was sufficient guide.

What we in this narrative call death, Darwin called natural selection. It was the second of evolution's great principles which he grasped before any other. If wisdom and progress and values exist in the history of living things, then it is only because natural selection, through death's agency, has allowed inferior beings to breed in fewer number than their betters. The ruthlessness of natural selection may appal us. If only one quarter of all those young wild birds that one sees in the autumn will live through a winter of starvation, predation, and disease to enter the territorial scrambles of the spring, then it seems a shame. And if only a fraction of the surviving male birds succeed in the springtime in gaining property, mates, and offspring, leaving the surplus to hunger and the hawks, then the calloused hand of natural selection may seem a grip harder than we care to grasp. But it is the hand that has guided us from the algae beds and a time of scum to a time of peacocks, leopards, and men.

Natural selection has made possible, through the accidents of individual variation upon the infinite fields of time, all that we know as life. But the three-legged stool that is organic evolution had one rickety leg when it emerged from the Darwin shop. His views on time and natural selection would stand up for a few more geologic eras. His view of variation was something else, and it collapsed quite shortly. Through the early decades of this century critics could correctly say that *The Origin of Species* had accounted for everything but the origin of species.

Variation's design, as Darwin saw it, was that of brothers who though their inheritance may be identical are never quite alike. But two gaping cracks appeared in such a construction. First, it could not account for the appearance of some radically new vital feature which has played no part in a creature's hereditary background: a lung that breathes air, a body that stays warm, a hoof, a horn, a mammary gland. And second, it failed to account for the discontinuity of species. Increasing knowledge of the fossil past made it more and more evident that no even transition exists between groups of beings. You are a chacma baboon, or you are a hamadryas baboon, but rarely will you be some half-way baboon. Transitional types appear in our fossil history but not enough by far to confirm Darwin's theory of variation. Discontinuity is the character of vital change. The road we have come by, read on a map, is a dotted line.

The theory of mutation rescued the theory of evolution. It is a concept as exalted as that of time or death.

The gene is a chemical unit of atomic proportions buried in every living cell. It determines the structure of an organism, and frequently its ways. It is capable of self-reproduction, and is inheritable. The gene developed as the determinant of life, in all probability, in the long beginnings of Pre-Cambrian simplicity; but genes by the thousands are required to handle the complexities of higher animals. And mutation is the abrupt change in the character of a gene in a reproductive cell, resulting in an abrupt and usually disastrous change in the character of the descendant organism. And while one might think that the change of a single gene among, say, a thousand would have small consequence, still it is not so, for genes operate as a system. The change of one changes the system and modifies the value of all other genes.

We may best compare the play of genes to a hand of draw poker. You hold the ten, jack, queen, and king of hearts, along with the nine of spades. The nine gives the other cards a considerable value, and you are in business with a high straight. But discard the nine of spades and draw. If you draw a lesser card, then you are out of the game. Your ten, jack, queen, and king of hearts are suddenly of no value; you have suffered a normal mutation, and you are dead. Or you may draw a higher card, any but an ace. Your high straight is gone, and you are reduced to a pair. You are not dead, but suffer many such hands and you will be out of the game. Draw the ace of hearts however. Every other card will leap in value. You will have a royal flush, the pot on the table, and in all probability a heart attack. In only this last qualification does such a draw differ from a benevolent mutation.

Nature's odds are poorer than poker's. One mutation in a hundred may be regarded as benevolent, and generally we may say that the other ninety-nine mutations will kill the organism immediately, or so damage its genetic system that natural selection will accomplish its discard. But when a change however rare opens a new evolutionary road better suited to an environment, then natural selection will protect and multiply the lucky heirs and seek further mutations among them.

The classic example of sudden mutation is that of the peppered moth. This moth was common in England, in the area of Manchester, in older times. Its colour lent the moth camouflage when it rested on tree trunks. Then came the industrial revolution. The smoke of the Midlands blackened the tree trunks and revealed the moths. But about a century ago the accident of mutation saved the peppered moth from extinction. A black mutant appeared. At an earlier date such a mutation would have been degenerative, the mutant conspicuous, and the gene eliminated by natural selection in the form of sharp-eyed birds. But now the situation was reversed. The birds continued to gobble up the ancestral peppered moths, while the mutant and his offspring vanished safely against sooty tree-trunks. The black is today the common moth of the Manchester area, the peppered the collector's item.

We may deal casually with such a story, yet in an oversimplified form it is the story of evolution. An environment changes, or competition may force individuals of a species into altered conditions of natural balance. In the new environment, the species carries some disadvantage and death begins its work. Slight variations are of small help. Time passes. Extinction presses. Generations of predators grow fat, generations of prey grow lean. Then—perhaps—the lightning strikes. Such was the situation of the human stock, in long-gone Pliocene times. And by such a marginal chance was the human promise saved.

Mutation is an accident, like the collision of cars on a highway. But it is a collision occurring on a sub-microscopic scale between a gene and a sub-atomic particle. And the chance that a gene in a reproductive cell will lie directly in the path of a flying particle represents the chance of mutation. What we do not know about the process of mutation looms today among the most enticing of scientific frontiers. But since Hiroshima that frontier is being rapidly penetrated. And radiation, we can now be fairly sure, is mutation's prime cause.

Fear of nuclear warfare may preoccupy us as we study the relation of mutation to nuclear forces. But never must we forget that mutation is the stuff of life, or that radiation has always been with us. Stand in the sun and warm yourself; sub-atomic particles released by solar fusion rain all about you. Stand in the peace of a starry night. Cosmic rays, of little known origin but all-powerful penetration, are coming your way out of the mystery of interstellar space. Stand on a mountain top. Your protection will be at a minimum. Stand in the lowland: radiation is reaching you from the earth's own inner places. The force of radiant energy is eternal, an intrinsic property of all physical existence. It was with us when life began and may well have been the force of life's creation. It will be with us when all life ends and may of course become the force of life's undoing.

Radiation is the killer; it is also the creator. Its impact on the gene is mutation, and on life, change. Drawn from hot, molten sources within our earth or from cold masses of our ancient granitic rocks; from sources beyond our planet, beyond our sun, beyond our galaxy; drawn from the most turbulent natal sources of intergalactic space, radiation is the force that has brought us where we are.

Time and death and the space between the stars—these are the ingredients of the woman who prepares your breakfast, or of the man who gets off the train as you get on.

3

Time and far space offer many a mystery that the human mind may never solve. But that mundane era called the Pleistocene is enough for this beholder. Our small continuum of time and space, the last million years on this planet, holds secrets that have baffled the most informed speculation. Yet this is the time and the place of man, and much of the human enigma remains enclosed in the Pleistocene mystery.

We have concerned ourselves with time in the long haul, since if we are to consider our African genesis we must have some respect for time's immensity. We have considered certain factors in the modern view of evolution, since if we are to investigate the origins of human and prehuman species we must have a modest comprehension of the evolutionary process. We shall before this chapter ends familiarize ourselves with techniques of ancient dating; for if we are to evaluate ancient evidences, then we must have some confidence in our information as to when events took place. But right now we shall look into the Pleistocene strictly for purposes of sublime confusion.

The reader should be warned, of course, that on this brief excursion into cosmic lunacy he may quite by accident learn something useful. The Pleistocene is, after all, the grand stage for the human drama; and familiarity with that stage will not diminish his interest in the following chapter. But as he concludes his excursion through the time of our kind, lurking figures should confront him. Was man a probability? Are we a product of orderly forces beyond human comprehension? Or an outrageous accident?

The Pleistocene is the time when the weather went mad, the time of the glacial onslaughts, and we are still in its strange embrace. Only twice before in the history of the planet have there been comparable eras. In Pre-Cambrian times at a date so ancient that we cannot define it we find the scour of ice on primordial granite. Again, two hundred million years ago, Permian ice-sheets left their scars in Africa, South America, India, and Australia.

The second era of glaciation closed when reptiles were only beginning their long, dynastic procession. Dinosaur and pterodactyl had yet to assemble their genetic monstrosities. The first true mammals like their first true birds lay far in the evolutionary future. Yet from the Permian to the Pleistocene, through an immense wash of time lasting over two hundred million years, no least sign of glacial movement may be found on the land. Then again came the madness.

We may appreciate even more keenly the extraordinary nature of our time if we glance at the African rainfall chart for the last twenty million years. It is the period of the

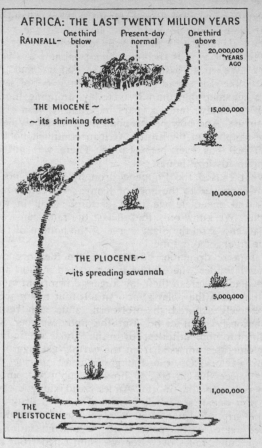

AFRICA: THE LAST TWENTY MILLION YEARS

RAINFALL— One third below   Present-day normal   One third above

20,000,000 YEARS AGO

THE MIOCENE ~
~ its shrinking forest

15,000,000

10,000,000

THE PLIOCENE ~
~its spreading savannah

5,000,000

1,000,000

THE PLEISTOCENE

emergence of the human stock. It begins in the Miocene, as you will see, the time of *Proconsul* and the other terrestrial apes of Kenya. The rainfall was heavier then than today, and the weather on the African uplands idyllic. Then slowly the rainfall lessens. The forests shrink, the savannahs and deserts spread. And at last we enter the terrifying Pliocene drought, unremitting, changeless, twelve million years long.

So intense was the drying up of the African land that the Portuguese diamond syndicate has found the red sands of the Kalahari desert, now confined to southwestern Africa, reaching northwards through Angola almost to the Congo River. We must assume that the Sahara and Arabian deserts likewise spread their vast arc in a wall of sand even more impenetrable than it is today, trapping the human stock for twelve million years in a mid-African evolutionary prison. And how prison conditions were may be judged quite simply. On the entire African continent no Pliocene fossil bed has ever been found. There was not enough water to fossilize bones.

What caused the Pliocene drought? We do not know. What happened to the apes of Kenya? We can only speculate—and speculate we most certainly shall in the next chapter. We know only that at last the rains came, and the Pleistocene. And the dizzy curve at the bottom of the chart is the track of our time.

Far more dramatic, however, is the Pleistocene of the higher latitudes where after two hundred million apathetic years glaciers spread their icy fingers down from mountains and out from the polar zones. In all, four major ice sheets successively scoured the northern land, each retiring as mysteriously as it came. But the antic weather was not confined to high latitudes, for in the Punjab we find boulder conglomerates amassed from the earthly garbage of Himalayan glaciers. On the Patagonia coast marine deposits show successive layers of boulder rubbish from upland glaciers originating in the Andes. And along every coast of every ocean sea-levels rose and sank as water, locked in the grip of distant ice, was released by melting then locked again. At the peak of the second glaciation twenty million cubic miles of water was subtracted from the sea.

What caused such wild swings of climate? And why has the Pleistocene existed at all? The questions would be academic and quite irrelevant to the problem of man were it not for a single, startling fact which we shall find revealed by our African genesis: At an evolutionary moment still unestablished but confined to the first half of the Pleistocene, the big brain came into being. For seventy million years brain enlargement had been the focus of the primate experiment, yet mutation and natural selection had combined to produce no brain larger than a pint measure. Then, coinciding precisely with the Pleistocene's first changes, and in a space of time no greater than an evolutionary flicker, the brain very nearly trebled in size and a creature called man walked the earth.

Is it possible to believe that the character of the Pleistocene was not in some measure a final cause for the appearance even by its mid-point of the new being, man? It has been the latterday fashion of anthropology to reject anatomical definitions of man and to extend the title to any creature capable of making tools. The cultural definition of man was premised by the entirely reasonable assumption that it was the enlarging human brain which had made possible the imagination and skills of such cultural achievement. But the East African discoveries of 1959 and 1960, which we shall inspect in detail in the next chapter, have exploded the assumption and rendered impractical the cultural definition. In the oldest deposits of Tanganyika's Olduvai Gorge lie the gorilla-brained australopithecines; in the next oldest, true men. And both made tools of stone. For anthropology now to cling to the cultural definition would be to deny with word-play the salient truth that one more characteristic of human behaviour, creativity, has been discovered to have its origins in the animal world; and to hide from philosophy's view a question of incalculable magnitude and controversy: If man was fathered by the sudden forces of the Pleistocene, then whose child was his time?

No one can suggest that our best minds have failed to investigate the question. Theories by the dozen have been advanced to explain the Pleistocene, and the reader will encounter them from time to time in the popular press. All are interesting; some have a certain substance; none cannot be shot down like a clay pigeon. And since it is not my intention, despite all rational temptation, to present man in this narrative in a package tidier than that prepared by nature, let us shoot down a few.

A favourite theory of the ice age is founded, for example, on the tipping pole. The famous astrophysicist, Thomas Gold, follows this most innocent of explanations. There is a certain small room—about the size of an empty intellectual clothes closet—for the notion that a wandering of the North Pole, not a change in climate, produced the successive glaciations. It is true that the northern glaciers affected Europe and America, but not Siberia, and that a location of the Pole in Greenland would spread an arctic climate over the better-known glaciated areas. But a temporary removal of the Pole to Greenland could scarcely account for the descent of the snow-line on Mt. Kenya, situated directly on the equator, by three thousand feet; or glacial activity in the Andes, which would now be farther from the South Pole than ever; or the drop in sea-levels all over the world. Of all the theories of the ice age, that of the tipping pole manages to explain a minimum of the Pleistocene's mysteries.

The comet theory, unlike that of the tipping pole, comes straight from space fiction. According to this one, a comet scoring a near-miss on the earth will leave fragments of its tail in our atmosphere. The contribution of particles will be sufficient to thicken the filter of the atmosphere, seed clouds in greater abundance, and reduce the solar radiation reaching the earth's surface while at the same time increasing the rate of precipitation. Thus an ice age is inaugurated. Gradually the particles will settle from the atmosphere and the earth will get back to normal. The theory has two major advantages: it is extremely difficult to disprove; and to explain previous ice ages we have only to presume more comets. The theory contains also an element attractively disturbing. Our four Pleistocene glacial onslaughts must be explained by four comets. It is statistically improbable that four different comets have come so close to us in a time so short. Therefore, what we must presume is that the same comet on four successive passages of its orbit has on each occasion scored a near-miss. We are left with the unsettling thought that with such experience at its disposal, on its next pass the comet may score a direct hit.

The comet theory, in fact, can be shot down with little effort. A comet follows an orbit that would bring it in our neighbourhood at regular intervals. The four major glaciations have not occurred at regular intervals, but in two pairs. Also, such a comet would appear suddenly in our midst and deposit immediately its maximum load of particles and produce its maximum effect on our climate. Slowly, very slowly, the cold, wet pallor cast on the earth would ameliorate with the settling of the particles. But this has not been the case with our ice sheets, for some have retreated more hastily than they have arrived. One parts with the comet theory with a certain regret, and passes on to the earthbound intricacies of the Milankovitch theory.

M. Milankovitch is a Jugoslav mathematician who in 1920 published in Zagreb a paper called *Théorie Mathématique des phénomènes thermiques produits par la radiation solaire.* No one concerned with the Pleistocene has quite got over it since. To follow the Milankovitch explanation we need postulate no tipping poles, nor angry comets. One needs only common sense, a plain record of our planet's movements, and a doctor's degree in mathematics.

We need not describe here the three variations in earth movement called perturbations. They are slight, and they proceed through very long cycles. Readers boasting strong mathematical stomachs may be referred for more elaborate consideration to Zeuner's *Dating the Past.* But it was Milankovitch's reasoning that although the cyclical variations were small, there were times in the past when they coincided to produce significant climatic changes. Having broached the theory in 1920, he proceeded for twenty years to put its ingredients through his mathematical meatgrinder. He emerged with charts showing for every degree of latitude north and south the climatic probability for every thousand-year period back for a million years. The results are stupefying.

The Milankovitch curves for Europe show the precise outline of the Pleistocene as geologists have come to know it. If the reader will refer to the large chart of the Pleistocene he will find some preliminary ice movements near the top. These are known as the Donau phases in the Alps. Argon studies published in 1958 show contemporary ice movements in California's Sierra Nevada as 870,000 years ago. Milankovitch's curve, prepared decades before the argon method of dating became available, shows the first bump of Pleistocene climatic change as 940,000 years ago.

Farther down the chart we come to the first pair of European glaciers: Günz, the least of the ice sheets, followed by a mild interglacial and then Mindel, towering in its severity. Classical geology has estimated the onslaught of Günz as six hundred thousand years ago; the first tall bump in this section of Milankovitch's curve falls at 590,000. Classical geology has likewise estimated the duration of the long, dry, Great Interglacial—following Mindel

—as two hundred thousand years. Milankovitch shows the last peak of weather disturbance during the first pair of glaciers as 435,000 years ago, the first peak of disturbance during the last pair as 232,000. One's wonder is divided between the geologist with his pick and Milankovitch with his calculating machine.

The final triumph of the Milankovitch theory is its revelation of minor climatic fluctuations resulting in inter-stadials, those temporary retreats of an ice-sheet which the reader will note on the chart. No other theoretical approach has even attempted to account for these. Yet there they are on the Milankovitch curve precisely as classical geology has described them.

After witnessing such a triumph of mind over madness, it seems almost bad taste to mention that something is all wrong. It is the supreme wonder of Milankovitch's curves that they have revealed so much proceeding from premises so false. His cyclical variations might produce certain fluctuations in climate, but they cannot be made to account for twenty million cubic miles of ice. Far worse, the earth perturbations were not invented by the Pleistocene. They have characterized our planet's course since its birth. If they have produced glaciers in the past million years, then what were they producing in the previous two hundred million? As Darwin's *Origin of Species* explained everything but the origin of species, so the Jugoslav's theory of the Pleistocene has explained everything but the Pleistocene.

One turns from the comet theory with reluctance because one hates to leave a good show. One turns from the Milankovitch theory with regret because one dislikes to discard a good try. And so one turns to the Simpson theory, the newest to bring uproar to science.

Sir George Simpson is one of the world's great meteorologists. For a generation or so he was in charge of British weather, and I can think offhand of no job more thankless. When I had tea with Sir George several years ago at the Athenaeum Club in London he was retired, eighty years old, tall, ruddy and when he complained vigorously about old age and his inability any longer to think about more than one thing at a time, I inquired as to how many things he had formerly been able to think of at once. "Oh, five or six," he said. "You know." I did not know.

Of all the theories evolved to explain the time of man,

my favourite is Simpson's. I enjoy it because it was created by a man who knew about weather. I enjoy it because its compass is worldwide, resting on a focus in Africa where the human emergence took place. I enjoy it because, though it may in the end fail to explain the Pleistocene, it describes it more successfully than does any other. But my real reason for enjoyment is that the Simpson theory is as mad as the Pleistocene itself. That the theory does not work, does not concern me. None of them work. And while it may seem an irony that a concept of such grandeur should be punctured by a few live birds and dead clams, still one must remember that the theory begins in irony, and so its end is appropriate.

Simpson's basic proposition is that glaciations are caused by a *rise* in world temperature; that the only force that could lift twenty million cubic miles of sea-water on to the continents, there to fall as rain or snow, would be an *increase* of solar energy as received on the surface of the seas.

It is a proposition so simple that one wonders why no one thought of it before. Sir George saw the Pleistocene as a consequence of oscillations in the energy output of the sun. Three times that output has risen, resulting in periods of abnormal rainfall each approximately two hundred thousand years long. These in Africa are known as pluvials. Twice the solar output has fallen below normal, producing worldwide droughts of equivalent duration. The five phases, three wet and two dry, make up the million-year span of the Pleistocene. If the reader will refer to the chart again, he will find these periods recorded in green and yellow.

The second of Simpson's awesome ingenuities was that a rise of solar energy if proceeding high enough will produce not one glacier but two. He visualized the first rise, a million years ago, as sufficient to cause worldwide rains and minor accumulations of ice, to break the Pliocene drought and bring about on all continents the new Villafranchian fauna. But it was not sufficient to cause ice sheets. While the rains near the equator may have started in the late Pliocene, this would be the general period of East Africa's oldest lake beds and of the first river gravels from the Kagera in Uganda to the Vaal of South Africa, in all of which we find pebble-tools. And the dry phase following would be the time when Dart's *Australopithecus africanus* was assembling his bone collection in the Makapan cave.

Not until the next great rise in solar output, approximately six hundred thousand years ago, was there sufficient water lifted from the seas to cause ice-sheets. Now Simpson's ingenuity comes into full play. Although world temperatures are rising, snow collects faster in winter than it can rise in summer and the Günz ice-sheet spreads across northern Europe. In the equatorial regions it simply rains. Lakes collect on Tanganyika's plains, and along their margins makers of true handaxes leave samples of their handiwork. The bush returns to the southern veld, and Broom's *A. robustus* and Robinson's *Telanthropus* leave their remains on the cave-floor at Swartkrans.

In the north, rising temperatures reach a point where the snow melts faster in summer than it collects in winter. Günz retreats. To this Pleistocene moment no sign of man or pre-man has appeared in Europe. But now a mild interglacial prevails. And Chellean handaxes of precisely the same degree of sophistication as those being made in East Africa appear in France. The approximately contemporary Heidelberg Man—for decades the earliest known true man—is found in Germany. And the most recent of all the sensational East African discoveries, revealed in February, 1961, is disinterred in the Olduvai Gorge. The bulging-browed being who stayed at home making Chellean handaxes is likewise true man.

Solar output having passed its peak, temperatures again fall but precipitation continues and snows again collect in the north. Massive Mindel holds Europe in icy austerity. The continent is depopulated. Asian Man—anatomically related to Germany's Heidelberg and probably to East Africa's Chellean—appears in China and Java. In East Africa the rains lessen and lake-levels fall but handaxe-makers continue to perfect their techniques. Then the great rains cease. The ice-sheet retreats; snow-caps vanish except from the highest mountains. The African lakes dry up and the handaxe-makers scatter, some to appear fairly shortly in Europe. Not for another two hundred thousand years will solar energy be sufficient to bring the long rains from the seas and another pair of glaciers to the land.

With the final presentation of the Simpson theory in

1957, the wildest vagaries of the Pleistocene seemed at last explained: why the glaciers had come and gone when they did; why the intervals between the ice-sheets had differed so markedly in character and duration; why in the brief interval between the last pair of glaciers Europe had been so incredibly warm that rhododendrons bloomed in the Alps and hippos grazed on English meadows. Human logic, it seemed, had bested even the Pleistocene. In fact, however, the one lasting consequence of the Simpson theory was a worldwide calendar based on the Pleistocene's worldwide phenomenon, rain.

It is a weakness of geology that the science originated in Europe where the peripheral adventure, ice, became the gauge for our time. From observations essentially provincial a solemn, planetary clock emerged acknowledging only the hours of the ice-sheets. Even in 1955 the Livingstone Congress in Prehistory while rejecting Dart's weapons reaffirmed a traditional time-scheme for Africa equating tropical rains with northern glaciers, inventing an extra pluvial so as to come out even, and crowding all of the turbulent African Pleistocene into the European measure. The consequence, apparent even to a novice, was a kind of faunal and cultural upside-down cake. No time space was left for the australopithecines. Villafranchian species like creatures in a Conan Doyle fantasy flourished in Africa long after their opposite numbers lay as extinct as trilobites in the north. A handaxe style demonstrably evolved in East Africa appeared in France before the moment of its faraway invention. A clear comprehension of the human emergence faces no greater source of confusion than anthropology's continued reliance on geology's European clock, which failed to strike all the Pleistocene hours.

Sir George Simpson junked the clock. He evolved his solar theory from a weatherman's plain recognition that a procession of rains and droughts, not a procession of glaciers, had formed the Pleistocene's fundamental pattern. Oversimplified the pattern may be. Local variations of significant magnitude may have sprung from shifting winds, displaced barometric centres, and from the diversion of such ocean currents as the Gulf Stream. But the pattern though rough has at last made possible a calendar of man— the chronology presented in this account—in reasonable accord with our time as we know it. Sadly, however, one must affix an inevitable footnote to the solar theory itself: it is probably false.

Cesare Emiliani of the University of Chicago has done studies of Pleistocene temperatures based on sea-bottom shell deposits. Temperatures in the past have ranged from one degree centigrade warmer to five degrees colder than today. If increased solar radiation caused our swings of climate, then the sun somehow failed to warm the seas. The theory crashes.

Another obscure bit of evidence denies Simpson's grand view. A scientific villain named Moreau once made a careful study of certain African evergreen forests, none older than the Pleistocene, scattered about the continent at altitudes above 4,000 feet. In these forests one finds a temperate bird fauna that must have its cool evergreen to survive. An isolated forest in the Cameroons is separated from one on the Iturbi highlands of the Congo by twelve hundred miles of the hottest lowlands in Africa. Yet the bird life is identical. How could the birds have dispersed had the forests not at one time been nearly continuous, and a cooler climate have prevailed? The solar theory demands an African past hotter than today. Yet here are the recalcitrant temperate birds—which if I were Sir George, I should assassinate—roosting cheerfully in the Cameroons.

Nature mocks man's mind. Sir George Simpson's very success at describing the Pleistocene makes his failure to explain it a calamity of a most horrendous order. Man is a creature of the Pleistocene, and the Pleistocene remains inexplicable. Theories may appease it, illuminate it, describe it, reveal methods in its madness. But none thus far explains it, so none explains man himself. The Pleistocene is larger than all our logic, and we are tiny, civilized minds clinging to its windward marches, the blast of the future watering our noses while to our flapping coat-tails clings the spectre of accident.

One broods. Order ranges the starry night, the evolution of life, the behaviour of animals. But the grinning face of the Pleistocene mocks alike the mind and the stars. Are we to believe that man, the most disorderly of creatures, is the mad stepson of an aberrant time? The mind recoils, and grasps for more theories. One passes from tipping poles

and earth perturbations to comets and the sun itself. None are enough. With a sigh one passes to the galaxy.

I herewith present with minimum humility the Ardrey Theory of Galactic Periodicity. It is original, I believe. If science without my knowledge has already come on this stunning interpretation of our times, then I suggest rather sharply that science should have better things to do. What the theory explains to my own immense satisfaction is why the Pleistocene should have happened at all. My contemporaries continually neglect this problem. No one suggests why the comets and tipping poles and solar oscillations which have driven our time to manic violence should have presented the Pliocene, the Miocene, the Oligocene and Eocene, the Cretaceous, the Jurassic, the Triassic and Late and Middle Permian all with a uniform *Pax Absentia*. My theory, and mine alone, offers a proper explanation.

The theory of galactic periodicity rests on an observation neglected by science: the elapsed time since the Early Permian glaciation, a bit over two hundred million years, is precisely the same as that required for one revolution of our galaxy. Now let us reflect. Our solar system lies in a far-flung arm of the Milky Way. We are a frontier garrison facing the eternal silence of intergalactic space, and doggedly we plod our formidable boundaries once every two hundred million years. Now let us reflect further. Modern astrophysics presumes that a galaxy is born from the condensation of vast gas clouds into those shining drops called stars. Thus was our galaxy born, and thus also our sun.

And so now let us make a postulation, since no theory worthy of the name fails to postulate something.

Let us postulate the drifting remainders of our own original gas cloud still floating at some point on our galaxy's fringe. It is free of our galactic field, and so does not revolve with us. But at the point of contact between galaxy and gas cloud atomic particles like driftwood in an eddy are still being caught by our magnetic majesty. Atoms pour in. And we, riding the frontier between the finite and the infinite, must every two hundred million years survive the storm's full fury.

Every two-hundred-odd million years our parent sun must absorb from space abnormal streams of particles snared by its magnetic field. Storms sweep its surface. Gas pains roil the solar bowels. The earth is likewise afflicted by the atomic shower. Those distant radioactive bands so recently explored by artificial satellites glow with the atomic collisions produced by invaders from space. On earth, the weather goes crazy. Then slowly we emerge into more peaceful fields. The sun takes bicarbonate of soda. The earth takes score of its glaciers and pluvials and uncounted mutations, buries its dead species, admires its new fauna.

There is a clinker, of course, in the Theory of Galactic Periodicity. There should be an upheaval of weather every two-hundred-million-odd years. We have our own Pleistocene. We have the Permian, one galactic revolution ago. There is the Pre-Cambrian spell of mad weather, easily accounted for as three revolutions ago. But where are the scars of Ordovician ice-sheets, four hundred million years ago? There are none. There is not a scratch.

I take a position. If an astrophysicist like Dr. Gold can ignore the snow-line on Mt. Kenya; if a mathematician like Milankovitch can ignore two hundred million perturbed terrestrial years; if a meteorologist like Sir George Simpson can ignore certain birds in certain temperate African forests: than a dramatist may ignore the Lower Ordovician. It was a long time ago, anyway.

4

Three forces have made possible the evolvement of living things: time, radiation, and that invention, death. Of the three, time is for many the most absorbing. Whether one is a lizard preoccupied with the origin of reptiles, or one is a weaver bird wondering back to the beginnings of feathered life, or one is a man groping about for the emergence of the human animal, still lizards, birds, and men must continually ask the same question: when did this happen? And how do we know?

It is not so very long ago, little more than a century, since Archbishop Ussher's calendar was still in vogue, and stipulated the creation as occurring in 4004 B.C. His dating was based on the Biblical begats. We believe today that more precise information has fallen into our hands. But the famous archbishop was sure of his sources, and how can we be more sure of ours? Neither australopithecus nor Pekin Man left dates scrawled on low cave walls. Yet we shall have little success coming to any but the most general conclusions concerning our past unless we hold fair confidence that seeming dates are real.

That confidence can be too easily come by. Kenneth Oakley tells the story of a Captain Brome, of Gibraltar, who towards the end of the nineteenth century dug up the fossilized bone of a horse. The degree of a bone's fossilization—its weight, its stoniness, its lack of remaining organic fibre—can easily speak of remote antiquity. Captain Brome was convinced that he had discovered a horse of some extinct species. He dug. He dug carefully. He exposed each bone with exquisite patience, reassembling the skeleton as he went along. It is a long job to develop such a fossil, but he dug with persistence. He dug, in fact, until he came to the horseshoes.

Captain Brome lacked the good right arm of carbon fourteen dating; and one would think from any brief glance at its wonders that no problems of ancient dating would now remain. But it is not so. Carbon fourteen is a rare isotope, radioactive, unstable, which behaves like carbon but by the discharge of one electron reverts to stable nitrogen. In 1946 Willard Libby, then at the University of Chicago, developed the process whereby carbon fourteen could be used for dating, and has since won a Nobel prize for his work. Carbon fourteen's property of behaving like normal carbon meant that living things—all of which must absorb carbon from the air or the water—deposit in their shells or bones or woody fibre telltale traces of C^{14}, in the same proportion as in the atmosphere; and so it must appear in your bones or mine. When we are dead, however, the slow beat of time takes its toll of the C^{14}. Every fifty-seven hundred years, half vanishes. And when we are disinterred and put through the machinery, only a portion of C^{14} will remain. We may be dated most nicely.

The limitation of the process is evident. There is not much C^{14} in the atmosphere to begin with. It takes a large sample and a process most delicate to detect and measure a fraction of an ingredient that existed in the first place in a proportion of one part in a billion. Recent dating may give results of incredible accuracy. The date of the final glaciation's last flurry is 11,000 B.P. (Before Present) with a probable error of only seven hundred and fifty years. But the farther back we go the larger grows the error that must be expected. Beyond forty or fifty thousand years so little C^{14} remains that the process despite recent refinements is of little help.

We in our investigations must concern ourselves with relics not forty thousand years old, but from four to eight hundred thousand. Other dating processes based on radioactive isotopes with half-lives longer and more useful than C^{14} are being perfected now. Argon dating, which I shall describe shortly, will within a few years confirm, modify, or deny the Pleistocene calendar put forward in this account. But as of the time of this writing the methods of classical geology must still be used to arrive at the dates which concern us. And the classical method of geology is to gather together every possible clue, climb out on a limb, and guess.

Geological clues may be gathered from innumerable sources: thickness and succession of beds of rocks; identification of extinct faunal species as compared with earlier or later forms; glacial traces and identification of which glacier; cave lime deposits resulting from prolonged periods of abnormal rainfall, and identification of which pluvial period; analysis of fossilized pollen signifying what forests and what climate prevailed; reference to old beaches or sea bottoms; even the variations in the annual deposits of sandy clays on the bottom of forgotten lakes. I spent many days myself, when I was younger and more tractable, copying on adding machine paper the record of varve clays left behind by a Wisconsin lake that had not existed since the last ice-sheet. My knees have never quite recovered from the experience.

By such methods the great German geologists, Penck and Brückner, developed the European glacial clock. That was in 1900. Through the use of every clue available they estimated the time since the last glaciation as twenty thousand years, and projecting this back as a yardstick made the first estimates in terms of absolute dates of the glacial chronology. It was they who reckoned the onslaught of Günz, the first major ice-sheet, as six hundred thousand years ago. How they did this one will never know, for the reckoning seems accurate enough to survive the most modern dating methods. Yet their yardstick, as carbon fourteen has demonstrated, was almost exactly twice too long.

A single observed discrepancy, however, is usually enough to upset a theoretical apple-cart. My first suspicion that something was wrong with the accepted four-pluvial African calendar came about from observation of an australopithecine site. Raymond Dart's 1924 discovery of *Australopithecus africanus* was made in a cave in an immense lime deposit near Taungs in the western Transvaal, on the arid fringe of the Kalahari desert. And one of the minor complications of studying the site lay in the simple fact that it was gone. Mining operations had removed the lime and the cave with it. But a geologist from the University of California, Dr. Frank Peabody, in 1948 made a painstaking survey of what was then left of the deposit, and an accurate reconstruction of its character and topography at the time of Dart's discovery.

Lime is deposited in southern Africa when it is dissolved by ground water from basic dolomite and carried to the surface. At no time during the twelve million years of the Pliocene drought was there sufficient ground water anywhere in Africa to accomplish such deposits. At no time during dry cycles of the South African Pleistocene has there been enough water, either, to do more than fossilize bones. Only during the wet periods, the pluvials, have significant deposits come about.

Without exception all discoveries of the southern ape have been made between the layers of such lime deposits. Elsewhere than at Taungs, the discoveries have been made in caves packed with the lime that preserved his bones, his teeth, his controversial weapons and his arguable fate. At

Taungs, however, the discovery was made in a cave *within* an enormous apron of lime which later became sealed by a succeeding deposit. No better opportunity could present itself to establish a date for the southern ape, if only one could grasp the chronology of the lime.

Peabody accepted the traditional European Pleistocene clock and found evidence of four deep mantles of lime, the last extending virtually to the present. The southern ape's cave had been formed in the first and could not have been entered after the second sealed it. Australopithecus must have occupied his cave in the interval between the first two pluvials. To Peabody, correlating African pluvials with northern glaciers, the southern ape seemed necessarily to date from a period corresponding to the first interglacial in the Alpine sequence, about five hundred thousand years ago.

What disturbed me was study not of Peabody's four lime mantles but of the intervals that had elapsed between. There had been a tremendously long interval of erosion following the deposit of the first mantle, and fissures had been filled with the drifting red Kalahari sand. True desert conditions had prevailed, and here was a genuine interpluvial, dry and long-extended. Then followed the second great wave of lime, even larger than the first and sufficient evidence of a second major pluvial. But it was the following dry period that initiated my disturbance. It was a genuine interpluvial, beyond question. Again the red sand of the Kalahari collected in caves and fissures. But erosion was nowhere as extensive, cave-cutting nowhere as prevalent. The second interval seemed of the same character as the first, but if anything of shorter duration. Yet in Europe the equivalent Great Interglacial had lasted two hundred thousand years, four times as long as the first.

It was consideration of the final interval between aprons of lime that induced my general scepticism for the accepted African correlation. No dry interpluvial existed at all. Two mantles of lime had been deposited, without doubt, testifying to two wet phases of climate. But the interval between had been of such short duration that little surface erosion had occurred; and in shallow depressions it was not the red sand of the Kalahari desert that had collected, but black earth. I recalled that in Europe the first and last interglacials had been of equal duration, about fifty thousand years. To equate this short hesitation in the African rains with the prolonged desiccation of the first—the time of the southern ape—was nonsense. The early dry period had been ten or twenty times as long.

The accepted correlation of four pluvials with four glaciers was dubious. Equally dubious was the dating of the southern ape as five hundred thousand years ago, on the basis of a supposed relationship between the first interpluvial and the first interglacial. Whenever he had lived, it had not been then. Simpson, of course, was to provide the solution.

No single line of evidence from the repertory of classical geology can establish an absolute date in the remote past. A single line, however, if it is ingenious enough, may establish a relative date of extraordinary subtlety. Such a triumph was posed just a few years ago by the amazing young South African, C. K. Brain, who at the age of twenty-seven turned from ancient caves to contemporary cobras.

The conditions of cave deposit are so special as to make uncertain most means of analysis. Failing roofs haunt the layman when he explores a cave; failing conclusions, the geologist. But the fearless Brain discovered that a pinch of sand, whether dusty or consolidated, from any level in an australopithecine's dolomite cave was enough to give him a diagnosis of the level's prevailing climate. If the ratio of quartz to chert crystals was high, the climate was dry, for quartz does not exist in dolomite and must have blown into the cave from a distance. A predominance of local chert, on the other hand, meant generally damp conditions that kept the desert where it belonged.

Brain did not stop there, however. He developed a checking process, based on the angularity of sand grains. If the crystals were well-rounded then they had been subjected to much wind-blowing before they finally came to rest in the cave; again, dry conditions had prevailed. If they were sharply angular, however, then few high, dry winds had rubbed them down. The times had been wet. Brain produced a relative calendar for all the existing australopithecine sites, by means of which a series of dampening levels at Sterkfontein cave for example could be related to a parallel cycle of change found at Makapan, two hundred miles to the north.

A few pinches of sand gathered from scattered sites give one a fair calendar of the southern ape's life and times. And while the scientifically elegant young Dr. Brain might disdain such shortcuts, the rough-shod layman finds himself overcome by lust for adventure. One scrapes a little sand from the matrix of some fossilized jaw-bone. Place the sample in a test-tube, and pack it down. An old aspirin tube will do. Now drip in water. How many drops will the sand absorb? The more wind-rounded are the grains, the less is the air-space between them. The more angular they are. the more drops of water will the sample absorb. One finds oneself with a seven-hundred-thousand-year-old relic in the one hand, and a weather report in the other.

Kenneth Oakley's analysis of the Piltdown skull was an exercise in relative dating by chemical means. Fluorine exists in most ground water, and is deposited in fossils. At a given site all fossils of the same age should contain approximately the same amount of fluorine. The problem of the Piltdown skull was its human-like cranium with bulging forehead, and its ape-like jaw. Were the two contemporary? The skull was found in England in association with various animal remains of ambiguous age, some Villafranchian, some a bit later. They indicated, however, that the fossil was the oldest known human specimen. Dr. Weiner, of the British museum, developed strong doubts concerning the anatomical congruity of jaw and cranium. Oakley confirmed those doubts for all time. His tests revealed three times as much fluorine in the skull as in the jaw. The Piltdown hoax was revealed.

A less-known but equally fascinating story of relative dating concerns Oakley's consequent analysis of the associated animal bones. The prankster who had planted the Piltdown skull had known his palaeontology. Carefully he had contributed certain teeth of *elephas planifrons*, a Villafranchian species, along with the later *elephas antiquus* and other Middle Pleistocene souvenirs. Where he had collected them, no one knew. Fluorine variations told nothing. But Oakley in the course of his experiments tried uranium which like fluorine exists in most ground water and is likewise deposited in fossils. Since it is radioactive, to analyse the uranium content of a fossil one has only to expose it to a Geiger counter and keep a record of the beta rays exuded. Oakley's uranium analysis of the Piltdown skull itself had been inconclusive. But when he turned his attention to the associated animal remains, astonishing events were recorded.

The Geiger counter, exposed to the various fossils found all in the same deposit with fraudulent Piltdown Man, kept up a fairly monotonous count of ten to twenty-five beta rays per minute. No significant variation was revealed. But when the Villafranchian elephant teeth came along, the beta rays rattled the laboratory. *Elephas planifrons* had bequeathed the British Museum at least one molar assaying in radioactive potency double that of low-grade uranium ore. Now the blood-hound, Oakley, went baying at the traces of Piltdown's perpetrator. Where had he found such a hot tooth? Not a Villafranchian site in Britain, the Continent, Morocco or Algeria could come up with mammal remains showing betacounts greater than 28 per minute. Oakley's three elephant teeth shook the Museum basement with 175, 203, and 355. At last a report came in from a site at Ichkeul, in Tunisia. *Elephas planifrons* was the commonest fossil there. And a sample ticked madly at 195 counts per minute. Piltdown's hottest companion, if not his perpetrator, had been treed.

Radioactive ingredients of the earth's crust will eventually give us a complete and accurate calendar from the time of the earth's creation down to the present day. As carbon fourteen gives us an accurate calendar of organic life for the last forty thousand years, isotopes of longer half-lives will reach farther and farther back into the shadowy recesses of ancient nights and days. Uranium is untrustworthy, although its disintegration into lead and helium has given us some interesting dates which seem fairly accurate and confirm remarkably the estimates of classical geology. Still the use of uranium can produce dates of the wildest improbability. It is argon, not uranium, that will give us our calendar.

Argon is the blue gas that one sees in electric signs associated with the red neon. It is a fairly rare element. But a radioactive isotope of a common element, potassium, decays into argon. That isotope is K^{40}, and through an enormously long half-life it produces A^{40}, or argon. Potassium crystallizes in any rocks produced by volcanic activity. No argon, however, crystallizes originally. Argon found in a crystal of potassium must theoretically have been produced by radioactive decay, the more the argon the older the deposit. But there is a difficulty, particularly for those concerned with man and the Pleistocene. The crystal can absorb under certain conditions a small amount of argon from the air.

The first efforts at argon dating began at various research centres in the United States in 1948. It was believed, however, that the process would be useful only as applied to very old deposits in which the quantity of transmuted argon was at a maximum and that of air-absorbed argon proportionately at a minimum. The last million years were entirely too recent. Then in 1958 Dr. J. F. Evernden and his associates at the University of California published a paper in Rome that should mean the end of all controversy concerning Pleistocene dating. They had developed an elaborate and most delicate process for pre-heating the rock in a vacuum. Atmospheric argon was driven off, and only the transmuted remained. Unless unforeseen troubles afflict the process, then any date above fifty thousand years—the horizon at which carbon fourteen becomes impractical— should remain a mystery little longer.

Argon dating will not put the geologist out of business, for its material must be volcanic. Absolute dates from California or Kenya or Italy, where volcanic activity has left its black signature, must be correlated with deposits on the veld or the prairie or the steppes where volcanic activity has been nil. The classic methods of fauna and sedimentation and erosion, of sand grains and pollen counts and lime deposits and the habits of temperate birds must still concern us in the relating of things that we don't know to the newly revealed things that we do. But by and large that rankling doubt—how do we truly know when it was?—will be settled forever by secret argon crystals annually enlarging in our radiogenic earth.

5

Time and death and the space between the stars remain the substance of evolution and of all that we are. They rest unseen in a gesture of farewell, in a handshake or kiss, or a child's goodnight. We read a book, or think of friends, or remember our grandmother's little grey house where a trumpet vine softened the kitchen windows. We go to bed, or build a pyramid, or accomplish a peak in Darien and stand hushed by the view of an unknown sea. We fear. We regret. We learn or love. It is all of a piece, and the moment of our consciousness is the moment of all things.

I will lift up mine eyes unto the stars, from whence cometh my help. Out of matter's resounding mathematics comes the force of change. In the fiery, farthermost fields of existence, matter transforms itself. And the rippling energy of the cosmic transaction probes with radiant fingers the last empty reaches, the last galaxy, the last burning star, the last modest planet and the least of living things. Ceaseless, questless, random and blind, the outflowing energy of matter transmuted forces change and mutation on vital affairs. Life springs where once was chemistry; legs where once were fins.

Death is the evaluator. Death moves among the chances, choosing. Out of the cosmos would come only chaos; out of all the collisions of ray and gene, purposeless and senseless, changeful and unevaluated, would come only mediocrity's wriggling mass, but death steps in. And death chooses: the wise from the silly, the pointed from the pointless, the fiery from the faint. Death stalks the fish eggs, the seedlings, the foetuses. Death is a leopard that sees in the dark. Death is a goshawk, a glacier, a serpent; a wind from the desert, a dispute among friends, a plague of locusts or viruses, a tiring of species. Chance proposes. Death disposes. The odour of jasmine may scent the night, and the conversation of mocking birds come to my window. I may ponder a thesis or comfort a child. We should all be lost in the wilderness of chance had not death, through a billion choosings, created the values of the world I know.

Still granting the potency of the radiant shower that rains on living things, and still granting the implacable judgement of death that chooses from the changeful, weighing and discarding; still neither random change nor selective death could have evolved a world from a scummy sea, had there not been time. Man could not be, nor mocking birds nor scented forests nor elephant tusks. Time—immense, unhurried, patient and impartial—has made possible the union of accident and value.

If I enclose within my genetic inheritance the potentiality of writing this account: the sufficient brain to encompass its details, the sufficient energy to explore its byways, the sufficient judgement to weigh conclusions, the sufficient concern for the human condition—then all has been made possible by time. It is not the time of my own life, or that of my traceable forebears, or that even of my species. It is rather that leisurely measure of time that could wait a billion years from life's first stirrings for the birth of the individual, and death's first sortings.

But time yet waited. It waited for the backbone that now supports me, it waited for lungs that could breathe air, and legs to crawl out of the sea. It waited for the accumulations of chance to produce warm-blooded animals with energy superior to the cold-blooded past. Now birds could fly, and mammals could inherit the dynasty of reptiles, and I could have energy beyond the lizard's. Still time waited, while my most distant, modest primate ancestors took to the trees that would be their home. Here cunning surpassed strength and judgement instincts in the tricky pathways of the arboreal life. The brain could enlarge, and chance and death, old partners, could select subtler instincts from old coarse ways. The values of society, of communications between individuals, of the education of the young, of group defence and care for one's fellow— all became part of the primate way, and mine. Seventy million years would have to elapse from the first primate moment until accident and value produced the human instant. But time could wait—as it waits today.

Time and death and cosmic fortune have combined to evolve a living world. But all are too large for the human scale. We are six feet high and seventy years long. We may speculate, measure, describe. We may delve into the lawless Pleistocene and strive for conclusions concerning our kind. But mystery continues to pervade all things. Time and death and the space between the stars remain still rather larger than ourselves.

Chapter 9

The Bad-Weather Animal

Of all the races of mankind, the race of aesthetes has its feet most firmly grounded in the fallacy that man is unique, special, and operates according to rules and by-laws given to man alone. That remarkable English critic, Mr. Clive Bell, took as stoutly as any the aesthete's wrinkled-nose attitude towards evolution when he wrote in his famous *Civilization:* "And if we reply, the sole end and purpose of man's existence be but to continue his species, if the individual has no value, save as a means to that end, does it matter? That any given race of apes should become extinct signifies not a straw, and if man is to live for no other purpose than that for which apes live, his continued existence becomes equally unimportant."

Some years after the publication of *Civilization,* Sir Arthur Keith considered with tenderness Mr. Bell's proposition. And he wrote, "It matters to this extent: if a certain optimistic branch of Miocene apedom had become extinct, then there would have been no Clive Bell, no *Civilization,* and the world would have been all the poorer. I feel confident that, if evolution had succeeded in tracing man from a fallen angel and not from a risen ape, Mr. Bell's antagonism to evolution would have gone by the board."

The story of man's low emergence from the cloistered forests of his primate past is the story, as Sir Arthur implied, not of fallen angels but of risen apes. It is also, however, a story of most haunting outline. Fragments lure us like locked-away segments of a disconnected dream, and one has always the sense of having been here before. It is little wonder. For hidden away in the fossil fastness are indications of Adam, and of Eden; of a Paradise lost; and of Cain, and of Abel. Our genesis in Africa has the ring of old, inexplicable bells.

Every indication of science points to Miocene Kenya as the Eden of the human stock. Argon crystals in long-eroded volcanic rocks yield us the date: twenty million years ago. Twenty times longer ago than the entire duration of the Pleistocene—forty times longer ago than the span of man with his mutant brain—an optimistic branch of apedom roamed the East African savannahs. And the refusal of some unidentified species to become extinct made possible, twenty million years later, the human condition: our dreams and our brutalities, our triumphs and illusions; even, perhaps, our snobs.

African palaeontology has always presented to its practitioners certain hazards peculiar to the continent. As early as 1909 suspicion grew in the government offices of Kenya Colony that there might be some interesting fossils around. In that year the provincial commissioner sent a government officer named D. B. Pigott to prowl about the shores of Lake Victoria near the little port of Kisumu to see what might be found. Mr. Pigott was successful. He collected a fascinating series of fossils, but Mr. Pigott himself was most unfortunately collected by a crocodile. After such an uneasy beginning, we may understand why so many more years went by before the great discoveries began to roll in from Lake Victoria's innocent shores. And most of those discoveries were to be made by the third wild man of African science, Dr. L. S. B. Leakey, whose stubborn refusal through a long career to being collected by crocodile or spitting-cobra, leopard or black-maned lion must be ranked among the wonders of a magical continent.

L. S. B. Leakey is today curator of the Coryndon Museum in Nairobi, and is Kenya born. He has the manner of a bull in search of a china shop. Leakey comes of that English tradition which has always regarded natural hazard as something to be flicked away. One of his mother's sisters, arriving alone in Mombasa before the turn of the century with an unfathomable desire to inspect the East African interior, was denied transportation by panic-stricken local officials and told to go home. She ignored them. Hiring a string of native porters, she grasped her umbrella and walked to Uganda. Her nephew today charges about the red uplands of explosive Kenya, the man-trap islands of Lake Victoria, and the lonely lion-infected plains of northern Tanganyika as if he were pursuing butterflies on the Sussex downs.

Of all the scientists involved at present in African research, it will be Dr. Leakey's name that the reader will encounter most in the headlines of the next few years. But it was as far back as 1926 that the young Kenyan got his first glimpse of the wonders to come. This was fifteen years or so after Mr. Pigott's encounter with the crocodile, and Leakey was taking the Lake Victoria night-boat at Kisumu for Entebbe, in Uganda. He had made the trip many times. But for one reason or another on this occasion the night-boat was delayed till morning.

Kisumu lies in western Kenya at the head of a long arm of Lake Victoria called the Kavirondo Gulf. When one passes out of the mountain-hemmed gulf into the broad freshwater sea, red islands break the surface. For the first time Leakey had the opportunity to pass Rusinga Island in the daytime. He inspected it through binoculars from his delayed night-boat, and made a mental note that the island seemed a likely hunting ground for fossils. Not for another five years, however, did he have a chance to return. By then several examples of long-extinct apes had come to light in other Kenya fossil beds. And on Leakey's first day on the island he picked up a fossil jaw. His colossal discoveries of Miocene terrestrial apes had begun. Over six hundred specimens now rest in the Coryndon Museum in Nairobi and the Natural History Museum in London.

To comprehend the significance of Miocene Kenya in the story of emerging man we must understand that only two examples of earlier fossil apes exist anywhere on earth. These were found in Egypt and are about ten million years older. In Miocene times, however, in the region of Lake Victoria, the ape came into his own. Why it should have been Kenya, we do not know. It was a time of intense volcanic activity, and fresh radiogenic materials may have produced abnormal mutation. Or perhaps it was simply that the time was right and the ape was ready. In any event, on the mile-high East African plateau we find the first great known hour of the human stock.

Kenya was cooler twenty million years ago, and better watered. Where today are endless savannahs there were then forest galleries following every stream bed with separating savannahs on the upland ridges. It was an Eden-like time. Fruit and green stuff abounded in the woodlands; space abounded on the prairies. A generalized, fruit-eating ape faced no necessity to become an arboreal specialist in order to gain a living. And he thrived.

To call him an ape, however, is to stretch the term, for an ape is anatomically specialized by his brachiating life. Unlike our contemporary ape, the Miocene beings had arms like ours, shorter than their legs. The brachiating mode of getting about had not come into their lives to distort the generalized primate anatomy. They pursued an existence partially on the ground, partially in the trees, thanks to the mixed environment of the Kenya Eden. And such an existence denied the benevolence of any chance mutation that anchored its recipient to one environment or the other.

In many strange ways *Proconsul*—as the family of Miocene apes is called—resembles man anatomically. Between man and forest ape, for example, there is a clean distinction to be found in the skull. Why this distinction has come about is entirely mysterious and probably accidental. But man's eyes look out through rectangular openings in the skull, the ape's through round. As you stand with the skull of a man in one hand and that of a gorilla in the other, it is as if the one peered back at you through windows, the other through port-holes. Now turn to *Proconsul*. He looked out through windows too.

We shall indulge in a comparative anatomy lesson shortly, so that we may better judge the physical consequences of our evolution on the African savannah. But on the whole, *Proconsul* was so generalized a creature that he possessed only one significant specialization that we did not inherit. He had the large, fighting canine teeth typical of the forest ape.

If you will take a good look at your own teeth, you will find that as in australopithecus the eye-tooth is little longer than the front incisors. Unlike the magnificent daggers sported by apes and baboons, our canine teeth are virtually useless when argument reaches its peak. That the Miocene apes of Kenya possessed specialized fighting canines was regarded at one time as evidence that they could not be ancestral to man. But the evidence does not hold up. Run your finger up the gum above the eye-tooth, and you will find a root out of all proportion to the size of the tooth it supports. That root is vestigial. It is like other vestiges of our primate past that we hide about our dignified persons; tiny bone developments, for instance, where once we sprouted tails, and little remnants of muscle left over from times when we wiggled our ears. The long root of our in-conspicuous eye-tooth is a nostalgic souvenir of those long-gone Miocene days when our ancestors grew natural weapons to settle discussions as we cannot.

The prevailing view of science today favours an in-terpretation of the Kenya apes as ancestral to all ape and human stock alike. The view is supported by the monopoly that Kenya seems to have held on apes in the Early Miocene times, by the density of their population, and by the variety of their types. Mrs. Leakey's discovery of a complete skull of *Proconsul africanus* has made this chimpanzee-sized species best known; but others come in all sizes from that of the gibbon to that of the gorilla. But while most evidence points to the view that this optimistic flowering of Miocene apedom produced through twenty million years of evolu-tion all ape and human stock, still it may not be true. The terrestrial creatures of the East African prairies could be the ancestors of man, and of man alone. And a closer in-spection of their earthly paradise—not entirely a blissful one—will tell us why.

The Lake Victoria that we know today is not the ancient lake on the shores of which these creatures died. Deep blue, immense, criss-crossed by steamers calling at ports in Uganda and Kenya and Tanganyika, rimmed by red rocks, papyrus swamps, crocodiles, and lake flies, our Lake Vic-toria occupies a shallow depression formed by earth move-ments in Kenya far more recent than *Proconsul's* day and was probably filled by the Pleistocene's first rains. What the old lake's depth and extent were, we do not know, so radically have the contours of violent Kenya since been altered. But the deeply cleft valley rimmed by volcanoes and filled by one arm of present Lake Victoria existed then, and the Miocene lake that filled it in those times ex-tended even farther into Kenya's green hills.

The fossil remains of the Miocene apes are found in the sandy clay of the ancient shore by no random chance. Here

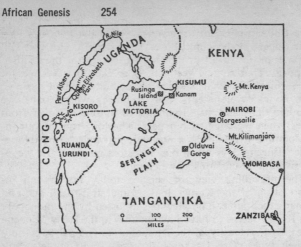

they came to drink, and here they were set upon by predators. Creatures by the tens of thousands suffered the same fate. Crocodiles took them from the lake itself, ancestral lions and leopards and hyenas from the shore. And when we look in London or Nairobi at the collected remains, we are looking at something that nature collected first—by a special trap with a special bait, successful only with special animals. It is not a broad sample of Miocene life. It is a sample, simply, of that segment of the Miocene animal world that either lived in the swamps like *Dinotherium* or *Teleoceras*, or lived on the land and was compelled despite fear of predators to come to the lake for water.

Forest apes do not come down out of their trees as dusk approaches to seek water at some nearby stream. In their arboreal pasture of fruit and leaves they gain all the water they need. The extreme poverty of primate remains in the worldwide fossil record is due to this feature of arboreal primate life that he need rarely expose himself to conditions insuring fossilization. He is born in the trees; in the trees, he dies. And when his body falls to earth it joins the mouldering fate of the forest.

The apes of Kenya found in Miocene lake beds may or may not be ancestral to both ape and human stock. Had the division between terrestrial and forest apes already taken place, there is no reason in all logic why remains of any but the terrestrial type should be found at these sites. And so all we can say with certainty is that an optimistic branch of Miocene apedom found life on the ground so rewarding that despite the mortality rate at the lakeside cemetery they refused the security of the trees. And with a terrible patience some clung to the indefinable rewards of terrestrial existence, as we shall see, long after Eden was gone.

One haunting detail must be added to our picture of these earliest known hominid creatures. It is a footnote, of a sort, that has its source in some peculiar fossilizing quality characteristic of the ancient lake. What that quality was, no one knows. The clays and sandstones are thickly mingled with volcanic ash, and Mt. Homa, standing directly on the shore, was in frequent eruption in *Proconsul's* day. Some chemical ingredient of its ash may have lent a preservative quality to the late water. Whatever was the cause, the water at times preserved flesh.

From the lakeshore fossil beds have been developed the fossils of no less than four thousand Miocene insects. A fossil, we must recall, consists solely of that hard portion of a creature, whether bone or shell, which can resist rot and last long enough to be transmuted to stone by natural process. But in Kenya I have seen fossil insects with their wings intact. I have seen a caterpillar twenty million years old, now a piece of stone, with every tiniest wrinkle of its soft body preserved in eternal perfection. And the most astounding fossil that I have ever handled is that of a Miocene bird that we must asssume fell into the embalming fluid of the mysterious lake. What one holds is the breast of the creature. No bones are visible. Inspect the flesh with a magnifying glass and you will see every muscle perpetuated in stone.

I have frequently wondered at the sight of Dr. Leakey, grey hair flying, charging like a Spanish bull down the corridors of his museum or along the crimson gravel roads so like straight bloody cuts on the face of shining Kenya. Gasping to keep up with him, I have wondered: Must he be in such a hurry? But I believe I know why he is in such a hurry. He is haunted, as I am haunted, by the possibility that one day on some ancient sandy shore he will break open a rocky matrix and find Something. And it will not be the 675th example of a fossilized lower jaw. It will not even be another perfect skull such as Mrs. Leakey found. It will be, instead, a face.

It will be a face, embalmed like a bird's breast in the strange waters of a forgotten lake. It will be a face protected by its rocky coffin from the eroding terrors of twenty million years. It will be a face, absurd or sublime, looking sightlessly into the face of its shaking discoverer. It will be the face of the Human Ancestor.

2

If you will go to the bathroom, lock the door, and observe yourself closely with neither shame nor pretension, you will discover yourself in the presence of a mammal so primitive and so generalized as to be difficult to describe. You have no distinctive horns arranged like a musical instrument on top of your head. Nobody would dream of shooting you for your tusks. Your hide is worthless, your vestigial fur of comic proportions. No intricate patterns adorn your surface; it has neither the camouflage value to make possible your vanishing into a landscape, nor such decorative value as to warrant your being nailed to a wall. Your teeth lack any special superiority, either for munching hay, chiselling through doors, or penetrating jugular veins. Your claws are so inadequate that while a kitten may scratch you, you cannot scratch the kitten back. And while it is true that you are warm-blooded, and that you do not lay eggs, and that you are edible, still the same may be said of all other mammals. How any creature could survive at least one hundred million years of mammalian evolution and acquire as few specializations as yourself is the chief wonder with which you might attract the attention of a zoologist visiting from another planet.

Evolution is largely a story of advancing specialization. Time, change, and natural selection combine to create natural values particularly adapted to special spheres of existence. From the point of view of evolution, therefore, it is the specialized animal that must be regarded as the more advanced; the animal retaining his generality, the more primitive. Unless we grasp this concept— that man, for instance, is on the whole a more primitive creature anatomically than the gorilla—then we shall have difficulty in tracing the human emergence through the obscure land-scapes of our antique past.

Let us look back far earlier than the Miocene to that era when the reign of the reptile came to its enigmatic end. For a long time even before that, the tiny, furry, warm-blooded mammal had been assembling its mutations, by slow trial and error arriving at a higher and more efficient organization of vital processes. Little larger than the shrew, he lived like the shrew on insects. And to stay out of the way of dominant carnivorous reptiles he lived in trees and cultivated modesty as the best of all defences. Then the reptile dynasty came to its end, and a wide world beckoned to the retiring little creature.

George Gaylord Simpson, in his *Meaning of Evolution,* speaks frequently of evolution's "opportunism," in other words, that in evolution what *can* happen *does* happen. With the decline of the reptile an environmental vacuum was created; and the mammal, anatomically ready, seized the opportunity. In all directions spheres of existence de-manding evolutionary specialization faced the energetic creature until then confined to the trees. Some took to the air, like bats; some to the water, like whales. Some became carnivores, like wolves and the cat family; some became herbivores, like rodents and the hoofed family. But in contrast to the multitude of specialized creatures that mam-malian evolution would inevitably produce the primates stayed in the trees. The primates retained the obscure life of the generalized, primitive mammal. And a hand with fingernails pointed our way.

We may now return to the bathroom, lock the door, and take another look. If we see no sign of spreading antlers or formidable spines, it is simply because our scampering an-cestors found such encumbrances a burden to the comings and goings of arboreal life. Even claws are a disadvantage to the arboreal citizen. We may spread our hands, think of our personal enemies, and regret the absence of such ever-present weapons. But to the early primate threading his high, narrow ways, an exquisite sense of touch could mean the difference between death and survival. Sensitive finger pads, protected by flattened nails, became standard primate equipment. Look at your hands. They echo the primate experience.

Fingernails are among the few primate anatomical

specializations. Another is the position of the eyes on the front of the head. Regard yourself in the bathroom mirror. Far more than similarity of hands and ears and bodies, it is this "human look" of the eyes that binds together all branches of the primate line, men and chimpanzees, baboons and bush-babies. And it arises from nothing other than the apparatus of stereoscopic vision, a primate specialty.

Snouts are normal to terrestrial mammals. Dogs, rabbits, kudus, bears, deer, leopards, weasels, rats—all find advantage in a keen sense of smell for detecting an enemy or tracking down dinner. But the keen sense of smell does one little good in the trees. Vision is what is needed. And it is a very special type of vision—depth perception—that prevents disastrous errors of judgement as you leap hurriedly from limb to limb fifty feet above the ground. And so, instead of dividing a field of vision between two eyes as do horses and mice and most other mammals, our primate line duplicated the field of vision in eyes set slightly apart. Even by fifty million years ago, before monkeys and apes and our ancestral line could go each its separate way, the flattening face with the stereoscopic eyes had become primate characteristics.

If you will inspect your unimpressive lower jaw, you will see that it makes a very poor gadget for carrying about packages. This was an early primate sacrifice which forced an increasing use of the hands. But the retreat of the snout and the shortening of the jaw brought on a structural problem. Simply stated, the longer and narrower and more typically mammalian was the jaw, the less was the need of bracing. The narrow V, like a steeply pitched roof, was a strong structure. But the more the primate snout retreated, and the less acute became the angle of the V, the greater became the need for reinforcement. The evolutionary means of meeting this situation was at first simply to thicken the jawbone. But then at some later moment in primate evolution came a very special mutation. A little bony brace appeared on the inside angle of the V, tying two sides together.

Feel under your jaw. There is a hollow. There is not the least sign of such a bone. Neither will you find it in *Proconsul* or the australopithecines. Yet you will find the brace, known as the simian shelf, in every living ape. It was a benevolent mutation that came about *after* the separation of our line and theirs. Some common ancestor of all forest apes received the accidental mutation, and it has been retained by every descendant species. We have been left with the primitive jaw.

The presence or absence of a simian shelf in a fossil jaw gives the scientific detective an immediate key to the human line. If the jaw presents a shelf, then it cannot be the remains of a member of our ancestral human stock. If, on the other hand, the jaw presents no shelf, then various interpretations are possible. The creature may be of our direct human line; it may be of a side-branch of our line; or it may, if it is old enough, be of the line ancestral to both forest apes and men. How long ago the lines separated we do not know, but it cannot be less than fifteen million years ago, by which time the shelf had come into existence.

Unlike the characteristic simian shelf, most of the modern ape's specializations result from his brachiating life in the trees. The early primates scampered on all fours, and so as a rule do the descendant monkeys. The ape alone swings from branch to branch, and heavy has been the mark left on his body. The legs have become short and unimportant, the arms long, the chest a barrel of muscle. The thumb, almost useless, in some cases has shrunk to little more than a hook. No bone or muscle of the ape's anatomy has survived the distortion of the specialized brachiating life.

Regard yourself once more. Your arms are shorter than your legs. You have retained the primitive proportions of the earliest primates. Look at your hand. The thumb is flexible, the fingers have preserved for seventy million years the exact proportions of your simple Eocene beginnings. There is not a mark on your hand or your body of an ancestor who ever swung habitually from trees.

It is not, of course, that you have entirely failed to acquire specializations. You have a moderately outsized head, and thoroughly outsized buttocks. Also, you have flat feet, a chin, and an embarrassing lack of fur. But a zoologist visiting from some distant planet, having overcome his first repugnance for a mammal almost as hairless as a hippopotamus, will probably not be unduly fascinated by your head-size. Enlargement of the brain is a primate, not just human, characteristic. What will enthrall him will be the magnificent development of the human buttocks, and the peculiar specialization of feet.

Nowhere in a world of marmosets and macaques, of gibbons and mountain gorillas, of lemurs and howling monkeys and chacma baboons will you find anything to compare with the feet and buttocks that you are now observing behind locked doors. Regard them with pride. They may be afflicted with broken arches and a bad sacroiliac. That is only because these marks of your kind have been recently acquired and could do with another mutation or two. But even as they will fascinate the visiting zoologist, your feet and your buttocks should fascinate you. They are the changes favoured by nature to promote your firm concord with terrestrial existence.

The specialized human foot makes possible a balanced, erect posture and rapid movement without recourse to an all-fours position. No ape or monkey has the capacity. He may stand erect momentarily, or stagger along for a distance, but his hands are never freed permanently for chores other than locomotion. Similarly, the special development of that mass of muscle centred in the human buttocks makes possible agility and all the turning and twisting and throwing and balance of the human body in an erect position. As the brain co-ordinates our nervous activity, so the buttocks co-ordinate our muscular activity. No ape boasts such a muscular monument to compare with ours; and it is a failure more fundamental than his lack of an enlarged brain.

Regard yourself. Take pride in your hat-size if you will, but it was the specialization of feet and buttocks that made all else possible, and that truly distinguishes you from all other primates, living and dead, with the single exception of australopithecus.

Let us sum up the anatomy lesson. You possess a body

of primitive, generalized proportions, hands of primitive, flexible simplicity, and teeth of primitive, all-purpose effectiveness. So did *Proconsul,* twenty million years ago. But sometime in the next nineteen million years before our first glimpse of the southern ape, significant changes came to your body. You gained erect carriage made possible by the development of specialized buttocks and ground-gripping feet. You became a carnivore, but strangely lost your fighting, killing teeth. Your brain increased somewhat in size, though not significantly in such a long span of time, and your snout flattened correspondingly though your jaws still protruded. These were the changes favoured by natural selection in the human stock throughout the African Pliocene, a vast, terrible, and mysterious time.

Between *Australopithecus africanus* and true man there is only one significant difference: your brain. And that we do not make impressive use of the organ does not diminish the impressiveness of the change.

There is one last distinction that came your way, and I have almost forgotten it. Peer into the bathroom mirror once more and observe that bony projection known as a chin. Feel it with awe. Apes had their simian shelf to tie the halves of the jawbone together. The human stock from *Proconsul* down through Neanderthal Man could do no better than to thicken the bone for strength. Then came your particular species in the human family, *Homo sapiens.* And at the last evolutionary moment chance presented your jaw with a flying buttress to reinforce the V.

By this single distinction, the chin, will palaeontologists of far distant times, sorting through the fossils, be enabled to classify our kind from all other primate kinds, human and prehuman, that have gone before us. There is no other final distinction. Shave it with respect.

3

The gentle Miocene vanished. Through million-year span after million-year span the rainy seasons shortened, arrived with less certainty, brought dwindling moisture. Rivers shrank. Lake levels fell. Winds ripped the savannah. And about twelve million years ago came the Pliocene.

No mind can apprehend in terms of any possible human

experience the duration of the Pliocene. Ten desiccated years were enough, a quarter of a century ago, to produce in the American southwest that maelstrom of misery, the dust bowl. To the inhabitants of the region the ten years must have seemed endless. But the African Pliocene lasted for twelve million. Then the rains returned and the Pleistocene—the time of man—was born.

What happened to the human stock in the Pliocene's dry inferno? The dusty bankrupt kept no records. For lack of lakes, we are left no lake-beds; for lack of streams, no valley terraces; for lack of ground-water, no lime-filled caverns. And for lack of all, we are left no fossils from the desperate Pliocene days.

The record now blank is one that time and research may some day fill in. Rare Pliocene fossil beds will be found. Shortages of money, of time, of scientists, and of limey souvenirs may ultimately be overcome. There will remain, however, a difficulty more significant than all the shortages: the over-abundance of Africa. To know man's past on a continent so large, so varied, so flamboyant, and so downright dangerous, is almost as difficult as to know his future. I find it a source of profound relief that the demands of this narrative require speculation not on the human condition in Africa five or ten years from now, but merely on the state of the human stock five or ten million years ago.

And speculate we must. For it was within the Pliocene's harsh jurisdiction that the human way was formed. We entered the crucible a generalized creature bearing only the human potential. We emerged from the crucible a being lacking only a proper brain and a chin. What happened to us along the way? We can only speculate. But we must conduct our speculations within the limits imposed by evidence. A dramatist-turned-scientist is presented, as it were, with a first act and a third. He must write the second. But the second cannot be pure invention. It must develop the premises of the known first act to bring about the known resolution of the third. Neither does science allow that the second act's setting be left to the dramatist's invention, nor certain situations affecting his characters. Within such limitaions he will undoubtedly stray from the reality of the lost second act. But it is unlikely that he will stray very far.

What are the things we know? Well, we know that in Kenya at a time when the ape seems to have existed nowhere else on earth, we have the largest collection of fossil hominids—man-tending primates—that has ever been discovered. And we know that from the lake shores of Miocene Kenya to the lime-packed caves of the Pleistocene Transvaal, as evolution flies, is about two thousand miles and almost twenty million years, and that in those caves we have in the australopithecines the second largest collection of fossil hominids ever discovered. Measuring the distance in other evolutionary terms, we know that the beings of the Transvaal are separated from the beings of Kenya by human carriage, human buttocks, human feet, and the human loss of the fighting canines. We know also that they were of two general sorts: There was *Australopithecus robustus,* largely a vegetarian, who had acquired as part of his dietary way certain specializations of skull and dentition marking him as a side-branch of the hominid line. And there was *Australopithecus africanus,* a carnivore, whose human teeth and smooth cranium left him with only a single evolutionary advance—enlargement of brain and consequent flattening of face—to project him across the human threshold.

We find on-stage, therefore, as the third act opens, two characters. One is a consummate predator, *africanus.* The other, *robustus,* was either no predator at all, or if so was less successful. And as the final curtain falls on the Pleistocene wilderness, one character alone will occupy the stage to face the judgement of time and the audience. That character, of course, will be man.

We have the beginning of the story in the Miocene Eden, and the end in the changeful Pleistocene. And the middle, we know must be the parching African Pliocene. The second act of the human drama is the story of Paradise Lost.

Let us now return to the Miocene Eden, with its ample rainfall, abundant riverside woodlands, and spreading prairies where the grass grows deep. Elsewhere in lower-altitude equatorial Africa the prairies give way to limitless jungle where the forest ape may flourish along his own evolutionary track. Throughout the later Miocene, before the drying northern deserts enclose him in his ancestral African home, the forest ape extends his domain to Europe and the farther reaches of the Old World. Gradually, mutation by mutation, he becomes a more specialized creature. His arms lengthen, his legs dwindle as he perfects his brachiating speciality. But even as he becomes a more efficient creature in his forest home, he becomes that forest's prisoner. It does not matter, however, so long as his forest still provides him with abundant space and abundant food.

Throughout the same period no great change, in all probability, affected our human stock. We may presume that the eternal pressure of the predator reduced the numbers of those species less gifted on the ground. Oakley has reasoned that any primate frequenting the lush Kenya prairies of the time would be subjected to considerable selective pressure favouring the capacity to stand and move, even though briefly, in an upright position. It seems unlikely, however, so long as the terrestrial ape depended on his riverside orchard for fruit, that any great specialization came about to establish him as a true biped. A flattened foot would have been an unfavourable mutation at the tree-climbing hour.

And so, while the arboreal ape became through specialization a prisoner of his forest home, the terrestrial ape remained in a sense a prisoner of his necessary generalization. He could not stray far from that mixed environment peculiar to high-altitude East Africa. But so long as weather permitted, he was all right.

Weather did not, indefinitely, permit. The gentle Miocene vanished slowly, but it vanished. And the climatic deterioration of the encroaching Pliocene brought a crisis to the whole ape world. As forest and food supply diminished with the rainfall, so diminished the evolutionary prospects of the higher primates. The arboreal apes were trapped wherever dwindling forests still existed. They retreated to the Congo, to the Himalaya-watered hills of India, and perhaps to those jungles of southeast Asia where sufficient equatorial rainfall yet made life possible. But for the terrestrial ape the crisis was more excruciating.

The mixed environment of the East African highlands simply disappeared. With every passing half-million years drought bit more deeply into riverside woodlands until at last both rivers and woodlands were gone. We may visualize the shrinking species of the terrestrial apes following through the drought-stricken ages the retreating forest rim as in a later era the mammoth and the woolly rhinoceros followed the retreating glacial margins along the course of inevitable extinction. Unlike the continental ice-sheets of the Pleistocene, however, the forests of the Pliocene never quite disappeared. In the heartland of Central Africa a vestige of the former jungle persisted like a mouldy museum of long-gone Miocene days. But in that jungle the ape of the African forest was making his last stand.

We may apprehend the savagery of the evolutionary conflict between the two ape stocks. Both demanded forest fruit to survive. The forest ape, imprisoned behind the locked doors of specialization, defended his shrinking territories and dwindling food supply against the raids of the apes of the field. In such a struggle for survival our kind could have only the worst of it. We faced in the overpopulated forests territorial proprietors with the psychic advantage that territory lends to animals. More important than that, we faced specialists. Our precious anatomical generalization, preserved through the ages by a generalized environment, proved sorry equipment for a struggle in the trees with brachiating acrobats fitted by millions of years of mutation for just such emergencies. We were like human swimmers in shark-infested waters. We were lost.

Why did not the human line become extinct in the depths of the Pliocene? The drama staged in some unknown African theatre was one of cosmic proportions. It was not merely the conflict between two lines of great apes. The primate experiment from its Eocene beginning had centred on the enlarged brain. The protagonists facing each other on the stark Pliocene stage were the possessors of the largest, most complex brains that natural selection had so far evolved. Would either protagonist survive? Or would evolution's experiment with beings of superior intelligence come to tragic failure? It was the crisis of the mind itself. And we know that but for a gift from the stars, but for the accidental collision of ray and gene, that intelligence would have perished on some forgotten African field. For it is the irony of the Pliocene drama that the forest specialist should triumph in his embattled trees, yet survive as an evolutionary failure. Whereas the battered, defeated ape of the field deprived of his forest margins, should by luck and necessity and generalized potential turn in time to vaster pastures and become the most successful animal that the world has ever seen.

Vast indeed were the pastures of the human future. Because the dusty grip of the Pliocene all but denuded the African continent, we must not conclude that it was a stage emptied of animal population. Those creatures perished that depended for survival on the forest. But where ancient jungles had once flourished, spread now the bush and the grasslands.

Take a small plane from Victoria Falls early one morning long before sunrise, and fly out over the immense savannah in northern Bechuanaland lying between the Zambesi's flat basin and the arid wastes of the Kalahari desert. It is Pliocene Africa. Fly low, not over a hundred feet above the ground. Near the Zambesi's back waters are patches of stunted woodland and ranges of bush. Here you will surprise a few browsing creatures who find leaves enough to supply their needs. A small, startled herd of elephants will turn at the quick approach of your plane; the cows will hustle into the patchy wood, and the bulls will rear, spread their ears at you, and trumpet defiance. A few giraffes like mobile monuments will lope with strange grace from the path of your noisy intrusion.

Then, however, you will leave the bush and the browsers behind and enter the treeless, interminable savannah. Your engine echoes from what seems a deserted world. But you will begin to see below you the very earth in movement. Herds of creatures beyond counting are in massive flight at your approach. Stripes of the zebra glint by the thousands. Impala, their coats reddened even more deeply by the sunrise, flee like an exquisite golden horde. Buffalo in anger and wildebeest in panic charge the empty places of the disturbed morning; while ostriches foot their ungainly way across the resounding earth. So quick is your passage that you cannot mark the crouching, bloody-jawed lion as he finishes his good night's work. But what you have seen is enough. You have passed like a bird of timeless passage above the unchanged scenes of Pliocene Africa.

And these were the scenes that our defeated ancestor faced. There was the brush, with its berries and shoots and leaves and roots. And there was the immense savannah alive with countless animals of most edible potentiality. But a physiological mutation does not come because somebody wants one. And any mutation in a primate species making possible the digestion of meat must be a transformation of revolutionary genetic proportions. How long did the mutation wait?

Recall that with the end of the Pliocene and the opening of the final act of the human drama, not one but two characters occupy the stage. Both are australopithecines. Both are true bipeds as totally specialized as man for terrestrial life. Both—most significantly—have lost in equal measure the ape's fighting teeth. But *Australopithecus robustus* is large, heavy-boned, and shows long-acquired marks of vegetarian specialization. His molars are square with enamel three millimetres thick. On his skull is a crest of bone like a gorilla's, the anchor for powerful jaw muscles demanded by the ever-munching life. *Australopithecus africanus*, on the other hand, has a cranium as smooth as our own. He is small, with light bones. His teeth have shape and size and crowns like ours, and enamel a single millimetre in thickness. There is not a mark of vegetarian specialization.

The two have likenesses and unlikenesses. Nothing but the evolutionary experience of a common ancestor can explain the similar terrestrial specialization and the similar reduction of fighting canines. And nothing but an evolutionary parting of the ways, a very long time ago, can account for the differences.

And so we must presume that their common ancestor—and ours—defeated by the ape of the forest, turned to a grubbing existence in the bush. With release from the forest necessity, any mutation must now have been benevolent that favoured terrestrial existence. Feet flattened, backs straightened, rumps thickened with muscle. Denied the physiological mutation that would open a way to the savannah, he was dependent on the berries and the roots and the shoots of the bush for a skimpy living. And no African environment so favours the predator as the concealing brush of the bushveld. Here only the large or the agile survive.

Agile we became, in our time in the bush, or we died. How long did we spend in the bush? A million years? Not long enough, we can be sure, to mark descendant *africanus*

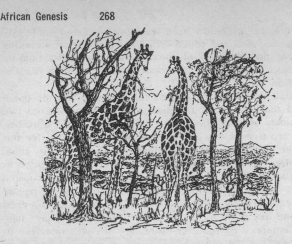

with the specializations of a root-eater. But it was long enough to create a true biped, to free the hands and to lose the necessity for fighting teeth.

In the first evolutionary hour of the human emergence we became sufficiently skilled in the use of weapons to render redundant our natural primate daggers. I know of no scientific explanation for the remarkable reduction in our canine teeth other than substitution of the weapon in the hand. Natural selection has tolerated such vestigial reduction in no primate other than the human line. And in our insufficient attention to the qualities of *Australopithecus robustus* (whom Robert Broom, as we have mentioned, called *Paranthropus,* to the confusion of science) we have failed to realize that the reduction must have occurred at an evolutionary moment *preceding* the separation of the two species of southern ape.

To say that we used weapons at such an early hour is not to say that we used them systematically or with purpose. But in our quarrels over territory or status or in our defence against the leopard, our freed hands found the expedient stone or the expedient stick an ally superior to a tooth however sharp and long. And so natural selection made its first evaluation on the basis of a cultural acquisition; it lost interest in the tooth.

Still the Pliocene drought deepened, and now even the bush dwindled with the forests. The ancestral gorilla, victor in his battle with the ape of the field, brought his unfortunate load of inappropriate mutations down from the trees and in search of food took his long, pathetic road towards inevitable extinction. And in the narrowing bush the terrestrial ape faced the grip of another crisis.

Larger and larger territories were needed to protect the thinning supply of roots and berries. Fewer and fewer were the bands of not-yet-men that the desiccated African earth could nourish. Higher and higher rose the mortality rate among Eden's outcasts: dead of hunger; dead of dispute; dead, in the dead of night, of a famished leopard's ambitions. Always before us lay the spreading savannah, but we could live on the antelope no more than on grass. A single commandment, unheard and unseen, overhung the birth of every infant: kill, and eat meat, or die. And we died. We died by the family, by the troop, by the race. We surrendered our flesh to the vulture, our bones to the hyena. And then the lightning struck.

Accident, incredible accident, befell us. In some scrawny troop of beleagured not-yet-men on some scrawny, forgotten plain a radian particle from an unknown source fractured a never-to-be-forgotten gene, and a primate carnivore was born. For better or for worse, for tragedy or triumph, for ultimate glory or ultimate damnation, intelligence made alliance with the way of the killer, and Cain with his sticks and his stones and his quickly running feet emerged on the high savannah.

Abel stayed behind in the bush.

4

We need a momentary descent into the pit of mathematics. The author guarantees the reader's safe return.

When you go out to London airport after an early breakfast to board a plane for Rome, you may safely assume that you will be there for lunch. Somebody there may accept it as a fact that you will arrive, and come out to the airport to meet you. A business conference will be arranged for the afternoon and a table reservation made at Dell' Orso for evening. But it is not a fact that you will arrive in Rome at lunch-time, or at any other hour. It is simply a probability. Experience indicates that not all airliners arrive at their destinations. But experience likewise indicates the statistical improbability of a sobering incident's affecting your flight. So high is the probability that you will arrive that you and your friends have every right to regard the probability as fact.

A reader confronted by scientific conclusions, whether in the popular press, or in the pages of the *American Anthropologist,* or in the observations of this author, has the obligation to raise his eyebrows and murmur to himself, "But is it a fact?" He must recall, however, that there are few facts in everyday life that are anything but statistical probabilities. And so it must go with the assessment of a scientific conclusion. If the probability seems high enough, then we may accept it as what passes for fact. But we must likewise—laymen and scientists too—keep in mind that those cornerstones of apparent truth which form the baselines for our thinking are rarely anything but exhibits of extreme likelihood. And that as experience broadens, today's fact may become tomorrow's improbability: today's doubt, tomorrow's divine revelation.

That the emergence of the human family from its animal past took place on the African highland is a conclusion which has risen so fast on the curve of probability that tomorrow it may enter the high sky of approximate truth. The likelihood that events recorded in the African earth were mere reflections of a reality transpiring elsewhere is an improbability diminishing like an extinct bird over a discarded horizon.

Not for a moment, however, should the reader accept as approximate truth the Pliocene emergence of our ancestral hunting primate precisely as I have outlined it. New discoveries will alter its details. Rival explanations may be compounded. There is Raymond Dart's theory, for example, of the predatory transition from ape to man. According to Dart's thesis every human distinction—buttocks, feet, erect posture, use of tools and weapons, reduced canines, the big brain itself—was a selective answer to the killing imperative. Dart's second act would therefore present the defeated ape of the field as turning directly to the life of the savannah. But while this nicely accounts for Cain, it does not seem to me to account for Abel. And somehow I cannot conceive of a primate line in the terrifying Pliocene, once having received the almighty munificence of the carnivorous mutation, as even partially discarding it to return to the life of the bush.

As we pass now, after this cigarette-smoking interval, to the third act of the human drama, another probability must be weighed. The emergence of the earliest true men must certainly have occurred on the African highland; but this does not say that *Homo sapiens,* our modern breed, found his place of birth in the same awesome setting. Where, in other words, did we pick up our chin?

We do not really know, for we have not yet come into possession of the fossil remains of that first chinful creature. And whether the natal moment was one hundred or four hundred thousand years ago, we likewise cannot say. And until an expedition properly stocked with funds, equipment, know-how, and lion-repellent undertakes true excavation of Tanganyika's fabled Olduvai Gorge, the precise moments and manners of modern man's beginnings will remain enfolded in its ancient earth. But a moderate probability must be accepted that every stage of the human genesis took place on Africa's high, equatorial plateau. And so as we return to our seats and let down the house lights let us think of the air traveller and consider one last probability which might confront him.

I have presumed that after breakfast in London you set forth for Rome. Now let us presume that instead of disembarking you stay on your airliner, cross the Mediterranean, and pass on south across the interminable Sahara wasteland and the mountains of Abyssinia until you come to bloody Kenya. At little Nairobi's magnificent airport you will disembark and there for the first time you will sniff the sweet, fertile fragrance that is the smell of true Africa. It is a heavy odour, as of some timeless greenhouse, and no passenger is unaffected by it. Whether your fellow traveller is returning to his office in Hardinge Street or hurrying to make a connection for Arusha or Zanzibar, he will suck as deeply as you at the fragrant African cup. Then you, the unfamiliar one, will proceed in leisure towards the airport's transit lounge to pick up a customary whisky. But on the way you will pause, astounded, at one of the more preposterous creations of the human mind.

On the edge of the apron of Nairobi airport stands the world's most arrogant road sign. It is a very tall post, and from it stands out a rising spiral of boards marking the highways in the African sky. Consulting this road sign you will find that New York lies 7,356 miles to the northwest, Timbuktu 2,873 miles almost directly west, Buenos Aires 6,473 miles to the southwest, and Cape Town 2,548 miles to the south. You will discover that Sydney lies 7,546 miles to the east, and such towns as London, Paris, and Berlin four thousand miles or so to the north. The implication is plain: the little mile-high African city with its banks and its night-clubs and its skyscrapers and its opaque future stands directly at the centre of human affairs.

Five years ago the magnificent absurdity of Nairobi's boast would have sent you chuckling to the transit room to order your whisky double. But the curve of probability has boosted the boast into the marching African sky. Two hundred miles to the west of the road sign on the margin of sprawling Lake Victoria lies Rusinga Island. Here are the bones of *Proconsul* and the Miocene beginnings of the human stock. In some unmarked region a few hundred miles to the west or south-west must lie the battlefield where the ape of the forest defeated the ape of the field, and the human emergence began. In the same general area, we must surmise, intelligence made alliance with the way of the killer, and the reasoning being became possible. Closer to the west are old lake beds at Kanam where emergent Lake Victoria beings a good million years ago dropped crude pebble-tools to mark the first horizon of the capacity to create. It is less than forty miles to other old lake beds at Olorgesailie where humanity's reservoir swelled when the later ice-sheets depopulated Europe. And less than three hundred miles to the southwest, deep-cleft in the Tanganyika plain, lies the hidden gorge of Olduvai with the innermost of mankind's secrets.

Nairobi may or may not be the centre of the human present, but it is the indisputable metropolis of the human past. And one does not laugh quite so hard these days, for what is Kenya's pride is man's.

5

The rains came.

For millions upon millions of years the world had known nothing but drought. So long had it been since snowcaps graced any but the tallest mountains, lakes sparkled on any but the world's most favoured uplands, river wound through any but the rarest, richest plains, that evolution in a sense had forgotten about them. Natural selection combined with accident to produce species for whom a parched, never-varying environment was normal. The late Pliocene was a stable time—stable in its climatic bankruptcy, in the level tenor of its desperate ways, in its reliable forecasts of tomorrow's calamity.

Hunting-primate bands fought over water-holes that tended all too often to vanish under the baking African sun. Any cycle of seasons worse than the disastrous normal saw reduction of game on the grasslands and enhanced hunger and competition among predators. No more preposterous a hunter than the little two-legged primate had ever been evolved in the history of natural selection. We lacked everything: size, speed, protective hide, claws, fangs. We lacked even camouflage. Yet in the bloody circus of the high savannah we had not only to survive the competition of the great carnivores, but their appetites as well. We were not only predators; we were prey.

How did we survive? Not too well, probably. Our numbers remained slim. But we had certain advantages denied the great cats. We had primate wits. We could learn more rapidly than could they. If the modern lion in the Kruger reserve can learn in three months to drive his prey against a newly-built fence, then it is highly unlikely that a hunting primate surviving the pressures of the Pliocene would have demonstrated tactical skill and adaptability of a lesser order. And besides our wits, we had the primate tradition of the social instrument.

The lion's hunting pride, as we have seen, is as disciplined and systematic a society as exists in the world of living animals. But the extinct hunting primate had social potentialities of subtlety, communication, and stability far exceeding that of the lion. The hunting life demands division of labour; the male lion flushes the game for the lioness to kill. It is difficult to believe that little *africanus* would not have organized his specialists even more finely. Division of labour demands communication between interdependent partners, but the lion is capable only of a roar. Again, I find it difficult to believe that even in the Pliocene days of pre-human experience we did not lay the foundations for human language. And finally there was the necessity for sharing placed on any hunters when the kill is made. We have seen such ruthless dominance in the lion pride that the chief source of mortality arises from conflict with juveniles at the kill. No primate society would tolerate such mortal waste. The amity compulsion characteristic of primate social partners must have dictated in *africanus'* hunting bands a sharing of the spoils far more nicely adjusted to need than the lion pride has ever known.

We had wits, we had society, but above all we had hands no longer prisoners of locomotion. Without those hands freed to grip a weapon we could not have survived.

Such was our life on the changeless highlands of Pliocene Africa. We were bad-weather animals, made by the natural disaster that had unmade the ape of the forest. It was a hard life, but for millions upon millions of years it was the only life we knew. Then the rains came to change the face of Africa and all the world's ways.

The Villafranchian rains that arrived a million years ago came scarcely as a sudden deluge. Through thousand-year cycle after thousand-year cycle the rainy seasons simply came earlier, lasted longer, and charged the dry earth with deeper moisture. Humidity returned to the atmosphere and a cooling cloud-cover to the sky. Sea levels fell. The Pliocene oceans had brimmed with almost all the earth's water. Now the immense terrestrial sponge began again to enforce its collections. Lakes like Victoria came into existence filling upland depressions that had never seen water before. Rivers ran. Snow appeared on the higher mountains. In Europe, the Alps were scarred a bit by preliminary glacial forces. In California's High Sierras, we may recall, earliest Pleistocene glacial movements have been dated as occuring about eight hundred and seventy thousand years ago.

In Africa, it was as if a painter's brush slopped green across the continent's broad yellow face. Forests sprang up where no forests had grown since Miocene times. The bush ate into savannah, and new grass grew in old arid places. Antelope herds migrated to pastures that had once been Pliocene deserts, and we followed along. But change was enormous: change of habits and habitats, and old natural balances. Then no sooner had we become adjusted to new homes and new ways than the mad painter's brush re-

versed itself. The rains dwindled, died away to Pliocene
dimensions. And the hand that had painted Africa green
painted it yellow again. The Pleistocene dance was on.

From the viewpoint of any individual being it is difficult
to describe changes lasting each two hundred thousand
years as dizzying. But from the viewpoint of stable, orthodox Pliocene species the Pleistocene represented a rat-race
from which almost all immediately withdrew. We, Pliocene
creatures though we were, had at least the advantage of
being bad-weather animals selected under conditions of
climatic emergency. And so we came marching back from
wherever it was that we had gone to.

We made our return engagement in the northern Transvaal's valley of the Makapan just about eight hundred
thousand years ago. It was our first appearance on-stage
in the human drama. We had no doubt hunted in this area
in Pliocene times but with the Villafranchian rains it had
gone too thickly to bush and forest. The succeeding Villafranchian drought, however, again spread the grasslands
over the hills and out across the denuded veld. Water was
scarce, but there was a fair supply in a cave in the Makapan valley and our bands occasionally stopped there.

You may inspect that cave today, and in the walls you
may read our story. It was a vast cavern perhaps thirty feet
high at its opening and thirty or forty feet wide. It extended
back deeply into the hills. Low down, you will find thick
layers of bright red mud and glistening white lime deposited during the opening rains. There is not a fossil. But
you will mark without difficulty the moment when our
bands returned to the area and began to use the cave. The
rains have stopped, the pure lime has ended, but enough
ground water still dripped in the cave to calcify into limestone breccia whatever collected on the cave floor. And
there are the bones. All through the dry interval close to
two hundred thousand years long you will find the drifts
of fossil-laden breccia in the old cave walls. The species
are mostly antelope, but opposite your knees, very low and
old in the record, is the layer of breccia in which was
found the jaw-bone of an adolescent southern ape who encountered a job of murder.

The bone-bearing breccia extends to the farthest reaches
of the cave. When Dart went to Livingstone in 1955, his
fossils developed at that time represented the remains of a

little less than five hundred individual animals. But the best estimate today is that there are half a million fossils in this single cave and that they represent the remains of about fifty thousand animals. We were able hunters.

Considerably above your head you will see in the wall a layer of rounded, water-worn pebbles. A stream broke into the cave at that time, something less than six hundred thousand years ago. By then the Middle Pleistocene rains had begun, the painter's brush for a second time was daubing Africa green, the bush had returned to the Makapan area, and the fossil record ends. Creatures of the savannah, we followed the savannah away. And we never came back to the Makapan area—not, in any event, as *Australopithecus africanus*.

The story is about the same at Robert Broom's Sterkfontein site, far to the south near Johannesburg. *Australopithecus africanus* occupied the cave through the same dry interval, appearing a little earlier and staying a little later. A strange circumstance, however, revolves about his disappearance from Sterkfontein's high veld, for in 1956 young Dr. Brain discovered pebble-tools fashioned of quartz in the cave's last high australopithecine breccia. The discovery shook the anthropological world. Who had made them?

A pebble-tool is the simplest of all stone implements, consisting of nothing but a fair-sized pebble usually smaller than one's hand and chipped at one end to achieve a cutting edge. Crude though pebble-tools may be, they mark the beginning of the human capacity to create—to take something found in nature and fashion from it an object the design of which exists only in the mind of the maker. For this reason anthropology has regarded them as the beginning of human culture, and probable evidence for the first presence of big-brained man.

But who at Sterkfontein could have made them? No evidence of true man exists in the area. There was Robinson's mysterious *Telanthropus,* of course, at nearby Swartkrans. By this time the rains had returned heavily to South Africa, and the open veld was reverting to bush. Brain's sand-grains indicate that the early level at Swartkrans could have been contemporary with the late level at Sterkfontein.

Also, there was Abel. With the return of the bush, *A. robustus* had made his appearance on the South African stage. But no more improbable candidate for the role of initiator of human culture could be found in all Africa than this long-lost brother species, this backward, inoffensive, non-aggressive being, this big, thick-skulled, small-brained, heavy-jawed, square-toothed root-eater with the crest of bone on top of his cranium.

There was *africanus* himself, of course. Raymond Dart in 1956 was beginning to assemble evidence that the hunting primate had not only used bones as weapons, but had fashioned them into tools. If he could fashion a bone tool, then there was no good reason why he could not have fashioned a stone one. But the case was unproven. And there was anthropology's assumption—one that I shared myself—that evidence for human culture was evidence for true man. There was an objection to *africanus,* however, far more reaching than assumptions. In all the lower Sterkfontein breccias, and among all the masses of Makapan fossils developed with such care by Dart's group, not one indisputable pebble-tool has ever been found. Whether or not the hunting primate had had the capacity to make a stone tool could be debated in the northern musuems. That he hadn't made them was evident in the South African caves.

Who had been the maker of the Sterkfontein pebble-tools? There was no apparent answer. But Brain's discovery—hailed with remarkable insight by Kenneth Oakley as the most important since that of Pekin Man—initiated a chain of African discoveries that flash today like summer lightning. One had the sensation at the time of standing on a dark, mysterious platform vibrating with the thunder of things to come. And something came quickly. The following year John Robinson found handaxes in the same late Sterkfontein breccia.

I was in Johannesburg at the time, and Dart phoned me

the news at my hotel. I was stunned. Pebble-tools were one thing, handaxes quite something else. I went out to the University and there they were, quartz and shining, oblong and chipped almost entirely around. They were crude but developed stone weapons.

But who had made them? Last year's question shouted for new answers. Robinson had found at least one of the handaxes in a single block of breccia together with remains of the hunting primate. But despite his presence, *africanus* was entirely ruled out. A handaxe is a product of cultural evolution, which like a heavy freight train takes a long time to get up speed. One might concede that the hunting primate in his last South African days had begun the fashioning of simple pebble-tools. But he could not have begun with an object like the most sophisticated of the Sterkfontein weapons with fourteen surfaces from which flakes had been removed to achieve its design. No background for such a creation existed at any australopithecine site. We were further from answers than ever. But a new means for analysis had come my way.

It was June, 1957. In Nairobi I had obtained from Dr. Leakey a preliminary copy of the Simpson theory, not yet officially published. On the basis of Simpson's description of weather cycles, I had begun the assembly of the Pleistocene calendar to which the reader has already been referred. Inspection of the new correlation revealed what had not been obvious before, that handaxes previously discovered in East Africa were not only the counterparts of the new discoveries at Sterkfontein; they were their contemporaries. And in the Olduvai Gorge lay the record of their cultural evolution.

An observer in Johannesburg in June, 1957, could come to just one conclusion: that the metropolis of the human creation lay farther north. Down here in cavernous limestone museums beneath the sky-swept southern plains had been preserved by provincial tranquillity certain conservative vestiges of our Pliocene experience. Flashes of the Pleistocene resolution might burst through: an unidentified stranger lying among beings of an earlier time; a single piece of Sterkfontein breccia in which, frozen in stone, lay the weapons of the future and the corpses of the past. But the third act of the human drama had transpired two thousand miles away in the equatorial, metropolitan north on the very same East African high plateau where twenty million years earlier the human stock had found its Eden.

Two years and a month later the lightning began flashing over Tanganyika's Serengeti plain. Mary Leakey found the skull of an australopithecine in one of the older lake beds of the Olduvai Gorge. Around him were scattered pebble-tools. The author of our human culture had been an animal—and, as we shall see, the wrong animal, at that.

With the Leakeys' discovery of what they termed incorrectly *Zinjanthropus* and announced incorrectly as true man a crisis not just for science but for all modern thought was launched with proper drama in a sea of appropriate confusion. It is a crisis fed today by announcements in the world press of still further discoveries none of which we are prepared emotionally, philosophically, or scientifically to meet. It is the crisis of man's estimate of man, and it will spread with deepening and broadening ramifications into the indefinite future as we come to comprehend its significance.

But it is a crisis which by the fortune of natural accident rests well within human definition.

The Serengeti plain, known to few but hunters, lies just to the southeast of Lake Victoria. It shelters the last vast reserves of wild creatures remaining on earth, and in fossil beds beneath its surface the limestone menagerie of the human beginning. As three times in the last million years Lake Victoria has brimmed and twice been reduced to a swamp, so three times the interminable plain has collected its lakes, witnessed rivers flow, seen its face turn green with brush and woodland, and twice been reduced to dust and sparse grasslands.

All today would be buried under time's accumulations but for a gift from the anthropological gods. An uplift came to the uneasy African land, and the Olduvai River when rains permitted cut a long, narrow gorge through the risen land. And so today's rare traveller standing at the bottom of the gorge is privileged to look up at bed after bed of ancient deposits exposed by the river's action. They tower above him three hundred feet high; and every bed, in every stage of its formation, contains the evolving stone implements of our human culture.

The Olduvai Gorge offers an almost continuous record of the human experience, a million years long, from the opening of the Pleistocene to the most recent past. We may debate the dates at which certain events in that record took place; and we may disagree in our interpretations of those events and in our identification of the beings who participated in them. But we cannot deny that what we are studying is the history of man, and that it can be found nowhere else on earth.

At the bottom of the Olduvai Gorge is the oldest deposit, known as Bed One. It is approximately one hundred feet thick, and consists largely of silty lake deposits in which one finds the pebble-tools that initiated our human culture. Its age is in dispute. Orthodox geology, tied to its inadequate glacial clock, calls Bed One Middle Pleistocene, half a million years old. The calendar presented in this account approximately doubles geology's estimate. Whatever be the truth, it was in Bed One, twenty-two feet from its top, that the Leakeys found the being with the pebble-tools.

Between Bed One and Bed Two there exists what geologists call an unconformity. A length of time passes which we cannot define since erosion carries away a portion of the earlier deposit. Dr. Leakey has found there little silicate formations called desert roses which can only come about under the driest conditions. Reference to the chart will show that this dry period of erosion corresponds most probably to the long, dry interval in South Africa when *Australopithecus africanus* left his fossil souvenirs in lime-packed caves. But whether under equatorial conditions the erosion at Olduvai carried away the deposits of a hundred thousand or a million years, we cannot know. In any event, it is this unconformity that makes most difficult any exact dating of events in Bed One.

With Bed Two, fortunately, things get more definite. The weather turns wet and lake beds again accomplish their deposits. This is the long, wet mid-Pleistocene period that brought brush and *A. robustus* to the South African veld and the first pair of glaciers to Europe and America. The rains opened approximately six hundred thousand years ago, and so far no sign of man, of pre-man, or of human culture appears anywhere on earth but in Africa.

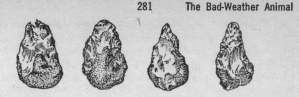

But from the very bottom of Bed Two we find handaxes being made around the Olduvai lake margins; and they have evolved directly from the pebble-tools of Bed One.

Who were the handaxe-makers who gathered around the earliest lakes of Bed Two? Were they small-brained australopithecines? Medium-brained transitional beings? Big-brained men? We do not know, though we should know quite shortly. But whoever they were, their cultural efforts had proceeded by direct evolution from the work of Bed One. Whereas the earlier being had simply chipped an edge on the end of a pebble, the handaxe maker continued the chipping around the edges to create a true shape. And whereas the earlier implement had been useful only for scraping and scratching and perhaps for whittling rough wooden spears, there was now being created however crudely the all-purpose weapon and tool the perfection of which would pre-occupy stone-age mankind for hundreds of thousands of years to come.

Bed Two is almost as thick as Bed One, and its lake deposits encompass a period roughly two hundred thousand years long. In this span may be recognized four major stages of handaxe evolution which correlate with events throughout all the Old World. The oldest deposits at the bottom yield handaxes known to anthropologists as Chellean 1. In this first stage they are crudely chipped, thick, and somewhat oblong in shape. These are the weapons that were brought to Sterkfontein, we may assume by migrant bands of the period. In the second stage the handaxe gets slimmer and takes on a beak. Then in the third stage the weapon at last takes on a true point.

The consequence of the improved weapon is immediate and may be read on our calendar, for with it man moves. The first known stone implements found anywhere on earth outside the African continent appear in France. And they are Chellean. From approximately the same period we have the first definitely human fossil found elsewhere than in Africa, Germany's Heidelberg jaw. Could the European memories be of anything but African bands following the movement of game northward in the mild interglacial climate?

Human migration now, however, becomes still more far-reaching. With the immensity of the second ice-sheet Europe is depopulated. Game and hunters retreat, some undoubtedly to Africa. But many thousands of miles away to the east true man makes his appearance in the caves of China and the valleys of Java. These heavy-browed beings known to anthropologists as pithecanthropines are regarded by anatomists as related to Heidelberg Man, and the presumption has been that their western representative appeared in Europe as a migrant from Asia. On the basis of the new Pleistocene calendar, however, I have advanced the hypothesis that all reached their destinations by migration from the African heartland. The hypothesis seems at least partially confirmed by a Leakey discovery announced in early 1961. In Olduvai's Bed Two the maker of Chellean 3 handaxes has at last been found and even the most superficial photographs of his skull reveal him as a probable pithecanthropine.

The cultural force released by the beings of Bed One may now be traced to the caverns of Choukoutien. There the Asian wing of early mankind will pursue its own evolutionary course and evolve its own characteristic flake implements. These characteristics will be brought back to Europe someday by the Asian descendant, Neanderthal, before he and the entire pithecanthropine line vanish beneath the full *Homo sapiens* flood. But meanwhile, at about the same time as the establishment of man in Asia, the Olduvai handaxe-makers pass a fundamental moment in the history of human technology.

The final stage in Bed Two's record of cultural evolution is the discovery of the principle of the chisel, the tool-to-make-a-tool. Chellean handaxes have been made by striking one stone with another, as were the earlier pebble-tools But now a piece of bone or hard wood is held where the flake is to be struck off, and the chisel is struck, not the stone. The flake flies off with a precision never before attained. Handaxes so produced are known to anthropologists as Acheulian.

Now—about four hundred thousand years ago—the pattern of radiation is repeated. The great rains end, the Serengeti dries up, the lakes vanish. Dry Bed Three shows a slim cultural record, for the handaxe-makers scatter. But the ice-sheet has withdrawn from Europe and men again move north. *Atlanthropus* appears in North Africa, and he is pithecanthropine, and his Acheulian weapons mark his origin as East African. Swanscombe Man is found in Thames River gravels, and his weapons too are Acheulian, made with a chisel. Throughout the two hundred thousand years of the Great Interglacial the Afro-European wing of early mankind is established from Britain to South Africa. But not till Olduvai's wet, populous Bed Four and the return of the glaciers to Europe will East Africa again become the metropolis of western man.

Our concern in this narrative is not with true man's growingly complex history, but with man's emergence from his animal past. And so now we must return to the vast filing case on the Tanganyika plain. Who made the first Chellean handaxes? The answer is there. Who was the being who invented the tool-to-make-a-tool? His bones are in the file. Under what mysterious circumstances did we acquire our big brain and the final determinant of our nature? And when did *Homo sapiens* insert his chinfulness into the human story? All must be in the file, but we know next to nothing. The story of man lies hidden and awaiting revelation in the towering, orderly beds of Tanganyika's Grand Canyon of Human Evolution. And the wonder is that we know anything at all.

A graceless observation must be made at this point. Romantic fortunes have been lavished on the restoration of temples and palaces in the Middle East. In Asia, the Rockefeller Foundation spent more money on the single site of Choukoutien, the home of Pekin Man, than has been spent by all sources in all time on the investigation of man's origin in all Africa below the Sahara. Even the direct cost to the author and his publishers for the research, the writing, and the publication of this account exceeds science's total investment in the four main anthropological sites in the world—Olduvai, Makapan, Sterkfontein, and Swartkrans. It is a preposterous fact that the wild men of African anthropology have assembled our main body of knowledge concerning the human origin with less funds available for direct research than have been needed to record it. Without the luck and the dedication, the experience and the genius, the courage and the perseverance of a handful of incorrigible scientific dreamers below the equator, we should know nothing. They have been on their own.

Luck, dedication, experience, genius, courage and perseverance guided Mary Leakey on July 17, 1959, to a fossil skull exposed by erosion in the oldest bed of the Olduvai Gorge. It was a skull crushed into four hundred fragments by the weight of the years that lay above it. The being who had once animated this skull had died on the shore of a vanished lake. All about him lay pebble-tools made of lava and quartz, and the bones of small animals which he and his band had eaten. And it was Abel.

A riddle to satisfy a Sphinx grinned out from the coffin of a forgotten beach. Square-toothed, heavy-jawed, small-brained Abel, with a crest on his skull like a mountain gorilla's, had been the fellow who had started it all.

Dr. Leakey, strictly in accordance with that anthropological fashion which extends the title of man to any hominid capable of making tools, announced the discovery of the earliest known true man. And following the best traditions of African science he created a new genus for the being and named him *Zinjanthropus*. But Dr. Leakey has with great courtesy allowed me to examine the fossil in Nairobi, and I have discussed its features with others who have studied it with greater authority than I can exert. And I do not believe that *Zinjanthropus* can be accepted as even a new species, let alone a new genus. It is a pure australopithecine, a variant of Robert Broom's old *Paranthropus* described in this text as *Australopithecus robustus*.

The being of Bed One stood a bit straighter than the Swartkrans vegetarian and had a somewhat longer and flatter face. But there is the same pint-sized brain, the same crest on the skull, and the same massive, grinding molars. In many ways the teeth are even farther removed from the human line than those of the southern *robustus*, for so wide are the molars that they give the impression of having been fitted into the jawbone sidewise. And so we are left with the riddle that while an australopithecine was the author of our human culture, he could not in any fair likelihood have himself been the ancestor of man.

One school of puzzled thought answers the riddle by suggesting that Leakey's creature was not the maker of of the associated pebble-tools but like the animal victims around him was the prey of the true but unknown tool-maker. The possibility exists, but I find it of low order. The small-animal collection surrounding him speaks of an evolutionary novice at the hunting game. As compared with *africanus'* appalling bone-pile at Makapan, there is even a touch of pathos. And there are no weapons. Any postulated Olduvai hunter incapable of killing game larger than this would have been incapable of killing a creature as powerful and agile as *robustus*. We must add to this a most significant and overlooked observation that early pebble-tools have been found so far in Africa *only* in areas of presumable bush reflecting wet conditions, the place and time of *robustus*. Leakey's lakeside ensemble makes sense only if we think of the tool-maker as a *robustus* breed who throughout his long stay in the bush became a highly specialized vegetarian, who in the late rigours of the Plio-cene acquired a digestive capacity for meat, but who lacked both the skills and the weapons of the developed hunter. Here he is, Abel, precisely as he would be.

Another school of puzzled thought accepts *robustus* as the creator of our culture, but despite all his specializations insists that a sudden, large-scale, systemic mutation could have converted this square toothed, gorilla-crested root-eater into true man. We know from our brief excursion into the field of genetics what can happen to a mediocre poker hand with the draw of an ace of hearts, and so the hypothesis cannot quite be discarded. But what one must suspect is that this school of thought in its devotion to the improbable is in fact expressing its devotion to the ro-mantic fallacy: Inoffensive Abel, despite all genetic im-probability, must be demonstrated as the human ancestor. That another species of australopithecine flourished in the same era on the same African highland and required no such mutational miracles to take his place as the human ancestor, is a skeleton in the human closet best kept quietly tucked away.

In the short two years that have elapsed since the dis-
interment of the equatorial Abel, discoveries have piled on
discoveries,* controversies have grown like pumpkins in
August, and the sea of confusion in which the original discovery was launched has threatened to swamp the discov-
erers and their science alike. In Washington Dr. Leakey
announces at a Press conference that an unidentified juvenile hominid found likewise in Bed One died a probable
victim of violence. Promptly London's *New Scientist* (to
March 1961) rebukes Leakey for putting into public cur-
rency "wild speculations—and they can be nothing else—
about the way in which beings 600,000 years ago met their
death." And while it is true that Dr. Leakey failed to offer
his science any material whatsoever to substantiate his
claim, still it is equally true that the *New Scientist* demonstrates no awareness whatsoever of any part of the evidence for australopithecine violence which we shall consider in the next chapter.

We approach the crisis in man's estimate of man, scientist and layman with arms locked in determined innocence. But to a dramatist-turned-scientist sorting through
the riddles only one field of probabilities offers a general
solution to the mystery of man's Pleistocene emergence.

The action of the final act of the human drama takes
place on a stage darkly shadowed. It is a scene shadowed
by all those things we do not know, by the mystery of a
continent that we still do not comprehend, and by a time
so inscrutable that no mind can explain it. But on this
stage, this African highland, we find brother species of not-

*On July 23, 1961, a sensational announcement from the Evern-
den group at the University of California gave the argon date of
Zinjanthropus (A. robustus) as 1,750,000 years ago. We may
conclude that the rains began falling earlier at the equator than
at higher latitudes, that the unconformity between Beds One
and Two represents an erosional gap of a million years, and
that the European clock should now vanish with happy dis-
patch from African affairs. If the date is correct, we may further
conclude that Bed One has now been established as the first
known Pliocene deposit in Africa, and that, in consequence,
speculations concerning the long evolutionary development of
the australopithecines in the African Pliocene, as presented in
this narrative, have survived their first test of evidence.

yet-men. And their paths have not crossed since the hour of their separation.

Through all the changeless millions of Pliocene years, Africa has stood still. Here was the eternal bush, there the eternal savannah. Here Abel pursued his digging, scrounging, grubbing existence. And there, faraway under vasty skies, Cain killed for a living. Which needed tools? Which, weapons? Which used the stones that were all about him? And which the bones of his prey? Each found and developed those skills and aids that his separate way demanded. And the two never met.

But then came the Pleistocene, and a hand painting and repainting the face of Africa. On the high savannah where Cain once hunted we find lakes and bush and Abel with his little chipped stones. Yet succeeding sweeps of the mad painter's brush will bring Cain back and send Abel away, then send Cain away and bring Abel back.

When did they meet? We do not know. But somewhere in the storeyed archives of the Olduvai Gorge there should be a record of the meeting of brothers. There should be that moment, frozen in stone, when Cain met Abel, and slew him, and made his weapons thenceforth of quartzite and lava, and fathered the human race.

Chapter 10

The Hyena Alibi

The human genesis took place on that continent where nature today exhibits a minimum of innocence. And I find it difficult to believe that Africa in the time of our beginnings was a continent where nature smiled more amiably than now.

The mamba that one encounters on a dusty, provincial road has a pedigree two hundred million years long. The cobras that inhabit your friend's garden, while you both have tea on the veranda and children play in the grass, have grandparents of the same generation. The crocodiles crowding the Zambesis shore, that you hope will ignore you while your little boat passes cast eyes no more friendly on the earliest of your kind.

I have often reflected: how long should I last dropped naked, clawless, fangless, and unarmed, in some remote region of the Tanganyika bush? And had I been the first man?

Linger, despite all regulations, on a backroad in some African game reserve while the dark rises up from the earth. You are comforted by the man-made armour of your car's top and sides. Your human smell is camouflaged by the odour of man-made petrol. You have nothing to fear. Herds of zebra and impala grazing nearby seem likewise to have nothing to fear. But day once disturbed by on-coming night will flee rapidly in these latitudes.

There is a moment when as peaceful as the graceful impala you are still taking colour pictures. Then the sunshine is gone. A ram lifts his head. And you will feel his tension most unexpectedly in yourself. You peer up at the sky through the windscreen. Flat-bottomed clouds are turning hastily mauve, their undersides purple. The ram is standing rigid, nostrils high. A zebra shifts. Several impala cease their grazing, look about. Dark places, like some fluid spilled, are spreading where the bush grows close. Birds still rattle about. Glance up again. The clouds have turned a very dark grey in a sky from which all colour, as from a hurt man's face, is rapidly draining. Against this sky the delicate leaves of a thorn tree are becoming black lace. And without warning the buck that has been standing rigid will cross the road and with three long, high, slow-motion leaps vanish into the bush on the other side.

Now all the herds are in movement, impala and zebra alike. Panic has spread its instant message and you are not immune yourself. The herds charge past your car, zebra trotting and clambering, impala taking obstacles like winged horses in a steeplechase. Out of the lingering light of the open road shining flanks vanish into the brush and your eyes try to follow them but night's dark fluid that moments ago merely blotted the bushes has spread into a single impenetrable pool swiftly flowing into the road to engulf you and your car and your petrol smell in a deepening black flood, while off in the brush the crashing of animals ceases suddenly and in the thorn tree above you birds no longer rattle. There is silence.

You try to see. You try very hard to see because night has arrived on the African continent and the importance of being able to see something has become in an instant an urgent matter. But you can see nothing. The zebra's shining rumps are out there, somewhere, but they are invisible. And so you try to hear something. You listen very hard and you find that you are holding your breath but you can hear nothing. The herd cannot be far away but it makes no sound. The birds that were your rattling companions only moments ago must still inhabit the thorn tree above you, but they give no sign. You are alone, quite alone, as each animal is alone in his pressing black silent world, each listening and waiting. And then it comes. It is a coughing sound, at first hard and slamming—then softly diminishing like an old-time steam locomotive pulling out of some distant junction. And whether or not you have ever heard the sound before, you will know that it is a lion.

Later that night at the permanent camp, where as around a native kraal a circular, continuous wall of living thorns keep lion and leopard out of all but fancy, you will reflect. Night has visited the African continent every twenty-four hours since the world was born. And here was our Eden. How would you have survived, O Adam, without fangs or claws or motor cars, without pointed horns or leather hide, or a snout to sniff with or feet to climb with, without even petrol to camouflage your smell—how could you have survived, O most vulnerable primate, tuskless in Paradise, had you not been created with a weapon in your hand?

2

Livingstone is a very small city several hundred miles from anywhere on the lost western fringes of Northern Rhodesia. It has a wide, dusty main street resembling a set for a fairly expensive Western film where one expects that at any moment cowboys will charge through shooting off guns. Aside from its main street, Livingstone possesses one of the finest museums in Africa, with a curator, Dr. J. Desmond Clark, who is among the most respected anthropologists in the world; an intercontinental airport where one may see airliners arriving from New York or Paris or London or Rome; a magnificently civilized hotel where in the early morning baboons investigate the tables on the terrace; a weird forest, a mile long and a hundred yards wide, surrounded by sunshine yet living in a perpetual downpour of rain; and that overwhelming improbability of nature created by the Zambesi River where it slides in cataclysmic grandeur into a slot in the earth's surface, the Victoria Falls, a phenomenon which of course makes all else possible.

It was at Livingstone, in July, 1955, that a hundred-odd anthropologists gathered from several continents to attend the quadrennial Pan-African Congress in Prehistory. And it was to Livingstone that Raymond A. Dart took his heavy boxes of fossil bones which he and his students had developed with such care; his anatomical analyses and his statistical distributions; and his argument that *Australopithecus africanus* had gone armed, and that among these Makapan fossils were the world's first known weapons.

Dart faced, in a sense, an international court of scientific opinion. It was a court of unrivalled excellence, authority, and integrity. It was a court the verdicts of which stood beyond reasonable appeal, since the judges would not ride the African circuit for another four years. It was science's Supreme Court on the subject of Man, meeting at a time when the creation of the ultimate weapon threatened Man with possible extinction. And it was such a court, meeting at such an hour in a quiet little town in the African hinterland, that accorded Dart twenty minutes to present his grave evidence; that received his argument in silence; that failed generally to inspect his exhibit; and that rendered a verdict that the bones were the work of hyenas.

L. S. B. Leakey himself was the chairman of that court. Two years earlier in his book, *Adam's Ancestors,* he had dismissed outright the possibility that the australopithecines could be ancestral to man, and referring to the South African sites had written: "There does not seem any justification for regarding these caves as their dwelling-places; their bones, as well as the other fauna, were probably dragged into the caves by hyenas and other predators." He placed the evolutionary separation of the human and australopithecine lines at approximately the Pliocene-Miocene boundary, twelve million years ago. Then, precisely four years after the Livingstone meeting, Mrs. Mary Leakey discovered in Bed One, Olduvai Gorge, that an australopithecine had been the author of our human culture. This discovery was properly hailed by world science. Great emphasis was laid on the demonstrable fact that the crude pebble-tools were not weapons. But no one suggested, so far as I know, that if one australopithecine had the capacity systematically to make stone tools, then another might quite probably have been able systematically to collect bone weapons. No one has suggested to this date that the case for Cain be reconsidered.

A scientist—and Dr. Leakey is a great one—has the right to be wrong. It is a right approximating an obligation, for if a scientist becomes more concerned with being right than with expressing the convictions of his judgement, then he violates a public trust. But back in 1955 the problem of Livingstone had not been that its chairman possessed a set of preconceived views which by a stroke of irony he himself would one day help shatter. It was rather that an entire body of scientific opinion, confronted by evidence disturbing the premises of its field and challenging all fashionable conclusions concerning the nature of man, chose to hide itself behind the hyena alibi.

That the hyena should have been nominated as the Makapan bone-collector, thus exempting the human line from responsibility, was a logical development in orthodox anthropology's appalling approach to the australopithecine problem. Other than the southern ape, only three possible animals could be blamed: the porcupine, the leopard, and the hyena. Leopards frequent caves, but somehow the leopard alibi never quite caught on. The porcupine, on the other hand, had a fair vogue. While it is not at all a carnivore, the creature has a strange propensity for dragging bones to his home-place where he sharpens his teeth and satisfies his soul by chewing on them. Ever since 1949 when Dart first published his claim that certain Makapan bones had been used as weapons there had been sporadic efforts to demonstrate porcupine responsibility. I doubt that the Livingstone rejection of the porcupine alibi, however, was based on the quite obvious fact that the fossil bones had not been chewed. Too few of the assembled scientists inspected the exhibit to note such a feature. It seems more likely that the grand absurdity of porcupines accumulating the remains of quite so many animals was a little too much for even this court. And besides, man's ancestral responsibility for the numerous dead animals at Makapan could be passed on to a hunch-shouldered, slope-rumped, ragged-coated, evil-smelling animal whom nobody liked very well, anyway.

Just who originated the hyena alibi is a little obscure, and the author is not apt to make a clean confession now. Leakey, as we have seen, recorded it in 1953. But at about the same time another famous scientist was expounding the same thesis at greater length. Gustav H. R. von Koenigswald is one of the foremost anthropologists of our time. His various discoveries of the pithecanthropus family in the Solo River Valley in Java have given us much of our knowledge of the Asian branch of early human kind. In 1942 von Koenigswald was taken prisoner by the Japanese, and spent the remainder of the war in prison camp. It was natural that when post-war political chaos in the Far East made further work there impossible, von Koenigswald should give thought to discoveries being made elsewhere in the world. And so on September 26, 1953, he addressed his thoughts on the australopithecine situation to the Akademie van Wetenschappen in Amsterdam. In the course of his paper he gave consideration to Dart's 1949 claim that various baboons had had their heads cracked by somebody's vigorous wielding of antelope bones. Von Koenigswald discounted the claim. He referred back to studies made many years earlier by Dr. Zapfe, in the Vienna Zoo, of the hyena's methodical if indelicate table manners. Having considered the characteristic leavings from a hyena dinner, von Koenigswald stated: "Such remnants are easily mistaken and have been mistaken for implements. A comparison of illustrations given by Zapfe and Dart leaves no doubt but that we are dealing with the same phenomenon."

To my knowledge von Koenigswald's was the first scholarly presentation of the hyena alibi. The weight of his reputation, together with evidence totally convincing to anyone totally unfamiliar with both Dart's bones and Zapfe's, must have been a powerful force at Livingstone; so powerful, indeed, that for many of the assembled court it rendered examination of Dart's exhibit unnecessary. Ignorance, immaculately conceived, could be immaculately perpetuated. But if the judgement at Livingstone seems unduly influenced by the mere authority of von Koenigswald and Leakey, then in all compassion we must regretfully drag another giant skeleton from anthropology's well-stocked closet—and discover to our consternation that we have seen it before.

No one, as I have emphasized before, can quarrel with Sir Solly Zuckerman's high rank in the dominant order of British scientists. He was knighted in 1956, and early in 1960 appointed "Scientific Advisor to the Minister of Defence and Chairman of the Defence Research Policy Committee." It has simply been bad luck, and far more of a comment on science than on Zuckerman, that his mighty authority has been seized upon to block both wings of natural science's contemporary revolution.

We have observed in detail the lasting influence of his sexual interpretation of primate societies based on baboon observations authoritative in 1932 and obsolete two years later. But just why Zuckerman should have felt compelled on foray after foray into a scientific field of unfamiliar terrain to prove that australopithecus was nothing but an aberrant chimpanzee is something beyond the province or comprehension of this observer. One of those forays in 1950 precipitated in the pages of *Nature* a controversy that reads now like a scientific comic strip. The contagion of Zuckerman's immense authority, however, has been such that not even a von Koenigswald, as we shall see, could remain immune.

That the southern ape was nothing but a veld-going chimpanzee is a thesis as old as Dart's original 1924 discovery. Hrdlicka among many others embraced it. By the mid-1940's, however, the argument seemed dead. But then in 1950 Zuckerman launched a new foray and with the aid of a junior colleague, Ashton, set dancing on the head of an australopithecine pin such a number of statistical ghosts as a medieval schoolman might envy.

The colossal paper consumed fifty pages in the *Philosophical Transactions of the Royal Society of London*. It was an attempt to apply "modern biometrical and statistical analysis" to the problem of whose teeth the australopithecine's resembled, the ape's or man's. The endless grinding of calculating machines produced a specific conclusion, for example, that the first milk molar of australopithecus had the same height as that of the chimpanzee, and the same breadth as that of the gorilla; and the general conclusion, rather less than surprising, that statistics proved australopithecus to resemble the ape more than man. Then the fun began.

Another great anatomist, Sir Wilfred Le Gros Clark, recorded in *Nature* his lack of enthusiasm for Zuckerman's premises, methods, and conclusions, and icily demanded that if a single ape specimen resembling australopithecus exists, "could we be informed where it is to be seen?" In reply Zuckerman changed the subject to the milk canine tooth and challenged Le Gros Clark to prove that the southern ape's differed from the chimpanzee's. Now Le Gros Clark submitted natural-sized drawings and asserted that they differed utterly in shape, and again demanded to see Zuckerman's single ape specimen. Zuckerman replied that he wasn't talking about shapes, but just sizes and that it was unreal to ask for a specimen.

How long the contest between the two anatomists might have gone on, I do not know, for it was interrupted by a communication from two of *Nature's* fascinated readers, one of whom was a professional statistician with the National Coal Board. Questioning Zuckerman's statistical methods they had put his dimensions through their own numbers-grinder and come up with a startlingly different answer. It seemed to them that the southern ape's much chewed-over teeth fell directly in the human range. By then it was 1951 and Zuckerman was showing signs of combat fatigue. But things only got worse. A month later two more statisticians got into the act. They too had inspected Zuckerman's arithmetic and found something very peculiar. They suggested that he recheck his figures. The correspondence closed shortly with a communication from Zuckerman. He had re-checked his ape figures, and admitted that he had forgotten to divide by $\sqrt{2}$.

One would think that such an absurd scientific excursion could be properly shelved and forgotten, since its conclusions pointed less to the aberrations of the great ape than it did to the aberrations of a great scientist. But it cannot be forgotten. Two years after the close of the debate we find in the same influential Amsterdam paper which established the hyena alibi von Koenigswald's flat assertion that "modern statistical methods" had proven the australopithecines to be unrelated to the human line. The "modern statistical methods" could only have been Zuckerman's.

From the follies and prejudices of its greatest authorities anthropology drew its Livingstone line of defence against Dart's sober evidence. Police and sociologists might be struggling with gangs of juvenile delinquents in the streets of New York. Anthropology, at Livingstone, refused to investigate evidence that the use of blackjack and bicycle chain may in adolescents be an uninhibited expression of animal legacy. Governments and peoples the world around might be striving for means to forestall nuclear war. Anthropology, at Livingstone, constructed from scientific fluff a bag to hide its head in. Dart's boxes might contain evidence that all weapons are a portion of our animal inheritance. Anthropology, the science of man, preferred the hyena alibi.

Following the Livingstone verdict, Dart prepared the counterattack that seemed to me wholly unsuccessful. The paper was published in February, 1956, and was called *The Myth of the Bone-Accumulating Hyena.* That no modern hyenas ever collect bones in caves is difficult enough to prove; were it possible, the evidence would still not extend to extinct species. Nevertheless, Dart chose to attack such ways as a myth concocted in the nineteenth century by the celebrated English geologist, William Buckland. It was a dangerous approach that served Dart's opponents more fully than his friends. When a defence for the alibi at last appeared, feeble though it was it consolidated most scientific opinion behind the Livingstone decision. That defence took the form of a paper by Dr. S. L. Washburn, published in August, 1957, by the *American Anthropologist,* and called *Australopithecines: The Hunters or the Hunted?*

Bad science on the part of able scientists has been the second most remarkable feature of the australopithecine controversy; the first has been the willingness, even the eagerness, of science as a whole to accept it. To all those eminent, dedicated, and proven spirits with whom I have had unhappy negotiations in these pages, I extend my apologies. It is grossly unfair—and I am acutely aware of the inequity—to turn hindsight's spotlight on yesterday's garden paths. But an investigation into the nature of man cannot in the name of good manners overlook the behaviour of the science of man when confronted by the australopithecine challenge.

Dr. Washburn, now professor of anthropology at the University of California, is I believe the most thoroughly informed American authority on man's early African horizon. He attended the Livingstone meeting. Later he visited the Wankie Game Reserve, in Southern Rhodesia, and reflected on Dart's analysis of the Makapan accumulation. Lions are common in the Wankie area, and there were the remains of a great many kills. At each of thirty-five kills Washburn noted the number and character of those bones remaining after the lion, hyena, jackal and wild dog had finished their carnivorous work.

Two years later Washburn published his evidence that the southern ape had not been the hunter, but instead had been the hunted, and that his remains in the cave like those of other prey were brought there by hyenas. In Washburn's opinion, the odd selection of bones as reported by Dart was due simply to the selective eating of carnivores. He recalls "the high frequency of jaws, skulls, and upper cervical vertebrae in the australopithecine deposits," (Washburn was evidently working from memory, since upper cervical vertebrae constitute exactly 1% of the deposit) and notes the corresponding frequency of these parts at the kills which he observed in Rhodesia. Then, with one of the most glorious non-sequiturs which I have ever encountered in scientific literature, he concludes that because at thirty-four out of thirty-five kills the skull remained in the field, disregarded by even the hyena, the hyena was therefore responsible for collecting the Makapan bone-pile with its high percentage of cranial remains.

I find it extremely difficult to believe that Dr. Washburn intended his paper to be taken too seriously. It has the reflective air of a wisp from a naturalist's notebook wafted into an argument by its author with no more final purpose than to see what will happen. But what happened was disaster. Washburn's scientific wisp became the scholarly justification for the alibi established at Livingstone. And the wonder is not that an eminent scientist could produce such a work, but that his science could receive it without scrutiny, without doubt, with none of that silent scepticism which it so lavished on Dart's six-year study. Anthropology *willed* to believe in Washburn, willed *not* to believe in Dart.

The measure of anthropology's will must concern us shortly. But what must face us now is that the Livingstone verdict has never been subjected to review. The hyena alibi still stands, reinforced by Washburn's remarkable testament. Popular magazines may present imaginative illustrations of the southern ape brandishing a cudgel of bone. But no man of science, other than Dart himself, has come forward since Livingstone to provide substance for the picture. The discussion has been closed.

In order that the discussion may be reopened, this observer presents in the following section twenty-four parallel lines of evidence that the hyena alibi is false. The general reader will find a few points repetitious in that they are drawn from statements made earlier. Most, however, will be unfamiliar even to the specialist, since they have been accumulated by this observer throughout the past five years and have never before been published. But since the evidence is presented not so much for the layman as the scientist—for the Zuckermans and von Koenigswalds, the Leakeys and Oakleys and Washburns, whatever the state of their prejudices or sympathies—it has seemed to me wise to draw all kinds of evidence into a single catalogue. Should the general reader find himself already convinced that the weapon is of animal origin, or should he find the presentation of the evidence tedious, he is invited to skip it.

3

Dr. Kenneth P. Oakley is one authority who, while demanding degrees of proof seldom forthcoming, has consistently kept a basic sympathy for the two propositions, first that the australopithecines were ancestral to man, and second that they made use of weapons. In *Antiquity* (March, 1956) he wrote: "It is agreed by the majority of anthropologists that the australopithecines were either part of, or very close to, the line of evolution that led to man." To describe the number of anthropologists who agreed with Oakley as a majority, in March, 1956, is an exaggeration. He proceeded: "It is of course highly likely that pre-human hominids were semi-carnivorous and that they made use of stones, sticks, and bones as ready-to-hand weapons and tools; but to prove it is difficult." To describe the proof of the second proposition as difficult is not an exaggeration.

What has beset all efforts to prove or disprove the intelligent, purposeful, systematic use of weapons by the australopithecines has been the tendency to pursue a single line of evidence. Such a feat is beyond achievement. Dart (1956) attempted to demonstrate that the hyena was not the agent of bone-accumulation at Makapan by the single line of evidence that the hyena never accumulates bones.

The single line collapses, as we shall see, when it encounters a single exception. Washburn (1957) attempted to prove that the hyena *was* the agent of accumulation by the single line of evidence that the normal eating habits of the modern hyena can account for the selective nature of the Makapan accumulation. The single line collapses on many grounds, and with it the case.

Proof of the weapons hypothesis can never be accomplished by such an approach. Any single line of evidence will always leave room for a degree of improbability which a conclusion of such vast significance cannot tolerate. With this thought in mind, I have assembled twenty-four parallel lines of evidence. Some are slender, some mighty. Many taken by themselves would seem inconsequential, but viewed as part of a panorama acquire weight they would not otherwise possess. And while a degree of improbability must exist in any one of the lines of evidence, it is my contention that the total assembly presses improbability to the vanishing point.

I proceed with the evidence that the use of the weapon is a human legacy from the animal world.

(1) The humerus bones

Dart (1949) described the fractured skulls of certain baboons found at Makapan, Sterkfontein, and Taungs, as the consequence of assault by a weapon. The peculiar nature of many of the injuries suggested to him that the weapon had been the humerus bone of the antelope. Six years later, after an analysis of 4,560 fossil fragments developed from the Makapan breccia, he found that 518 were portions of the bone in question.

Since I have developed elsewhere in this account the evidence of the humerus bone, I summarize it briefly at this point. The baboon injuries consisted of a double-depressed area which could be caused only by the distal (elbow) end of the humerus bone. The proximal (shoulder) end could not cause it. Among the total humerus bone fragments Dart found 336 distal ends, 33 proximal ends.

If we are to postulate a hyena as the author of the Makapan deposit, then we must visualize one with a strong disinclination to consume bones or parts of bones useful for killing baboons.

(2) The predominance of useful parts

In his analysis of the 3,500 antelope fragments (discounting loose teeth) Dart uses 38 anatomical classifications, by body part, each of which is divided into four categories determined by the size of the animal. The 3,500 fragments are therefore divided into 152 brackets. Five of these 152 brackets contribute twenty-two per cent of all the remains. They are the humerus bone distal end (238), metacarpal bone distal end (135), horn core (122), and lower jaw (98), all of the medium antelope; and the lower jaw (191) of the small, impala-sized antelope. Again we have a statistical distribution that could not occur except through some agency of selection.

Was the hyena the agent of selection? Three categories are inedible, two edible. No generalization concerning the consequence of eating habits is possible. But it is noteworthy that four of the five predominant categories have an apparent utility for the life of an armed hunter in need of bludgeoning, stabbing, and slashing or cutting instruments.

(3) Transportation of bovid carcasses

We may safely assume that a carnivore the size of a hyena, overpowered by a mystical urge to bring back antelope heads to his cave, would have more difficulty transporting the head of such a giant as the kudu than that of those smaller relatives, the waterbuck or impala. Yet among the Makapan specimens, in which cervical vertebra are rare, almost forty kudu-sized antelope have contributed 36 neck bones, whereas 254 smaller types have contributed only nine. When bringing back whole heads, the collector favoured the largest size. Why?

The anomaly is explained if we presume the collector

to have been a hunter in search of arms, who brought back from kills those parts useful to him as weapons. The large antelope is the only type with snout and upper jaw heavy enough to be used as an axe-like weapon. It is likewise the only type in which upper jaws outnumber lower. In the three smaller categories, lower jaws outnumber upper by 342 to 125. Seeking as a rule from the small animals only the useful lower jaws or horns, he detached them in the field and did not trouble to transport the head. Needing the snout of the kudu size, however, he was sometimes forced to bring back the entire head with a vertebra or two still attached. It is a speculative explanation. But if we presume the collector to be the hyena, then there is no explanation at all.

(4) Duiker mandibles

I have covered elsewhere the evidence of the lower jaws of the very small antelope, and will briefly refer to it here. Buck of the duiker size have the sharpest, most closely set teeth in the antelope family. A portion of such a jaw— particularly the lower—offers obvious utility as a knife; and 53 jaw fragments occur in the sample. But the body bones of this type are too fragile to be of value. And out of the sample of 3,500, not one appears.

Did the hyena consume an animal so small, bones and all, leaving only the jaw? It could be possible. But if this was the case, then he exhibited a greater appetite for upper jaws than lower. Of the 53 jaw fragments, only 13 are upper.

(5) The hyena who choked on a bone

As we turn from the evidence of antelope remains in the Makapan breccia, we must brood on the fate of that particular hyena who swallowed a bone too large. His skull is almost complete. From his throat protrudes a lower leg bone of a medium-sized antelope. He has swallowed it so forcefully that both his palate and the rear of his cranium are fractured, as well as his zygomatic arch.

(6) Maturity of individual antelopes

One more selective quality appears in the bovid fragments from Makapan. Alun Hughes and James Kitching, Dart's two assistants who have had the greatest experience in handling and analyzing the specimens, have found almost all of the individual animals to be either fairly young or fairly old. If the hunter weighed eighty or ninety pounds, lacked claws and fighting teeth, and was armed only with the crudest weapons, then his inability to bring down mature buck is not suprising. But if the collector was the scavenger hyena and the original killer that traditional African predator, the lion, then no comparable distortion should appear. Any predator will always favour game most easily brought down, and if the observation were confined to antelopes as large as the kudu and eland, then one could understand. But any lioness incapable of killing mature waterbuck, nyala, and wildebeest, let alone such smaller creatures as impala and springbok, would be a lioness unworthy of her pride.

(7) Dietary preferences of the hyena

Seventeen individual examples of the hyena are to be found in the Makapan sample. They have contributed 31 head fragments, and 5 bones back of the neck. In contrast, 293 antelopes have contributed 859 head fragments, and 2,610 bones from the limbs and body.

If what we behold in the Makapan breccia consists of the fossilized leftovers of the hyena table, then we must conclude that his appetite for antelope was far less hearty than that for his own kind.

(8) The testimony of the giraffe

Giraffes have left four upper jaws and seven lower in the Makapan breccia; and nothing else. The remains speak of a most curious situation. Either hyenas of perverse nature brought only these most inedible portions of the animal back home to their children; or else we must visualize teams of hyenas transporting giraffes, necks and all, to their beckoning lair, there to consume everything but the farthest-flung portions, the inedible jaws.

(9) The testimony of the rhinoceros

The rhino remains in the Makapan breccia present us with an enigma as puzzling as those of the giraffe. Two body bones appear. But there are eight portions of upper jaw representing a minimum of five individuals. The rhino, as is fairly well known, is a large animal. How did the hyena get five of these cumbersome creatures into his cave, there to practise on the carcasses his arts of selective feeding?

(10) The bone flakes

We cannot present as evidence in one controversy conclusions derived from another. If Dart's current claim is correct, that certain bone flakes found in the Makapan deposit are in fact purposefully fashioned weapons and tools, then the hyena will automatically vanish from the australopithecine debate. Leakey's discovery (1959) that the australopithecine of Olduvai breed was capable of fashioning tools of stone would scarcely reduce the likelihood that the breed flourishing at Makapan was capable of fashioning tools of bone and horn. Dart's case, however, is still incomplete. But in the course of his investigation one undoubted piece of evidence has been established which should be included here.

Among the bone fragments developed in 1955 were 2,600 flakes and scraps. At that time they were regarded as nothing but the inconsequential debris left behind by bone breakage. But among them are innumerable flakes of peculiar character, long, slim, and pointed. And Dart's assistant, James Kitching, has since demonstrated that a green bone, no matter how it is pounded or how it is crushed (as by the teeth of a hyena) simply will not produce flakes of this shape. The texture of a bone is such that to produce such a flake, the bone must be twisted. That such a twisting motion could be accomplished by the paws of a hyena seems to this observer a probability of low order.

(11) The case of the decapitated baboons

Before we leave the internal evidence of the Makapan fossils, let us consider the baboon, that unhappy, set-upon creature who started the entire controversy in 1949. In the Makapan sample are the remains of a minimum of 45 individual baboons. They have contributed 103 fragments, aside from loose teeth, 101 of them cranial. No animal appearing in significant number has left so little testimony as to what happened to its body. And among the cranial remains, while a little over half are the customary jaw portions, 47 are fragments of skull, many of them so complete that twelve have yielded brain cases, and fifteen were among the objects of Dart's 1949 study.

Something went on with the baboon. Why does only his head appear in the Makapan deposit? Can such a selection be the residual consequence of the normal eating habits of carnivores? His brain is large, his skull flimsy. His skull bones, in fact, are the most fragile part of the entire skeleton. Why have they remained, whereas his skeleton has vanished? Shall we presume that *hyaena makapani* had such a developed taste for baboon brains that he brought home like a plum pudding only the head? But then why did not such a bone-eater consume the skull along with his dessert? How could he have avoided it?

A better answer is suggested by what happened to human skulls at Choukoutien. Pekin Man represents the earliest known true man of whom we have significant remains, and while we rarely publicize the unpalatable truth, he was a cannibal. Many of the skulls, four hundred thousand years old, had been forced open so that the brains might be extracted. Anatomical evidence shows that the Transvaal baboons received similar treatment. Somebody at Makapan had a pre-human taste for brains, but unlike the hyena had no taste for bones.

(12) The direction of assault
Of the 42 baboons studied by Dart and Mackintosh in 1949, only two showed damage on the right side of the skull. In these two cases the blow was delivered from the left. If we are to postulate the hyena as the killer of the 42 baboons, then we must likewise postulate an armed hyena, and not only that, but a right-handed one.

(13) The murdered young southern ape
The baboon was not the only victm of assault in the time before true man. We have the adolescent mandible of a young southern ape, discussed elsewhere in this account. There is the heavy jawbone, fractured on either side. There are the four missing front teeth, and the smooth flattened area on the front of the jawbone where the blow seems to have fallen. In the light of parallel evidence shall we regard this specimen as the consequence of the selective eat-

ing habits of carnivores? Or shall we regard it as evidence of intentional violence?

(14) Other australopithecine victims of assault

When Dart made his 1949 study of baboons that had met violent death, he added the cases of six australopithecines from the various deposits. All showed skull fractures, and one from Sterkfontein showed definitely the same double-depressed fracture as the baboons. In another case the rock that had caused the fracture still lay imbedded in the fossil skull. Had it been an accident occurring to an old skull lying about the cave, the cranium would have been shattered; but the bone was otherwise intact.

Not all the specimens demonstrate conclusively death by purposeful violence. But a curious case of what could only have been intentional, armed assault came my way in 1955 when Oakley, in London, gave me the plaster cast of a small portion of an australopithecine skull from Swartkrans. The skull showed two small round perforations, about an inch apart. The holes could not have been of animal origin, since no carnivore has canines set so closely together.

I was on my way at the time to Pretoria, and so Oakley asked me to inquire of John Robinson whether the original specimen (this was only a cast) showed the crystals of fossilization down into the holes. Could the marks, in other words, have been of post-fossilization origin? In Pretoria, Robinson gave the answer. The holes showed crystals all the way through. The living australopithecine, three quarters of a million years ago, had been struck with something. Not only had he been struck once. He had been struck twice. The holes came from slightly different directions.

(15) The yellow stain

Almost all of the evidence that we have so far considered has been of a nature available to any specialist. Many of the points that we consider now, however, rest either on familiarity with the australopithecine sites, or on this observer's good fortune at being present when illuminating events took place. The striking evidence of the yellow stain could not otherwise have come my way.

One southern autumn when the cold Antarctic winds were beginning to swing like a scythe across the high South African veld, Dart called me at my hotel. He had a man named Wilfred Eitzman in his office. Dart had told me earlier of Eitzman. In the 1920's he had been a science teacher in Pietersburg, in the northern Transvaal. One night in a local pub he had encountered a Scottish prospector named Maxwell who was prowling the region for lime deposits. Becoming aware of Eitzman's interest in fossils, Maxwell told him of the cave he had found in the Makapan valley where, besides lime, there was in his opinion the largest deposit of fossils that he had ever seen. Eitzman went to Makapan, found the cave. He recognized immediately that the bones were of extinct species and that the deposit was of great antiquity.

Raymond Dart was at this time in the midst of the highly publicized controversy that had sprung up with his discovery of the Taungs skull. Eitzman had been following the controversy in the South African press. He suspected that the Makapan deposit might interest Dart, and sent him samples of the fossil bones. It was in this fashion that Dart learned of Makapan.

That had been in 1925. Dart at that time we must recall was an anthropologist by accident. His professional concern was with the building up of the Medical School's anatomy department. He had no time for a personal investigation of the remote Makapan valley. For a while he corresponded with Eitzman, but by the mid-1940's, when Dart's students made their first expedition to the Makapan cave, the Pietersburg school teacher had dropped from sight. And this cold afternoon in 1957 was the first time that Dart and Eitzman had met.

I joined them in Dart's office. Our curiosity was immense. By the end of the Second World War when the students first visited the site the original character of the cave was entirely altered. The lime deposits had been exhausted. The cave was no longer a cave but resembled a narrow canyon in the valleyside, for its roof had been largely demolished by the limeworkers. There were the kilns, where the miners had burned the pure lime. And there were the dumps of useless breccia which had been piled in the valley below. From these dumps the great collection of fossils would be extracted. But what exactly had been the character of the cave before the miners had demolished it? And what precisely had been the location of the bone breccia before the limeworkers had consigned it to the dumps?

Eitzman's memory was clear. Although he had moved away from the area in the 1930's and had not seen the cave in over twenty years, he had visited it on many occasions in the old days. On his first visit the mining operation, begun in 1924, had reached only fifty feet back into the deposit. He recalled the stratification of breccia clearly. In the dumps Dart's workers distinguish three types by colour, grey, pinkish peach, and red. By careful checking with breccia still *in situ* in the walls, the grey has been identified as the oldest, the peach as the next oldest, and the red as the final deposit that filled the cave to its roof. Eitzman recalled each, the thickness of the bed near the cave entrance, and the quantity of pure lime separating the breccia beds. Then Alun Hughes showed Eitzman a lump of grey bone breccia with a deep yellow stain.

I had never seen reference to yellow breccia in the literature, nor had I happened to observe it in the Makapan dump. Hughes was asking Eitzman if he recalled the location of breccia so stained. Eitzman replied firmly that he did, that it occurred where the grey breccia made contact with the dolomite wall of the cave, and that he had always assumed that the stain proceeded from some chemical reaction of the dolomite and bone-laden limestone. Hughes nodded, and left the room with his yellow breccia.

I followed Hughes to the corridor. What had that been about? Hughes said that he had, in fact, merely been testing Eitzman's memory. The yellow breccia was rare. If Eitzman could recall it after this many years, his memory was remarkable. Concerning its situation against the walls of the cave, he and Kitching had formed the same conclusion years before. I asked, what was the significance of the yellow breccia? Hughes said that he and Kitching had been attracted to it because as a rule it was the breccia containing australopithecine remains. They had learned this so early in their search that they invariably set aside all breccia stained yellow, to give it immediate attention.

I felt a wave of excitement. The remains of the southern ape himself had *not* been distributed evenly throughout the breccia! His bones had *not* been left indiscriminately with the bones of kudu and wildebeest, baboon and hyena, that filled the broad cave floor. What remained of a dead southern ape had been placed to one side, as a rule, against the dark cave wall. Who had accomplished such discrimination? The hyena?

Despite the foul weather, we all went to Makapan the following weekend. Dart, Hughes, Kitching, C. K. Brain, Eitzman and I were possessed by the same desire to reconstruct in our imaginations the actuality of the original Villafranchian cave that had existed three-quarters of a million years ago. In the rain we put together the geological reconstructions of Brain, the experience of Dart and Hughes and Kitching, and the recollections of Eitzman. A hundred conclusions need not concern us here. But that the yellow stain had touched only those remains cradled by the old cave wall must haunt any investigator into man's legacy from the animal past.

(16) Fire

One of the most telling arguments against the interpretation of the Transvaal caves as australopithecine living sites was made originally, I believe, by Kenneth Oakley. The argument was simple: that until man could guard the entrance of a cave with fire, and thus keep predators away, such a cave would prove more of a trap than a refuge; and man and his predecessors would be unlikely to live there. Dart had made the claim that australopithecus, at Makapan, indeed controlled fire. Oakley largely disproved it. But with the discovery by Brain and Robinson of handaxes in the old Sterkfontein cave, the argument vanishes. No evidence for the use of fire exists at Sterkfontein (or anywhere in Africa until much later times) yet the unidentified makers of the handaxes undoubtedly occupied the cave.

(17) The bone-slide

Another argument, less telling, against interpretation of the deposits as prehuman living sites has been that the bones did not originally accumulate in the caves but piled up at the entrances from which point they slowly slid down into the cave recesses. I can only assume that this tenuous assumption was advanced as part of the hyena hypothesis: since evidence exists that hyenas on occasion accumulate

bones outside their lairs, then the bone-sliding argument would account for the undoubted deposits within. Such a situation is possible at Sterkfontein where the floor of the cave slopes sharply down from its entrance. The situation, however is impossible at Makapan. Hughes and I, on the expedition in the rain, marked a deposit of bone breccia four feet thick, deep inside the cave. We measured its distance from the ancient entrance as determined by Eitzman and Brain. The distance was approximately four hundred feet, and uphill for the last hundred.

(18) The one with a rock in his head

I have referred elsewhere in this compilation of evidence to an australopithecine whose skull was fractured by a rock. So heavy was the blow that the stone, about two inches in diameter, was found inside the skull. The evidence of the damage would indicate that it could not have been of a post-mortem sort. The australopithecine was killed by the stone.

How did he die? In any verdict we may come to, the argument that the cave deposits were not of australopithecine origin is again demolished. All likelihood points to death by assault with the rock the weapon. If this be the case, then a carnivore as the wielder of the rock becomes a fairly improbable figure. But although the rock seems too small and too light to have caused such disastrous damage simply by falling on the creature's head, let us still grant the possibility. The rock is most definitely not a meteorite, and so we must exclude as a possibility the occurrence of an accident in the open, for rocks do not otherwise fall out of the sky. If the accident did not occur in the open, then the only interpretation must be that the rock fell from the cave roof. And in this case, it is difficult to form any conclusion other than that the victim lived there.

(19) The absence of pebble-tools

Since Leakey's discovery of pebble-tools associated with the remains of *Zinjanthropus*, at Olduvai, a new argument has arisen against the Makapan breccia's being of australopithecine origin. The argument runs this way: if a branch of the australopithecine family made stone implements in Tanganyika, then the absence of stone implements from the grey and peach breccias at Makapan demonstrates that contemporary australopithecines could not have lived there. Were such reasoning applied to the European invasion of the New World, in the sixteenth century, then one would be forced to conclude that since the white race was armed with muskets and cannon, then the American Indian must have been so armed too.

The argument dissolves with any close inspection of the Makapan site. The cave overlooks a valley five miles long and about one half-mile wide. It is a valley in places steep-walled that today resembles a box canyon in the American West. In Villafranchian times, however, it was much shallower and more gently formed.

The evidence indicates that over a period no less than one hundred thousand years—and probably nearer to two hundred thousand—animal remains accumulated in the cave. Among them were the remains of the southern ape. If we are to assume that like his northern cousins he made pebble-tools, so that the certain absence of pebble-tools from the older breccia demonstrates that he did not live there, then we must conclude that he lived in the open, near the river, where he was occasionally snatched by a predator to provide bones for the cave. But the river flows less than three hundred yards from the cave entrance, and in Villafranchian days flowed closer. And if he lived in the open, then we must face the incredible conclusion that over a period of perhaps two hundred thousand years not one single tool-making australopithecine wandered into the neighbouring cave, there to drop one single stone implement to mark his lone adventure.

(20) The ecological approach

In October, 1953, two American ecologists—Bartholomew and Birdsell of the University of California at Los Angeles —published a paper in the *American Anthropologist* which expresses the essence of this observer's view: australopithecus, like early man himself, could not have survived had he not been armed. Ecology is the divsion of the zoological sciences that considers the animal in relation to its environment. Its techniques are infrequently used by anthropologists. *Ecology and the Protohominids* consists of a general survey of the australopithecine problem using these techniques. In part, the paper states:

"The terrestrial adaptations of the hominid line represent a step into a new and previously unexploited mode of life in which the critical feature was bipedalism. Among mammals changes of this magnitude have occurred only rarely since the middle Cenozoic . . . The extreme rarity of bipedalism among mammals suggests that it is inefficient except under very special circumstances. Even man's unique vertical bipedal locomotion when compared to that of quadrupedal mammals is relatively ineffective, and this implies that a significant nonlocomotor advantage must have resulted from even the partial freeing of the forelimbs. This advantage was the use of the hands for efficient manipulation of adventitious tools such as rocks, sticks, or bones . . . Man has been characterized as the 'tool-using animal,' but this implies a degree of uniqueness to man's use of tools which is unrealistic . . . Rather than to say that man is unique in being the 'tool-using animal,' it is more accurate to say man is the only mammal which is continuously dependent on the use of tools for survival. This dependence on the learned use of tools indicates a movement into a previously unexploited dimension of behaviour, and this movement accompanied the advent of bipedalism. With the assumption of erect posture regular use of tools must have preceded this in time."

Considering the Bartholomew-Birdsell statement, one must introduce two modifications. First, the term "tool-using animal" is incorrect. The "tool-making animal" is the term used in anthropology, and there is a fair gap of meaning between the two. Second we must keep in mind that when any scientist writes the word, "tool," he as a rule refers to weapons. This is a euphemism, the use of which we shall consider elsewhere, normal to all natural sciences. Having introduced these two modifications to the argument, however, I find its logic undiminished. The ecological evidence, intangible though it may be, seems to me the most profound of all arguments for the presence of weapons in the australopithecine deposits. Had they never been discovered, they would still have to be there.

(21) The canine tooth

For those who dine at the table of man's pristine innocence, a question must hover like Banquo's ghost: what happened to man's canine teeth? The most ancient, primitive mammals had long, sharp eye-teeth. All primates but the hominid line have retained them. We still cling to the big root as a vestigial badge of our ancestry, but the big tooth itself is gone. And it had vanished in equal measure from the dental apparatus of the earliest man and all known australopithecines.

What happened to our canine teeth? There is only one answer, and so far as I am aware no other answer has ever been seriously advanced. With the use of weapons, fighting teeth became unnecessary. The natural dagger that is the hallmark of all hunting mammals—the wolf, the lion, the leopard, the tiger—became in the armed hunting primate a redundant instrument. With the advent of the lethal weapon natural selection turned from the armament of the jaw to the armament of the hand. And the canine tooth, neglected by evolution, suffered its consequent reduction in size.

If the evidence of the canine tooth is correct, then the antiquity of the use of weapons is confirmed. By the time of australopithecus the reduction was as complete as in ourselves.

(22) Right-handedness

Before we proceed to the two final lines of evidence that the Makapan deposit could not have been of hyena origin, there is one more point confirming the antiquity of the use of weapons. Considered by itself, right-handedness in the australopithecines cannot be regarded as proven. But considered as a parallel to the evidence of ecology, and the evidence of the reduced canine tooth, it becomes a point not to be neglected.

Of Dart's 42 assaulted baboons, we may recall, only two were struck from the aggressor's left. Since most were struck from above, and only seven definitely from the right, this suggests but does not prove that australopithecus was right-handed. The suggestion however is of very great significance. The delicate nervous pattern whereby the left lobe of the brain becomes dominant and by the crossover of nerves in the spine produces human right-handedness, is not something that the hunting primate could have acquired in a hurry. Yet Oakley (1954) has demonstrated that right-handedness in all probability is a consequence of the use of weapons and tools.

The ape in a state of nature is uniformly ambidextrous. He manipulates food, objects, tree-limbs, and his neighbours' anatomy with complete indifference as to choice of hand. Only the specialized capacity for manual dexterity demanded by the continual use of weapons and tools can seem to account for the development of that singular human attribute, the dominance of one hand over the other. Just as control of the right hand is centred in the usually-dominant left cerebral hemisphere, so is the control of speech centred there. It was Oakley's reasoning that a high degree of manual skill, as a survival value, had favoured the specialization of one hand in the use of weapons and tools, and the consequent dominance of the corresponding part of the brain; and that since the associative areas controlling speech were likewise centred there, speech as well as right-handedness had probably developed from the necessities of the specialized manual way.

We need not here be concerned with the evidence of speech, for of course there is none. But if right-handedness was a characteristic of the southern ape, then like his vanished fighting canine it is evidence for long acquaintance with the armed way of life.

(23) The London testament

During the month of November, 1956, I was in virtual residence at the British Museum in South Kensington. The Hungarian revolution had just taken place, and for most of the following year the consequences of that event would absorb me. But before leaving for Vienna and resuming my normal role as a dramatist, I felt the necessity to prove or disprove, to my own satisfaction, the weapons thesis. If I could not convince myself of its validity, then I would discard it from future consideration. On November 22 and 24, two critical days just preceding my departure for Eastern Europe, I found the decisive pieces of evidence that by themselves were enough to determine my future commitment. Since neither has been published heretofore, I describe them in detail.

In 1950, following Dart's baboon paper and his claim that certain bones in the Makapan breccia had in fact been the weapons of the southern ape, the British Museum requested and received a sample of the Makapan breccia. It came as a single, fair-sized lump of stone. Technicians at the Museum developed the fossil content. Throughout the entire weapons controversy a perfect sample of the Makapan specimens lay available for study in a drawer in London. Since I wanted to photograph a few of the specimens, Oakley made them available to me. And since the Museum's palaeontologist was a specialist in the hyena, we made an appointment with him to join us. In preparation for the examination we found a copy of the paper by Dr. Helmuth Zapfe on the feeding habits of hyenas, which von Koenigswald had quoted as leaving no doubt but that Dart's fossils had been of hyena origin.

Sixty identifiable fossil bones had been developed by the British Museum technicians from the single block of breccia. They lay in trays. In Zapfe's monograph he described the joints at distal or proximal ends of bones as gnawed, split, or grooved. No single joint showed a groove, a split, or evidence of gnawing. In Zapfe's monograph he described "the characteristic fang marks" left by the hyena on uneaten bones. Not one of the sixty specimens revealed a fang mark. In Zapfe's monograph he speaks of the bones themselves as "split" or characteristically "crushed." Only one of the sixty specimens could be called "split," or "crushed." In Zapfe's monograph there is reference to the great mass of "crushed bones and splinters." The block of breccia, which had yielded sixty identifiable bones all but filling a large drawer, had yielded two small trays, each about eight inches square, of flakes and splinters. Von Koenigswald's argument, to my mind, lay in still smaller splinters.

I, however, might be dismissed as a prejudiced observer. The hyena specialist, Dr. A. J. Sutcliffe, could not. He was in this period absorbed with the excavation of a hyena cave in Devon. Raymond Dart, the previous spring, had published his paper denying that the hyena had ever accumulated bones, and Sutcliffe was finding masses of them. He approached the specimens with a notable lack of enthusiasm for anything Dart had ever claimed. For about ten minutes I worked on my notes while Sutcliffe examined the dusty exhibit, bone by bone, flake by flake. And then I asked him, who had been responsible for the bones? And Sutcliffe said, "Not hyenas."

(24) The hyenas of Devonshire

November 24, 1956, was a Saturday, and a very dark day. Early in the afternoon I walked in the rain and the fog through Regent's Park to the Royal Archaeological Institute where Sutcliffe was assembling his hyena collection. For many months he had been excavating Tornewton Cave, at Torbryan in South Devon. It was a cave that had tolerated a variety of occupants through succeeding phases of the Pleistocene. Five layers of deposit were so far excavated. The fifth and oldest had been made by cave bears, in a time of cold. It had been succeeded by a warm era, the fourth layer, when hyenas had made the cave their lair. Then in the third the cold had returned, and with it the bears.

If calculations were correct, then this hyena deposit had

been made during the strange warm time about one hundred and thirty thousand years ago between the last two glaciations. It had been the time when Neanderthal Man was entering Europe and dropping handaxes here and there to mark his open camp sites. It had been the time when rhododendrons bloomed in high Alpine places, and the hippopotamus flourished in Britain's pleasant land. It had been a time when the extinct cave hyena, of a species closely allied to a single specimen found at Makapan, had occupied a Devon cave and left a mighty collection of bones to affirm the myth of the bone-accumulating hyena. Here at last was an opportunity to observe a true hyena accumulation made under conditions comparable to the Makapan deposit. How would they compare?

Sutcliffe had his collection in a tiny, upstairs room at the Institute in Regent's Park. Tray upon tray was filled with bones and teeth. He bounded from specimen to specimen with remarkable enthusiasm, for he was the only man I have ever known with a positive affection for hyenas. And as tray followed tray before my eyes, the indisputable truth leaped up like flame. What hyenas collected, when they collected anything, was the remains of their fellow hyenas.

From the fourth layer of the deposit in Devon, Sutcliffe had identified the remains of 110 individual hyenas. That it was an undoubted hyena lair and not the accumulation of some other collector was proven by the proportion of young. Of the 110 individuals, forty were juveniles. But the startling proportion was that of hyenas to non-hyenas. Compared to the 110 individual hyenas that the deposit had yielded, there were only twenty others of all species. In the Makapan sample there had been seventeen hyenas out of a total of 433 individual creatures. And loose teeth confirmed the proportion. 100 were non-hyena, 1,000 hyena. At Makapan the proportion had been very nearly the opposite, 682 to 47. The two deposits bore no relation whatsoever.

A true hyena deposit is a graveyard for hyenas, and little else. The remains of five loins and half a dozen foxes skimpily filled one tray. A second tray held all that was left of a rhino, an ox, and the remaining non-hyenas. When the hyena finishes his dinner, he leaves few souvenirs for the palaeontologist. And what little he leaves bears the mark of his manners, precisely as described by Zapfe. There were the fang marks and the fractured joints. It is difficult to forget a lion's long canine tooth, with the furrow of a hyena's fang grooved deep in its hard enamel.

How does a hyena treat his own kind? He eats him up. Of the 110 individual hyenas, little remained but foot-bones, knee-caps, and teeth. So few body bones remained, in proportion to teeth, that one could only conclude that the cave hyena devoured the carcasses of his own kind if possible to the last morsel.

One last point of evidence remained—if any more could be deemed necessary—that a true hyena cave deposit has nothing in common with an australopithecine deposit. Many observers had pointed to the presence of hyena coprolites at Makapan to suggest that the deposit had been the work of hyenas. Coprolites are fossilized hyena faeces. Sutcliffe found the soil of the Devon breccia to be fifty per cent coprolite. Yet Dart and his assistants found only two hundred coprolites in five tons of breccia.

I left Sutcliffe with his trays of teeth and bones, and walked back through the rain to my hotel. Fog shrouded alike the soggy gardens of Regent's Park and the bombed-out ruins still standing from London's time of trial. The following day I left for Vienna and the frozen Hungarian border. Beyond that border another courageous people was having less luck defending its aspirations from the crushing veto of the superior weapon.

4

In the ocean depths off Madagascar, obsolete fish keep their laggard appointments. In the depths of the human mind, obsolete assumptions go their daily rounds. And there is little difference between the two, except that the fish do no harm.

When Raymond Dart in 1953 prepared his paper, *The Predatory Transition from Ape to Man*, he stated the thesis that man's animal ancestry was carnivorous and predatory. The hunting life in a creature ill-armed by nature made necessary the use of weapons. The use of weapons and the predatory way perfected the specialized human anatomy, and demanded complex nervous co-ordination never before experienced in the animal world. And so, as a final answer to evolutionary necessities of unprecedented complexity, came the big brain and man. The human being in the most fundamental aspects of his soul and body is nature's last if temporary word on the subject of the armed predator. And human history must be read in these terms.

So profoundly did Dart violate our fundamental human assumptions that the most eminent anthropologist in Africa could not obtain publication of his paper by any reputable scientific journal. It was published by a journal of small prestige and less circulation, and remains today all but unread. To complete the unconscious boycott, science at Livingstone established the hyena alibi. But the evidence presented in this account should leave small future for that fragile construction. Science and all branches of modern thought must at last reckon with Dart's terrifying thesis.

Weapons preceded man. Whether man is in fact a biological invention evolved to suit the purposes of the weapon must be a matter of future debate. As I have recorded, many factors contributed to the Pleistocene's supreme evolutionary invention. And certainly our animal inheritance cannot be summed up in terms as simple as those expressed in the *Predatory Transition*. Other forces of enormous power, all similarly derived from the animal world, play their instinctual roles in the drama of human conduct. We have investigated a few of them: the drive to acquire private property; social groupings based on the defence of a territory held in common; the commandment to gain and hold individual dominance within such a society; the contest between males for superior territory or superior status; sexual choice exercised by the female in terms of the male's acquisition of property or status; the hostility of territorial neighbours whether individual or group; and the dual code of behaviour, prevailing in the members of a group, demanding amity for the social partner and enmity for individuals outside the territorial bond. All these are human instincts derived from ancient animal patterns. But to them must now be added those particular attributes of the hominid line: the way of the predator, and the dependence upon weapons.

Man is unique, says modern thought; and all babies are born innocent. Science has done its mighty best to uphold the tenets of the romantic fallacy. If anthropology now finds itself pressed to the brink of failure, then the scientist cannot be blamed. He has given his all. With a thousand thumbs and consummate heroism he has blocked a thousand leaks in the scientific dike. No better example of the genius which he has brought to this desperate chore can be found than in his euphemistic use of the word "tool." I have suggested that we glance through the illustrations in the British Museum's edition of Kenneth Oakley's authoritative *Man the Tool-Maker*. With few exceptions, they are pictures of weapons. Or consider one of the most stupendous passages in scientific literature, drawn from Bartholomew and Birdsell's admirable *Ecology and the Protohominids:* ". . . Intrasexual combat is characteristic of the males of virtually all strongly dimorphic animals. Australopithecines are dimorphic; but they do not have the large piercing canines so characteristic of most of the larger living primates. This striking reduction of canines implies that even in intrasexual combat, the australopithecines placed primary dependence on tools."

Science has willed to believe in the innocence of man. And even the uncommon scientist (unless he be a Raymond Dart) who attacks the assumption, will still make use of the euphemisms of his trade. For a Dart, science will arrange the reception of a troop of howling monkeys for an extra-territorial bachelor with unwanted genes in his loins. And yet the anthropologist defending obsolete assumptions concerning the nature of man has been no more guilty of inattention to truth than the psychiatrist or sociologist, the educator, the statesman, the philosopher, the author, or the anxious man in the street. If in the course of this account the man of science has found himself occasionally standing in the cruelest of lights, then I owe him an apology. He has simply been the man on the spot.

The time has long passed when modern thought can afford the luxury of heart-warming but obsolete assumptions. Those ancient fish dragged up from some Madagascar deep may go their appointed, watery rounds holding firmly to the assumption that Cretaceous times have not passed. Ponderous tortoises may waddle about the margins of the Galapagos Islands, musing on past, distant glories and convinced that the reptile still reigns. The Loch Ness monster, for all we know, may be fathering baby Loch Ness mon-

sters beneath some ledge in his Scottish lake, happily dedicated to the proposition that for Loch Ness monsters day
is about to dawn. But for a sapient being, the mightiest
predator that the world has ever known, to attempt to resolve his difficulties through an assumption that his species
is both innocent and unique, is to court a fate more severe.
Evolution may abandon the experiment with the enlarged
brain, serve him with the extinction that he so grossly
deserves, and turn natural selection to the more hopeful
merits of the ancient citizens of the Madgascar deeps.

Chapter 11
Cain's Children

What are the things that we know about man? How much have the natural sciences brought to us, so far, in the course of a silent, unfinished revolution? What has been added to our comprehension of ourselves that can support us in our staggering, lighten our burdens in our carrying, add to our hopes, subtract from our anxieties, and direct us through hazard and fog and predicament? Or should the natural sciences have stayed in bed?

We know above all that man is a portion of the natural world and that much of the human reality lies hidden in times past. We are an iceberg floating like a gleaming jewel down the cold blue waters of the Denmark Strait; most of our presence is submerged in the sea. We are a moonlit temple in a Guatemala jungle; our foundations are the secret of darkness and old creepers. We are a thriving, scrambling, elbowing city; but no one can find his way through our labyrinthine streets without awareness of the cities that have stood here before. And so for the moment let us excavate man.

What stands above the surface? His mind, I suppose. The mind is the city whose streets we get lost in, the most recent construction on a very old site. After seventy million years of most gradual primate enlargement, the brain nearly trebled in size in a very few hundreds of thousands of years. Our city is spacious and not lacking in magnificence, but it has the problems of any boom town. Let us dig.

We are Cain's children. The union of the enlarging
brain and the carnivorous way produced man as a genetic
possibility. The tightly packed weapons of the predator
form the highest, final, and most immediate foundation
on which we stand. How deep does it extend? A few million, five million, ten million years? We do not know. But
it is the material of our immediate foundation as it is the
basic material of our city. And we have so far been unable
to build without it.

Man is a predator whose natural instinct is to kill with
a weapon. The sudden addition of the enlarged brain to the
equipment of an armed already-successful predatory animal
created not only the human being but also the human
predicament. But the final foundation on which we stand
has a strange cement. We are bad-weather animals. The
deposit was laid down in a time of stress. It is no mere
rubble of carnage and cunning. City and foundation alike
are compacted by a mortar of mysterious strength, the
capacity to survive no matter what the storm. The quality
of the mortar may hold future significance far exceeding
that of the material it binds.

Let us dig deeper. Layer upon layer of primate preparation lies buried beneath the predatory foundation. As the
addition of a suddenly enlarged brain to the way of the
hunting primate multiplied both the problems and the
promises of the sum total, man, so the addition of carnivorous demands to the non-aggressive, vegetarian primate
way multiplied the problems and promises of the sum total,
our ancestral hunting primate. He came into his Pliocene
time no more immaculately conceived than did we into
ours.

The primate has instincts demanding the maintenance
and defence of territories; an attitude of perpetual hostility
for the territorial neighbour; the formation of social bands
as the principal means of survival for a physically vulnerable creature; an attitude of amity and loyalty for the
social partner; and varying but universal systems of dominance to insure the efficiency of his social instrument and
to promote the natural selection of the more fit from the
less. Upon this deeply-buried, complex, primate instinctual
bundle were added the necessities and the opportunities of
the hunting life.

The non-aggressive primate is rarely called upon to die in defence of his territory. But death from territorial conflict is second among the causes of lion mortality in the Kruger reserve. The non-aggressive primate seldom suffers much beyond humiliation in his quarrels for dominance. The lion dies of such conflicts more than of all other causes. The forest primate suppresses many an individual demand in the interests of his society. But nothing in the animal world can compare with the organization and the discipline of the lion's hunting pride or the wolf's hunting pack.

We can only presume that when the necessities of the hunting life encountered the basic primate instincts, then all were intensified. Conflicts became lethal, territorial arguments minor wars. The social band as a hunting and defensive unit became harsher in its codes whether of amity or enmity. The dominant became more dominant, the subordinate more disciplined. Overshadowing all other qualitative changes, however, was the coming of the aggressive imperative. The creature who had once killed only through circumstance killed now for a living.

As we glimpsed in the predatory foundation of man's nature the mysterious strength of the bad-weather animal, so we may see in the coming of the carnivorous way something new and immense and perhaps more significant than the killing necessity. The hunting primate was free. He was free of the forest prison; wherever game roamed the world was his. His hands were freed from the earth or the bough; erect carriage opened new and unguessed opportunities for manual answers to ancient quadruped problems. His daily life was freed from the eternal munching; the capacity to digest high-calorie food meant a life more diverse than one endless meal-time. And his wits were freed. Behind him lay the forest orthodoxies. Ahead of him lay freedom of choice and invention as a new imperative if a revolutionary creature were to meet the unpredictable challenges of a revolutionary way of life. Freedom—as the human being means freedom—was the first gift of the predatory way.

We may excavate man deeply and ever more deeply as we dig down through pre-primate, pre-mammal, and even pre-land-life levels of experience. We shall pass through the beginnings of sexual activity as a year-around affair, and the consequent beginnings of the primate family. But all the other instincts will be there still deeper down: the instinct to dominate one's fellows, to defend what one deems one's own, to form societies, to mate, to eat and avoid being eaten. The record will grow dim and the outlines blurred. But even in the earliest deposits of our nature where death and the individual have their start, we shall still find traces of animal nostalgia, of fear and dominance and order.

Here is our heritage, so far as we know it today. Here is the excavated mound of our nature with *Homo sapiens'* boom town on top. But whatever tall towers reason may fling against the storms and the promises of the human future, their foundations must rest on the beds of our past for there is nowhere else to build.

Cain's children have their problems. It is difficult to describe the invention of the radiant weapon as anything but the consummation of a species. Our history reveals the development and contest of superior weapons as *Homo sapiens'* single, universal cultural preoccupation. Peoples may perish, nations dwindle, empires fall; one civilization may surrender its memories to another civilization's sands. But mankind as a whole, with an instinct as true as a meadow-lark's song, has never in a single instance allowed local failure to impede the progress of the weapon, its most significant cultural endowment.

Must the city of man therefore perish in a blinding moment of universal annihilation? Was the sudden union of the predatory way and the enlarged brain so ill-starred that a guarantee of sudden and magnificent disaster was written into our species' conception? Are we so far from being nature's most glorious triumph that we are in fact evolution's most tragic error, doomed to bring extinction not just to ourselves but to all life on our planet?

It may be so; or it may not. We shall brood about this in a moment. But to reach such a conclusion too easily is to over-simplify both our human future and our animal past. Cain's children have many an ancestor beyond *Australopithecus africanus,* and many a problem beyond war. And the first of our problems is to comprehend our own nature. For we shall fashion no miracles in our city's sky until we know the names of the streets where we live.

2

Man is a zoological group of sentient rather than sapient beings, characterized by a brain so large that he uses rather little of it, a chin distinctive enough to identify him among related animals, and an overpowering enthusiasm for things that go boom. Aside from these attributes—and the chin merely distinguishes *Homo sapiens* from earlier members of the human family—it is difficult to say where man began and the animal left off. We have a quality of self-awareness uncommon among animals, but whether this is a consequence of the enlarged brain or was shared with our extinct fathers, we do not know.

In any event, we do have the power to be aware of self, and to visualize ourselves in a present or future situation. And the power dictates as entirely natural our curiosity concerning the human outcome. Whether self-awareness will actually influence that outcome must strike any observer of human behaviour, on the basis of past performance, as dubious. When human consciousness of potential disaster has in the past come into conflict with instincts of animal origin, our record has been one of impeccable poverty. No past situation, however, can compare with the contemporary predicament of potential nuclear catastrophe. And self-awareness, generating mortal fear, may at least partially forestall an evolutionary disaster.

How great will be the role of reason in such inhibition or diversion of the weapons instinct must be entirely of a collateral order. The human brain came too suddenly on to the evolutionary scene, and lacking animal foundation lacks the command of instinct to enforce its directives. The mind's decrees rank merely as learned responses, and we cannot expect too much of a learned power placed in opposition to instinct. We cannot expect too much from the human capacity to reason, anyway, since its most elaborate energy is channelled as a rule into self-delusion and its most imposing construction erected so far has been that fairy-tale tower, the romantic fallacy.

The human mind, nevertheless, however sorry it may seem on a basis of past performance, cannot be ignored as a potential participant in some future human resolution. Granted a fresh comprehension of human nature and casting off pretence that reason carries power, the human mind can make alliance with animal instincts profound enough in our nature to engage forces for survival larger than the mind itself. We shall return to the thesis later in this chapter, but let us now look into the contemporary crisis of war and weapons, and see if our enhanced understanding of human behaviour benefits us at all in the illumination of the possible outcome.

I find it convenient to consider the contemporary predicament in terms of three possible outcomes of varying probability, and the reader must forgive me if I do not seem to take the first two seriously. There is the first possibility—which I regard as remote—that *Homo sapiens* will obey his weapons instinct with minimum inhibition, put to full use his intellectual resources, and commit himself and his planet to a maximum explosion. The experiment of the enlarged brain, by its final action, will have been demonstrated a total failure. Allied to the vegetarian way, the big brain failed to survive as a significant evolutionary factor the dusty challenge of the Pliocene drought. Allied to the carnivorous way, reason in one fiery instant will have demonstrated its inadequacy as a guiding force for living beings.

To believe that man has the capacity, however, even through a maximum effort, to bring an end to all life on our planet is a melodramatic expression of the Illusion of Central Position. We have no such power. The ancient insect has mutational receptivity equal to our best efforts. While a giant effort on the part of man could conceivably bring extinction to all land vertebrates, it is impossible to believe that a world of insects would not survive. We may regret the passing of the lion, of the elephant, of our partners the horse and the sparkling dog. But natural selection, regretting nothing, will turn its attention to the instinctual promise of the termite, the ant, and the subtle bee.

I find that I have small patience with this first outcome— purple in its hues, pat in its outline—which has so entranced our neo-romantics. And so I leave it to consider the far higher probability of the second. This second field of probabilities grants like the first that man, sooner or later, will obey his weapons instinct. Though we be raised under canaries for four generations, as Marais raised his weaver birds, still no conditioning force can eradicate our genetic affinity for the weapon. Given access to traditional materials, Marais' weaver birds built their nests again complete to the horse-hair knot. Given access again to our traditional materials, we shall proceed with alacrity to blow up the place.

The second outcome presumes, however, that we fail to do quite such a job of it. The instinct to preserve the species runs deep in all animals, and it may compromise the effectiveness of our weapons compulsion. Or the enlarged brain may not succeed in perfecting a cataclysm of such devastating proportions. Whatever the ingredients of the partial disaster—whether instinctual, ineffectual, accidental, or even thoughtful—the second possible outcome presumes that a portion of mankind survives.

If I were a fox, or a reedbuck, or a rabbit, and I found myself among perhaps twenty per cent of my kind to survive a holocaust, I should face the future with equanimity. In a few generations select territories, abundant food supply, and compensatory breeding would restore my kind to its former fullness. But I am neither fox, nor reedbuck, nor rabbit. I am a human being dependent on society and technology. And were I to find myself among the twenty per cent of human beings to survive a contest of radiant weapons, I should much prefer to have been numbered among the victims.

One may of course take a hopeful view of such a colossal weeding of the human garden. Five hundred million people remain, but overpopulation will cease to be a problem in India, and traffic jams in New York. The Riviera will no longer be crowded in August, and there will be seats on commuter trains in the six o'clock rush. The diminished ranks of children will have school rooms in plenty, the diminished ranks of tenants, apartments galore. Were that all there was to it, we should all be as happy as unpursued foxes. But of course it is not.

Starkest in horror of the three probabilities is the partial catastrophe. The survivor will face plague unrivalled in the middle ages, and famine unknown in China's worst seasons. Social anarchy will grip him. The peasant will be murdered by marauding bands, the city man withered by his dependence on society. Disease, hunger, predation, and

suicide will decimate the five hundred million, and mutation will alter the remainder's descendants.

Yet a certain strange hope exists. We need not quarrel over the actuarial rates of post-apocalypse insurance companies. Premiums will be high. But there is something we know of a more exact order and of far greater evolutionary significance. Any radiant catastrophe killing a presumed four-fifths of the human population will induce mutations in the majority of the survivors. Ninety-nine out of every one hundred mutations will be unfavourable. One will be benevolent. And here, should the second outcome provide mankind with its fate, lies evolution's hope.

It is the paradox of the contemporary predicament that the force we have fashioned and that can destroy our species is the same force that can produce another.

Let us assume that among the five hundred million immediate survivors of a nuclear contest, one hundred million survive the post-apocalypse. Of the hundred million, perhaps half will have descendants suffering mutations. Forty-nine million five hundred thousand will be doomed. But a half million will have descendants with endowments superior to the ancestral line. And it is on the shoulders of this slim half million that primate hopes must rest.

What happens to the rest of us, the unmutated, is of small concern. Rats may eat us, or our fellow men. Mutant germs for which we have no resistance may sweep us away with diseases for which we have no names. Famine may waste us. Our predatory instinct, for which our intelligence was never a match, may now unchecked by social patterns drive us into ceaseless conflict until *Homo sapiens* becomes extinct.

A grand and tragic breed will have passed from the earth; and the engine of our creation will have proved the engine of our destruction. But we shall leave behind no barren tidings. Here and there, in unlikely valleys and on unlikely plains, a few mutant beings will roam the byways as others once haunted the Lake Victoria shore. And natural selection will find them, these superior creatures: a few here, in a moss-draped swamp of the Mississippi delta; a few there, in a windy Himalayan pass; a handful, wandering the green velvet of an Argentine grassland; a solitary figure on the old Greek island, pausing in wonder before a marble memory. Slowly, ever so slowly, the mutant beings of a fiery creation will assemble their genetic promises, and a new species will be born. Is it too much to hope that in such a species reason may not be an instinct?

The first outcome of the modern predicament must leave evolution to the neo-romantics. The second, more probable and more horrid in outline, at least allows man his evolutionary dignity. Our interest in either outcome, of course, must necessarily be of an academic nature. It is in part for this reason that I have treated neither too seriously, although in far larger part because I take neither too seriously. Likelihood, in vast array, rides with that group of probabilities centered on the third outcome, in which very little happens at all.

The third outcome assumes that we have already seen or shall shortly see the end of general warfare. Either a contest of ultimate weapons will never take place; or if it does take place, the contest will be of small biological significance in which no more than two or three hundred million people are killed. In either case, sufficient inhibition will have been created to hold in check the weapons instinct. And I regard this outcome as the most frightening if for no other reason than that it is the only one that we shall have to live with.

There are other and more immediate reasons for regarding the third outcome as a nightmare of unpredictables. For generations we have been enchanted by the romantic fallacy. Assuming that man is unique, innocent in his creation, noble by nature, and good in all his potentialities when not distorted by personal or social experience, modern thought has contented itself with the question, "How can we bring an end to war?" No one making such assumptions could be impelled to ask, "How can we get along without it?" Yet today the honest observer must conclude that man is noble in his nature only in the sense that he partakes of the nobility of all living things; that he is unique to no greater degree than that of any fellow species; that far from being created innocent, he originated as the most sophisticated predator the world has ever known; and that amity in his nature, while partly founded on animal values, must largely be erected as a learned response by the social conditioning of each baby born.

How can we get along without war? It is the only question pertaining to the future that bears the faintest reality in our times; for if we fail to get along without war, then the future will be as remarkably lacking in human problems as it will be remarkably lacking in men. Yet war has been the most natural mode of human expression since the beginning of recorded history, and the improvement of the weapon has been man's principal preoccupation since Bed Two in the Olduvai Gorge. What will happen to a species denied in the future its principal means of expression, and its only means, in last appeal, of resolving differences? What will happen to a species that has dedicated its chief energy to the improvement and contest of the weapon, and that now arrives at the end of the road where further improvement and contest is impossible?

Let us not be too hasty in our dismissal of war as an unblemished evil. Are you a Christian? Then recall that Christendom survived its darkest hour in the fury of the Battle of Tours. Do you believe in law? The rule of law became a human institution in the shelter of the Roman legions. Do you subscribe to the value of individual worth? Only by the success of the phalanx at Marathon did the Greeks repel the Persian horde and make possible the Golden Age. Are you a materialist? Do you regard as a human good the satisfaction of economic want? The *Pax Britannica*, made possible by the unchallengeable supremacy of the British fleet, gave mankind the opportunity to lay the broad foundations of the Industrial Revolution.

I am free to uphold in the pages of this account certain views challenging the orthodoxies of my time because I belong to a nation that obtained freedom for its citizens through war, and that has successfully defended my freedom, by the same means, on all occasions since. You are free to read this book, and to consider, evaluate, reject or accept my views, because we are all members of a larger civilization that accepts the free mind as a condition of such profound if painful value that on innumerable occasions it has been willing to fight for it. Do you care about freedom? Dreams may have inspired it, and wishes promoted it, but only war and weapons have made it yours.

No man can regard the way of war as good. It has simply been our way. No man can evaluate the eternal contest of weapons as anything but the sheerest waste and the sheerest folly. It has been simply our only means of final arbitration. Any man can suggest reasonable alternatives to the judgement of arms. But we are not creatures of reason except in our own eyes.

I maintain in these pages that the superior weapon, throughout the history of our species, has been the central human dream; that the energy focused on its continual development has been the central source of human dynamics; that the contest of superior weapons has been the most profoundly absorbing of human experiences; and that the issues of such contest have maintained and protected much that I myself regard as good. Finally, I maintain that deprived of the dream, deprived of the dynamics, deprived of the contest, and deprived of the issue, *Homo sapiens* stands on a darkened threshold through which species rarely return.

The true predicament of contemporary man is not entirely unlike the Pliocene predicament of the gorilla. The bough was the focus of his experience as the weapon has been the focus of ours. It provided him with the fruit that was his nourishment, and with his means of locomotion. It dominated his existence even to the specialization of his anatomy: his hook-like thumbs, his powerful chest, his long arms, his weak and truncated legs. The bough was the focus of gorilla tradition, gorilla instinct, gorilla security, gorilla psyche, and of the only way of life the gorilla knew. Then a natural challenge deprived him of his bough. And the gorilla took to the ground. There we find him today, a depleted crew of evolutionary stragglers. Every night he builds a nest in tribute to ancestral memories. Every day he pursues the unequal struggle with extinction. His vitality sags. He defends no territory, copulates rarely. And the story of the gorilla will end, one day, not with a bang but a whimper.

Deprived of the contest of weapons that was the only bough he knew, man must descend to the cane-brakes of a new mode of existence. There he must find new dreams, new dynamics, new experiences to absorb him, new means of resolving his issues and of protecting whatever he regards as good. And he will find them; or he will find himself lost. Slowly his governments will lose their force and his societies their integration. Moral order, sheltered throughout all history by the judgement of arms, will fall away in rot and erosion. Insoluble quarrels will rend peoples once united by territorial purpose. Insoluble conflicts will split nations once allied by a common dream. Anarchy, ultimate enemy of social man, will spread its grey cancerous tissues through the social corpus of our kind. Bandit nations will hold the human will a hostage, in perfect confidence that no superior force can protect the victim. Bandit gangs will have their way along the social thoroughfare, in perfect confidence that the declining order will find no means to protect itself. Every night we shall build our nostalgic family nest in tribute to ancestral memories. Every day we shall pursue through the fearful cane-brakes our unequal struggle with extinction. It is the hard way, ending with a whimper.

How can man get along without his wars and his weapons? It is the supreme question of the contemporary predicament. Have we within our human resource the capacity to discover new dreams, new dynamisms? Or are we so burdened by our illusions of central position, our romantic fallacies, and our pathetic rationalizations of the human condition that we can acknowledge no destiny beneath the human star but to go blindly blundering into a jingo jungle towards an indeterminate, inglorious, inexorable end?

The reader must sort out for himself, according to his own inclinations and judgement, the probabilities of the human outcome. But before we pass on to certain other consequences of our total animal legacy, I add a suggestion: If man is unique, and his soul some special creation, and his future is to be determined by his innate goodness, nobility and wisdom, then he is finished. But if man is not unique, and his soul represents the product of hundreds of millions of patient years of animal evolution, and he approaches his crisis not as a lost, lonely self-deluding being but as a proud creature bearing in his veins the tide of all life and in his genes the scars of the ages, then sentient man, sapient at last, has a future beyond the stormiest contradiction.

3

The contemporary revolution in the natural sciences presents us with what seems to be a most unpromising portrait of man. He is a creature dominated by ineradicable animal instincts, with sapient powers devoted largely, thus far, to the task of hiding from himself all those truths which he deems disagreeable. Now the contradictions of his own nature have brought him face to face with storms beyond forecast. And were this all that contemporary science could say of man, then our future might be regarded as foreclosed. But it is not all.

Man is a bad-weather animal, designed for storm and change. And he is the luckiest creature on the earth's green face. We are a mathematical improbability.

At an earlier stage of this account I described the Illusion of Central Position in its relation to human maturity. The baby is born with the conviction that he is the centre of all things, and through slow disillusionment attains his maturity. But I noted that if an individual ever succeeded in attaining perfect maturity, and perfect Disillusionment of Central Position, he would probably surrender and die. Such perhaps is the limitations of our species. And so, since I assume that the reader is no less limited than myself, I recommend a grain of Central Position, and a closer inspection of the circumstance of man.

Four specific developments contribute to our existence. There was first, seventy million years ago, the launching of the primate experiment in which the generalized body was combined with an enlarged brain. This may be regarded as a logical probability that would occur in any evolutionary series of living creatures on our planet or any other. But the second development twenty million years ago, that of the terrestrial ape, was quite another matter.

Why did one line of primates break with arboreal tradition and take to the Kenya earth? I can think of no mechanistic answer. It was a risky venture to surrender the protection of the high bough and accept the hazards of the open savannah; the frequency of corpses in lakeside cemeteries furnishes ample testament. While population pressures in a time of arboreal abundance may have forced certain species to earth, it is a dubious assumption for which there exists no fragment of evidence. The emergence of the terrestrial ape cannot be regarded as logical, normal, or to any degree predetermined. It was a break with primate orthodoxy in the name of what can only be described as adventure.

The Pliocene emergence of the hunting primate was the third development contributing to the human circumstance. That development rested on not one but two extraordinary elements. The outright acceptance of the carnivorous way was a break with primate tradition—by then at least sixty million years old—which no other primate has ever succeeded in making. And the singular environmental pressure which commanded the break—the twelve-million-year African drought—was a climatic condition so far as we know with few rivals in the earth's long history. Granted the bad weather, the emergence of the hunting primate became at least possible. But nothing about the Pliocene drought may be described as normal or predetermined.

The final development of the human circumstance was the appearance of the big brain. We know that in the early Pleistocene, three-quarters of a million years ago, the pint-sized brain still prevailed. Since Leakey's discovery of *Zinjanthropus* in Bed One of the Olduvai Gorge, we know that such a brain was capable of conceiving in form and realizing in material the first stone implements. From Raymond Dart's exhaustive studies since 1955 we know that a comparable brain could so skilfully direct the activities of an armed predator that not just five hundred but fifty thousand animal victims grace the fossil deposits of a single cave. The predatory transition may account in part for the brain's subsequent enlargement. But if the hunting primate was doing this well with the brain he had, one may ask, why was natural selection in such a hurry to pick a larger one? By the Middle Pleistocene—within the course of two or three hundred thousand years—the brain leapt to the human condition.

Wrapped in the enigma of the Pleistocene lies the final extraordinary circumstance of man.

Let us recall that on only three occasions in a billion years of geological history do we find the scars of glaciers on our planet's rocks. There was the first occurrence among the hazy horizons of pre-Cambrian times. There were the Permian glaciers that left their marks on rocky outcrops two hundred million years ago. And there are the glaciers of the time of man. No scientific mind has ever succeeded in dispelling the mystery of the icy visitations. What cosmic storms or earthly disarrangements have combined to produce such violent and unlikely times, we shall perhaps never know. And so all we can say is that they are violent, that they are extremely unlikely, and that they are unexplained; and that one of these times has been ours.

Let us recall that our own era has been marked by equally inexplicable cycles of change. Our million-year Pleistocene has seen five major periods of rain or drought with fluctuations of temperature even more rapid. Each change transformed the earth's environment and the conditions faced by all forms of life. The forest spread, the desert retreated; the desert spread, the forest retreated. New species of animals appeared, old species became extinct. From the viewpoint of the human observer with a lifespan of seventy years, such cycles of climate may seem relatively stable. But from the view-point of species, the Pleistocene has been a climatic roller-coaster of a dizziness beyond evolutionary recollection.

Now let us finally recall that the hunting primate, a Pliocene creature, survived the first two cycles of change. The opening rains were sufficient to break the Pliocene drought and produce the Villafranchian fauna; but the change was insufficient to bring ice-sheets to Europe. It was the third cycle—the rains in Africa represented by Olduvai, Bed Two, and the period in Europe crushed by the first two major ice-sheets—that witnessed the manic-depressive Pleistocene in its first full disorder, that killed off the new Villafranchian species, that saw the last of the hunting primate, and that presented the planet with man.

Is it possible to form any conclusion other than that the big brain, after seventy million years of slow development, came about when it did in an evolutionary instant as an ultimate answer to the Pleistocene's unprecedented demands? The fourth and final condition of human development is inextricably mingled with the enigma of the Pleistocene. And if anything normal, logical, or predictable can be said for the Pleistocene wilderness, then it is a statement that has eluded the best scientific minds of our day.

Man is a mathematical improbability. Astronomers may assault the Illusion of Central Position with the estimate that our galaxy alone affords one hundred million planetary possibilities for sapient life. Against that estimate must be read the record of planet Earth. We have produced in the course of some billions of respectable years a current crop of perhaps a million species of animate beings. Of them, one may loosely be described as sapient. And that one has come about through fortune's most dazzling display. Were we not so evident, an impartial observer would be forced to conclude that we could not and do not exist.

Man is neither unique nor central nor necessarily here to stay. But he is a product of circumstances special to the point of disbelief. And if man in his current predicament seeks a fair mystique to see him through, then I can only suggest that he consider his genes. For they are marked. They are graven by luck beyond explanation. They are stamped by forces that we shall never know. But even so, in the hieroglyph of the human emergence certain symbols must stand for all to read: Change is the elixir of the human circumstance, and acceptance of challenge the way of our kind. We are bad-weather animals, disaster's fairest children. For the soundest of evolutionary reasons man appears at his best when times are worst.

4

The most remarkable development in the contemporary theatre has been the appearance in America of an art form lacking a name. We call it a "musical," or sometimes a "musical comedy" in honour of its humble parentage. But in truth, the American musical is a new creation under the artful sun, and its someday potential as a form of human

expression lies beyond a dramatist's guess. That potential has best been indicated at the time of this accounting by a work called *West Side Story*, a tale of juvenile life in the New York streets. No other work of art that I know of offers such a vivid portrait of the natural man.

West Side Story is a supreme work of art for many reasons not the least of which is truthfulness. The authors treat the romantic fallacy as if it did not exist. On a stage laid bare, and in young hearts laid naked, we watch our animal legacy unfold its awful power. There is the timeless struggle over territory, as lunatic in the New York streets as it is logical in our animal heritage. There is the gang, our ancestral troop. There is the rigid system of dominance among males within the gang, indistinguishable from that among baboons. There is the ceaseless individual defence of status. There is the amity-enmity code of any animal society: mercy, devotion, and sacrifice for the social partner; suspicion, antagonism, and unending hostility for the territorial neighbour. And there is the hunting primate contribution, a dedication to the switch-blade knife as unswerving as to the antelope bone.

I find it difficult to believe that the authors were aware of *Australopithecus africanus*. They observed their subject with honesty and without illusions and that is all. But the artistic consequence is an australopithecine interpretation of human conduct. There is more, however, in *West Side Story* than animal behaviour. We have the addition of human self-awareness, and the pitiless ridicule by the delinquent of those who would see his soul as sick. And we have the human complication of the youth touched by the inhibitions and ambitions of civilization, the struggle to free himself from animal bondage, and the tragic star-strewn failure. An accountant of a scientific revolution can add little to *West Side Story* in its portrait of that natural man, the juvenile delinquent.

Juvenile delinquency is a battleground where the romantic fallacy meets the new enlightenment head-on. What in adolescent conduct may be regarded as a consequence of abnormal frustration, what as a consequence of normal instinctual endowment? The delinquent today is an international figure who cannot be identified with any particular social or political system. In New York he is a JD, in London a teddy boy, in Cape Town a tsotsi, in Pekin or Moscow a hooligan. Everywhere he is a figure arousing concern, puzzlement, sometimes denunciation, more often guilt. Nowhere, to my knowledge, is he understood.

"Delinquency is a disease of society, just as cancer is a disease of the individual." "Every child who feels rejected is a potential delinquent." "Delinquency is the prerogative of the underprivileged." "The hooligan of today is the reactionary of tomorrow." "Love is the answer." "Delinquency cannot be attributed to a single cause. Mental disturbance, broken homes, poverty, and parental rejection contribute equally and in combination to the problem of the streets."

Where among these is an answer that does not speak from the spacious balconies of the romantic fallacy? Goodness, conscience, and nobility are attributes of man; and when youth fails to demonstrate such qualities, then youth must be sick or deprived or rejected. In *West Side Story*, youth snickers.

For the authors of such statements as those I have quoted —and to publish their names would be to bore the reader with the pages of *Who's Who*—there is a recent study that should provide bottomless embarrassment. It was published by Harvard University, supervised by Sheldon and Eleanor Glueck, and prepared by a large staff of physicians, psychiatrists, and other specialists. It represents the most carefully controlled examination of juvenile delinquency that to my knowledge has ever been made. In the Glueck report, the histories, behaviour, and attitudes of five hundred delinquent boys are compared with the histories, behaviour, and attitudes of five hundred non-delinquents, all of comparable backgrounds And we find the delinquent, by and large, superior to the non-delinquent in energy and physique. We find conforming children with a greater sense of insecurity, of being unloved, unwanted, or rejected, than delinquent children. And among the five hundred boys who had smoked at an early age, kept late hours, played with other delinquents, frequented neighbourhoods far from their homes, persistently and seriously misbehaved at school when they did not persistently and seriously play truant, and who had rolled up in every individual history a fair record of repeated burglary, larceny, assault, and public disturbance—among the ranks of this inglorious five hundred we find far fewer neurotics than in the ranks of the non-delinquents.

And why should it not be true? The citizen of the streets whom we watch in *West Side Story* is Rousseau's natural man, all but full grown, and by one means or another untouched by corrupting civilization. If he does not possess what society regards as a conscience, then it is because conscience is a social invention. If he displays a singular lack of neurosis, it is because his instincts have encountered few civilized inhibitions. Society flatters itself in thinking it has rejected the delinquent; the delinquent has rejected society. And in the shadowed byways of his world so consummately free, this ingenious, normal adolescent human creature has created a way of life in perfect image of his animal needs. He has the security of his gang, and finds his rank among its numbers. He has sex, although it does not preoccupy him. Without any learned instruction, he creates directly from his instincts the animal institution of territory. In the defence of that territory his gang evolves a moral code, and his need to love and be loved is fulfilled. In its territorial combats, the gang creates and identifies enemies, and his need to hate and be hated finds institutional expression. Finally, in assault and larceny, the gang and its members enjoy the blood and the loot of the predator. And there is always the weapon, the gleaming switchblade which the non-delinquent must hide in a closet, or the hissing, flesh-ripping bicycle chain which the family boy can associate only with pedalling to school.

Why should the delinquent not be happy? He lives in a perfect world created solely by himself. And if he is caught by that larger society against which he offends, and for which he holds the most knowing, cynical, and deserved disrespect, then follows the last, vast irony. He will be excused. He will be understood. Society will blame itself.

For years now, hundreds of thousands of the world's most civilized, adult human beings have formed the audience for *West Side Story* and found in it a fragment of their innermost dream. Nightly, in the dark hypnotism of the theatre, we lose ourselves in envy, in yearning, and in a terrible nostalgia which we cannot comprehend. And make no mistake. That is exactly what we do.

Any society must deal with its new-born members—since acquired characteristics cannot be inherited—as if they were each the first human baby on earth. Whatever be our main social principles—whether they be based on collectivism, individualism, vegetarianism or cannibalism, militarism, pacifism, feudal rights or Buchmanism, tribal doctrine or parliamentary law, human slavery or votes for all—whatever be the principles on which a society is founded, the problem remains the same: the new-born baby, that perpetual antique, must somehow be brought around. His instincts must be conditioned.

Any society makes use of the same techniques in the taming of its new wild citizens. Fear and satisfaction, punishment and prize, disapproval and acclamation, sublimation and expression all tend to sort out the instincts to fit the ultimate social purpose. If we do not know what our instincts are, then of course we face many a difficulty. An educational system, for example, that attributes to the human species an immaculate conception, will naturally consider its students as having been born as noble as goose eggs. The process of education then must become the application of a maximum of learning with a minimum of repression, so that the goose eggs will not be crushed. The educator may wonder why his end-product shows such an alarming devotion to illiteracy, to vandalism, to the pecking order, and to getting rich quick; and he will tend to blame it on home influences.

On the whole, however, a society unaware of the instincts of its members has a way of accepting disaster with equanimity. A collective society dedicated to human justice will find room in its pantheon for tyranny, inequality, and the right to peck, all obvious gods in a just world. And a free society inspired by the noblest of human motives, finding its citizens inspired by little but material success, will conclude that the satisfaction of economic wants is the sacred way to the ultimate temple. The enlarged brain does not lack imagination when the need arises to invent disastrous purposes to explain disastrous ends. But sometimes a society will be rocked beyond rationalization by a catastrophe beyond comprehension.

The Hungarian Revolution provided for the observer of human conduct a fiery laboratory of elemental behaviour without parallel in our time. From the viewpoint of the western sympathizer the Hungarians died for democracy, for justice, for expression of man's innate nobility and dignity. In fact, of course, they died for none of these things. Hungarians died for Hungary. On October 23, 1956, an unpredictable incident let loose the territorial instinct of an entire people, inner compulsion triumphed over reason, and in the days that followed the world witnessed the full flowering and the full, inevitable tragedy of an enterprise which for mad magnificence our century provides no equal.

The most impressive demonstration of the uprising, however, was neither the storm of energy lying latent in the territorial demand, nor the extent to which the amity-enmity code could grip a people themselves propelled by a full head of territorial steam. Both demonstrations were striking, but neither could compare in lasting importance—whether viewed from west or east—with the role of the young people.

Had I been a Kremlin master in the autumn of 1956, I presume that I should have regarded the Hungarian uprising as the most appalling outbreak of juvenile delinquency that a civilized society has ever been asked to endure. From start to finish it was a revolution of youth. From start to finish its heroes were children, its most fearsome battalions the armed adolescents, and its most implacable leaders men little their seniors. Never had west or east anticipated such a situation. We had believed that young people in a closed society could act none but the charades they had been taught, and that only those members old enough to recall the open fields of freedom would be capable of revolution in its name. The east, equally innocent, had presumed that its most trusted citizens were to be found in the ranks of the sheltered young. The Hungarian uprising demonstrated that the opposite was true.

In the aftermath of the revolution I encountered a Hungarian attorney who told a most curious story. On the day of the uprising he had been a prisoner in a vast lodging for the politically restless which the regime provided at Pecs. There he had been for seven years, since the days of the Rajk trial. At the time of the uprising he shared a cell with seventeen other men. Necessarily, he knew them all well. But imprisoned as they were, they knew nothing, saw nothing, heard nothing of the event that was shaking the world. And so, on the fourth day after the outbreak, they sat on their benches and crouched on their floor unaware that Hungary was free. But then an odd thing happened. Their incommunicative jailer entered with food. And something was wrong with his cap.

My attorney friend recalled the moment as something both hazy and terrifying. All eighteen men stared at the jailer's cap, groping to know what was wrong with their world. And only as the jailer left the cell did it come to them—and to all simultaneously. The red star had been torn off. Suddenly madness possessed them and all were screaming and some were breaking benches and pounding on the door of their cell and others were fighting those who screamed for freedom and were trying to restrain them, and from down the corridor all could hear the same madness overtaking cell after cell with the jailer's progress and there were the same screams for freedom, the same shouts of restraint, the same blows between prisoners, the same crashing of broken benches on broken doors. And in a stupendous jail-break the prisoners of Pecs fought their way out of their cells and out of their prison yard, and on the other side of their prison walls found themselves in a free Hungary.

The incident at Pecs was one among thousands—all dramatic, all ironic, and most of them inexplicable—that made up the cryptogram of the Hungarian uprising. What haunted the escaped young attorney, as he recalled his own incident, was a clear recollection for which he had no explanation. In the moment of maniac frenzy that followed the recognition of the missing star, there had been a division among the prisoners. Not one man under forty-five years of age had failed to scream for freedom. Not one man over forty-five had failed to fight for restraint.

The masters of Soviet society have explained the Hungarian uprising as the work of reactionaries and foreign agents; and for all I know they may believe their own lie. But, in truth what they faced was their own total failure to condition the instincts of a subject people; their own fatal ignorance of what those instincts were, and of the shattering power released when animal compulsions throw aside the learned restraints of human experience; and their own incapacity to deal with such power except by the use of superior weapons, and of force bared naked for all to see.

Man is a wild species, and every baby born is a wild young thing. Advancing age, weakening vitality, and a long accumulation of fears and experiences may at last work a general inhibition on certain animal sources of human behaviour. But the dilemma of any society, closed or free, finds its chief place of residence in the birth-rate. Every accouchement delivers to society a creature who somehow must be tamed. Every accouchement—today, tomorrow, and until the end of our species' time—presents civilization with an aspiring candidate for the hangman's noose. Yet truly to domesticate him means probably to destroy him.

The domestication of man—that is, the weeding out of the less socially acceptable instincts through controlled breeding—is not impossible, although extremely difficult. Adolf Hitler made a rough attempt in this direction with his crematoriums and gas chambers for those elements deemed undesirable by the society which he was attempting to create. Any universal government holding a monopoly on force would find the castration of Hungarians and other juvenile delinquents a tempting solution to the recurrent problem of the animal nature. It is a temptation frequently overlooked by such wise men as Bertrand Russell when they advocate the surrender to a universal government as preferable to death by nuclear annihilation. Controlled breeding, on the other hand, must naturally appeal to such Nobel prize-winning geneticists as H. J. Muller, who see in the potentialities of their speciality the realization of a brave new world.

In fact, however, the reliable taming of a wild species is a remarkably difficult chore. After thousands of years of domestication, the bull to be rendered socially tractable must first be turned into an ox. And though the timid, the recessive, the obedient, and the humble may be chosen through centuries of selective breeding to produce in the end a pure, tame creature, still all may be gone in a night. Mongol herdsmen produced in Asia herds of domesticated reindeer. But the intrusion of one wild male into a domesticated herd would leave behind it, without exception, progeny as wild as their sire. Whatsoever is the wild determinant, it proceeds through a dominant gene.

Since man is a primate with weaker instincts than the reindeer, the horse, and the goat, he may be a readier subject for domestication. We cannot be sure. Human slavery has represented man's only persistent attempt to tame his fellow man. The slave as a rule, however, was cheaper to buy or to capture than to breed; and so we cannot interpret the collapse of slavery as the failure of controlled human breeding. We and our greater philosophers must grant, I believe, that the masters of a universal society with the aid of a captive science might just possibly succeed in producing, over a long enough period, a lasting answer to the problem of our animal nature: a universal human slave inherently obedient to other people's reason.

Whether through sentimental attachment or rational choice, I find myself moved to prefer the wild creatures among whom I was born to the more literal *Homo sapiens* that science and tyranny might unite to produce. I may in my preference be a victim of a new self-delusion, and be looking at human affairs through another transparent curtain. But I find that I cannot disbelieve in nature. I cannot but believe in the pure wild gene, in natural selection as opposed to human, and in the strength and balance of our natural endowment as sufficient foundation for our species, ambitions.

We are a transitional species, without doubt. We are a pioneer creature testing the potentialities of the enlarged brain. The first species to be blessed by such a mutational marvel, we must be forgiven if sometimes we use it badly. Lacking instinctual authority for our mind's decrees, we must not be embarrassed if all too often human thought amounts to little but a faint, fizzing sound. We are simply doing the best we can. And if we do not behave too badly, then we shall pass on the power of thought, one day, to a descendant species who may count it a part of their animal endowment. They, not we, can found kingdoms on its strength.

We can trust no such kingdoms to the fragile constructions of the unauthoritative mind. We can use human thought and its limited powers to understand our natures; to explore our avenues of conduct; to weigh our best interests; to distinguish the false from the true and the dream from the waking. Confronted by the contemporary predicament of survival or self-annihilation, we may even do quite a distinguished job of it. But if we use our intelligence to its keenest advantage, then we shall note that the mind sits without a sovereignty. Allied to an instinct, judgement may act. In conflict with instinct, human thought becomes a wish.

In the balance of forces that make up our whole nature we must place our trust. It is the debate of our instincts that will determine our final testament.

5

The enlarged brain may lack a sovereignty; but it likewise acknowledges no chains.

Towards the end of his life, we may recall, Charles Darwin expressed the "horrid doubt" as to whether human convictions were of any value. If the human mind had evolved from origins in the lower animals, how could it be regarded as free? What value could be placed on intellectual conclusions concerning either morality or truth? If the human mind had come into being as a consequence of natural selection, then what confidence could be placed in any of its works, including its understanding of natural selection?

Darwin's profound self-doubt was a consequence of the inadequate knowledge of instinct prevalent a century ago, and which has managed somehow to remain intact to the present philosophical moment. So long as we regard natural selection as a force choosing and discarding among creatures driven by a single overwhelming instinct, to survive, then small confidence could indeed be placed in a mind created by such selection. But we know or should know today the wealth and the subtlety of our animal endowment. And if Darwin's survival be regarded as an infinitely tall, infinitely slender needle pointed high into the human space, then it is braced by a myriad of instinctual cables founded each in most ancient rocks.

The winds of chance and catastrophe may press on the human outcome. And a horrid self-doubt may overcome us: of what use is mind, and civilization, if in the end our animal endowment must determine our radiant fate? But our instincts are not that simple. And intelligence can discover allies.

It may be useful at this moment to recall a story, as startling as it is charming, told by the Austrian naturalist, Konrad Lorenz. It is a story concerning a family of jewel fish kept under observation by Lorenz and his students. And as we ponder the story, we must keep in mind that the jewel fish, unlike man, is no evolutionary newcomer. His ancestry goes back to the Devonian seas of three hundred and fifty million years ago.

Instinct and anatomy have combined in the jewel fish to eliminate certain of our more anguished problems. Juvenile delinquency, for example, can scarcely keep jewel-fish parents awake at night, worrying what their children are up to. Evolution has provided the jewel-fish young with a deflatable air chamber. When the child is placed in the nest at night, the chamber deflates. And so there the baby stays till morning whether he likes it or not.

The parents, of course, must have their complementary instincts to make juvenile deflatability a jewel-fish asset. And so, as the first darkness creeps through the water, the parents abandon their feeding. The mother rounds up the babies and nuzzles and fins them towards the nest. The magic touch of the sandy, scooped-out home-place has its immediate effect. As each of the small fry reaches it, he flops. But the enviable life of the jewel-fish mother has more even than nature on its side. It has also the father. The male is a reliable creature whose responsibility at night-fall is for strays. While she does her nuzzling and finning of that portion of the family schoolable in one piece, he darts about collecting truants. When he catches a baby with ideas of its own, he simply takes it in his mouth. And now another superb jewel-fish instinct takes charge. The touch of the father's mouth has the same magical effect on the baby as the touch of the family nest. Captured, the baby promptly deflates. And the father has no further problem than to swim to the home-place and spit out his son.

Any human parent may be forgiven if he condemns nature for not having contributed this system of child disposal to our own evolutionary legacy. But we cannot conclude that the jewel-fish father always has things so easy. The story concerns a moment when he did not.

Late one afternoon Lorenz and his students returned from an outing to discover that the jewel fish had not been fed. It was already beginning to get dark. Hurriedly they minced up some worms, dropped them in the tank. And then, in horror, they watched disaster's opportunity unfold. The male was already pursuing a fugitive child. And just as he snapped up his son in his mouth, a piece of worm came sinking past. And he snapped that too. The human audience stood about the tank like stark monuments to the baby's fate. But an odd thing happened. The hungry father made no motion to swallow. For seconds he hovered without movement as if paralyzed by the flavour of dilemma. Then abruptly he spat out both son and worm. The two fell to the sand. The father had determined his course of action. He first scooped up the portion of worm and swallowed it, then scooped up his son, swam home, and spat him in the nest. Lorenz records that the human audience burst into cheers.

It is difficult to read such a story without attributing to the father jewel-fish some process of thought. How else could he reach a complex decision in a situation unprecedented? Yet what the Austrian scientist and his students had witnessed was in fact the debate of the instincts. Survival of the individual threatened survival of the kind. And survival of the kind—the stronger—prevailed. No thought provided the material of decision. Neither for that matter did thought enter into the suicidal decision of Marais' two heroic baboons when in the dusk of the lonely South African Waterberg they attacked the leopard that threatened their troop. Nor does thought in reality determine the action of the human male when he chooses to die for his country.

The command of the kind may be expressed by the survival of the jewel-fish family, the survival of the baboon troop, the survival of a modern nation, or the survival of a gang of juvenile delinquents in a rumble on the streets of New York. In every case the command lies contrary to the individual's instinct for survival. And the debate of the instincts will determine his way.

The growing exercise of human thought has arisen as an extension of the animal debate of the instincts. Our primate line developed such an increasingly complex instinctual pattern that thought as we know it became necessary. The primate's sexual life is not confined to a season. Which at a given moment must he pursue, the hunger of his loins or the hunger of his stomach? His social life is confined to no simple family. Which must he defend, his troop or himself? Sex, society, status, nourishment, territory, children all clamour for his instinctual attention. Which at a given moment must take innate preference over what? Copulation? Defending his mate? Defending the monopoly he enjoys with his mate? Defending his rank in the order of dominance? Obeying the instinctual mores of his society? Getting his dinner? Protecting his young? Joining in the defence of his social territory?

We cannot know the entire range of instincts which must enter into the debate of any primate faced by the necessity to act. But another complication critical to the development of human thought enters the life of ape or monkey. He is a creature afflicted also by learned responses. Instinct commands his hunger. But learning and instruction have taught him which fruits are poisonous and which are not. Instinct has commanded his drive for status. But learning teaches him the opportunities and hazards that the rank he accepts may dispose. The debate of his instincts must sort out not only his primal necessities, but also those learned responses which have come to adorn them.

In contrast to the strain of decision on the primate, the lower animal has an easier life. Here instinct determines all, and patterns of life are simpler. There is a breed of sea-otter that lives along the California coast, and that boasts of an astonishing achievement. When the sea-otter dives for a hard-shelled clam on the sandy shallow sea-bottom, he comes up not only with the clam but with a solid, flat-sided pebble as well. Then turning on his back in the water he places the pebble on his chest and smashes the clam-shell against it. Amply rewarded by his ingenuity, he eats the clam. But what may appear as ingenuity is not. *Always,* when he gets a clam, he gets a pebble. The use of a tool by the California sea-otter is pure instinct in his kind.

The relation of experience to instinct in the conduct of animals is of elemental concern to the history and potentiality of human thought. Yet our ignorance of the subject is characterized largely by abundance. What is instinct? What is habit? What is ingenuity based on experience and rudimentary thought? The lesser flamingo, at Lake Natron in Tanganyika, builds a pedestal of clay ten inches high topped by a shallow depression. In the depression the female lays her eggs. The pedestal makes it easier for the long-legged mother to squat on her nest. The custom among present day flamingos is an instinct. But how could the cultural instinct have been initiated, in some ancestral species, except for the ingenuity of a bird with tired legs?

Darwin discovered on the Galapagos islands a bird-world of finches. Cut off from the South American continent, the islands had never received their normal complement of bird species. And so finches, with enthusiasm and finesse, had filled all the evolutionary niches. There were seed-eating finches. There were insect-eating finches. There was even a woodpecking finch, a species called *Cactospiza*. But the woodpecking finch had been faced with a problem. Nature had offered it the luscious opportunity of pecking insects out of bark, but nature had evolved no bill for the finch in his drilling operations. And so the woodpecking finch—today by instinct—solves the problem with minimum fuss. He holds a cactus thorn in his little beak. But how could the instinct have come about, except through ancestral ingenuity?

A final, puzzling example of ingenuity among the lower animals is recorded in one of Kenneth Oakley's studies. The great tit, we may recall, is a bird capable of unorthodox behaviour. It was a male of this species who encountered all the perils of bigamy in Miss Howard's garden. Some other English great tit—which one we shall never know—took not too long ago a more constructive flight into unorthodoxy. He learned how to open milk bottles. But this was not all. Within a very few years every great tit in the British Isles had learned the trick. Some British dairies in consequence had to change their milk-bottle caps.

How did the great tit do it, and how was the trick spread? We cannot even make a guess. But how also did the woodpecking finch first learn to use cactus thorns as a substitute for a drilling beak? And how did the long-legged flamingo first learn to build a pedestal to ease the cramps in her legs? One can only say that when experience facilitates an instinct then experience can soon become instinct itself. And while birds are notoriously open to suggestion, it is difficult to believe that modern man, pressed by chance and catastrophe, should be less.

Human thought is an extension of the animal debate of the instincts. It carries in itself no police power. It cannot act with final authority to impede this instinct, or advance that. But it can probe through experience and ingenuity the various means to a variety of ends. The paramount distinction between human and animal intelligence, so far as we know, lies not in complexity, or profundity, or creativity, or memory, but in man's capacity for conceptual thought, and his power to see ahead.

When Wolfgang Kohler conducted his research into chimpanzee mentality at an experimental station in the Canary Islands, he formed a central conclusion. "The time in which a chimpanzee lives is limited in past and future." It is a characteristic not unknown in the human being. But in the chimpanzee, most intelligent of living animals, it is absolute. The chimpanzee has a limited grip on his past; none at all on his future. He may solve a present situation through experience or occasional ingenuity. Still he cannot anticipate a future situation towards which present experience may be directed.

Foresight, and the capacity to create in terms of a mental image, are among living creatures the exclusive prerogatives of man. Yet the contemporary revolution in the natural sciences has revealed, in our African genesis, that even these have animal origins. Both were contributions of the extinct hunting primate, and were simply the last to enter the evolution of human thought.

That the hunting primate should have used bones as weapons is no more remarkable than that one of Darwin's finches should use cactus thorns for pecking wood. Our forefathers compensated for lack of claws and fighting canines, the finches for lack of a drilling beak. That the hunting primate should have picked up a stone and hurled it at enemy or prey, granted his anatomical capacity, is again no more remarkable than that the baboon on occasion will use a pebble to kill a scorpion or will roll rocks down a hill at an intruder. But that *Australopithecus africanus* should have systematically selected useful bones in the field, and should have collected them in his Makapan cave for future assault or defence, is quite something else again. This was foresight. And that *Australopithecus robustus* should have carried to his Olduvai lakeshore shaped tools made of lava from a deposit twenty-five miles away represents not only foresight but the dawn of conceptual thought. He created a form that did not exist in nature.

Both foresight and the capacity to form a mental concept reflect the same intellectual capacity: imagination. Whether we are considering a situation that does not exist in the present, such as nuclear annihilation, or a shape that does not exist in the hand, such as that of man's animal legacy, we exercise obviously the human faculty of imagination. And what we must now stress is that imagination existed before true man. It is part of our animal endowment. In the ancient rocks of Africa, three-quarters of a million years old, imagination lies fossilized as truly as antique bones.

Human thought is founded in our animal endowment. All of its ingredient processes, including even imagination, had come into existence before man's big brain. We cannot say, of course, that the power to reason—as man exercises that power—antedates the coming of our kind. The complete human faculty of thought requires speech, communication, the formation of symbols, and the necessary warehouse space in the cerebral associative centres for the storage of symbols for future use. As Oakley has expressed it, until experience can be summarized by symbols—whether words or manual gestures—and the symbols grouped, filed, isolated, and selected to perform the thinking process, then experience is no more than an endless silent film. But the capacity to relate past to future, to deal in symbols however rudimentary, to foresee contingencies and take present steps to meet them, is an inheritance from our animal past.

Intelligence is no human sideshow but an evolutionary main event. The power to foresee, to call upon the past in terms of the future, to evaluate, to imagine solutions, is a power flowing from old time springs. The human mind may be denied the policeman's privilege of arresting this instinct or that. It may sit as no more than a moderator in the eternal instinctual debate. But it is a moderator with unlimited investigative powers.

Darwin's horrid doubt was unjustified. The human mind is free, and the creature of no single instinct. It can discover a truth, as it can create a lie. It can paint a Madonna, as it can arrange a battle. It can conceive of a brotherhood of man, as it can envision a community of death. It can postulate treaties or symphonies, massacres or gas-chambers, songs in the morning or dirges at night. It can probe the margins of a new enlightenment, or it can perpetuate the delusions of a romantic fallacy.

The human mind is uncommitted. In a single day it may dedicate its energies to the designing of a missile with no other known purpose than the massacre of millions; to the raising of funds to promote racial integration; to a quarrel with a neighbour, or a wife; to a protest against deterioration of local standards of education; to a decision to buy a second Cadillac, since a rival has only one; to a brief but serious contemplation of certain pages of Tolstoy; and at bedtime, to equally serious reflection as to whether the local scoutmaster is capable of inculcating the eternal standards of loyalty, honour, and devotion in the youthful members of his Boy Scout troop. The day of course may have been punctuated by a visit to the doctor for the treatment of an ulcer, or an hour's meditation on a psychiatrist's couch.

The human mind stands free, in the sense that it is the servant of no given instinct. In the debate continually rag-

ing within us, one instinct may and will act to inhibit another. The mind cannot. The mind may act as witness,
at times impartial. It may act as a brilliant investigative
agency, at times uncorrupted. But on every occasion it
will ride with the winner, whatever be the winner's cause,
and devote to that cause in full, splendid measure its loyalty, honour, and devotion.

It is the mighty paradox of human thought that incapable
of imprisoning an instinct, it is at the same time imprisoned
by none. And that is mentality's most massive power, and
humanity's second best hope.

6

An investigation ends. The detective puts away his magnifying glass, his thumb-print powder, his gum-shoes and his
fake moustache. In various corners of the world the revolution in the natural sciences proceeds quite unshaken by his
absence. Somewhere George Schaller arranges his final
conclusions on the behaviour of Congo gorillas. In a California laboratory secret crystals of argon yield up the
calendar of the human past. In a Johannesburg laboratory
Raymond Dart puts together his evidence that *Australopithecus africanus* authored a fashioned bone culture to
which man added little for almost half a million years. On
the dusty, inaccessible Serengeti plain the Leakeys face
cobras, rhinos, leopards, black-maned lions, and a twenty-
five-mile-long gash in the Tanganyika earth that will reveal,
some day, the authentic story of the human beginning.

For this investigator, however, a case is closed. The evidence has been assembled. Some bits may be dubious, some
misinterpreted. Some may be modified, even nullified, by
future discovery. But for the purpose of this investigation
the whole of the evidence should still support a rough yet
glorious conclusion.

Not in innocence, and not in Asia, was mankind born.
We are a fraction of the animal world, and to its subtle
ways our hearts are yet pledged. We are children of Cain.
And were it not so, then for humanity there would be small
hope.

A case is closed. The scientific role of detachment may
be cast aside. Guided by the arrows of the new enlighten-

ment, we may indulge in that happiest of human entertainments, sheer speculation. Now tables may be pounded, tempers may rise, faces may grow red, and in the grand manner of the howling monkey we may all return to the most blissful of human transactions, out-shouting each other. But we shall conduct our negotiations in a brand new room where old values like old statues stand now on their heads. And the bright new wines that inflame our thoughts are wines never tasted before.

It passes beyond the jurisdiction of this investigator to close a scientific narrative with an orgy of speculation. I feel that the reader, however, keeping in mind my boyhood days in the cozy basement of a Chicago church and recalling my undying enthusiasm for swinging chairs in the dark, should out of compassion if nothing else grant me a very small orgy. While I indulge myself, he may feel free to hide behind a door in panic, to grope for another chair and come after me, or if such is his nature, to get himself as rapidly as possible out of the church basement.

I assert first the paradox that our predatory animal origin represents for mankind its last best hope. Had we been born of a fallen angel, then the contemporary predicament would lie as far beyond solution as it would lie beyond explanation. Our wars and our atrocities, our crimes and our quarrels, our tyrannies and our injustices could be ascribed to nothing other than singular human achievement. And we should be left with a clear-cut portrait of man as a degenerate creature endowed at birth with virtue's treasury whose only notable talent has been his capacity to squander it.

But we were born of risen apes, not fallen angels, and the apes were armed killers besides. And so what shall we wonder at? Our murders and massacres and missiles, and our irreconcilable regiments? Or our treaties whatever they may be worth; our symphonies however seldom they may be played; our peaceful acres, however frequently they may be converted into battlefields; our dreams however rarely they may be accomplished. The miracle of man is not how far he has sunk but how magnificently he has risen. We are known among the stars by our poems, not our corpses.

No creature who began as a mathematical improbability, who was selected through millions of years of unprecedented environmental hardship and change for ruggedness, ruthlessness, cunning, and adaptability, and who in the short ten thousand years of what we may call civilization has achieved such wonders as we find about us, may be regarded as a creature without promise.

My second assertion, flying farther into the speculative sky, is that civilization is a normal evolutionary development in our kind, and a product of natural selection. So far as we know it lacks direct animal origin. Like the jackdaw flock our civilization is the bearer of social wisdom and the accumulated experience of our kind; but unlike the flock it carries no instinctual authority over the conduct of its members. Nevertheless, I believe that civilization has come to mankind as neither accident nor ornament. It reflects the command of the kind. It rests on the most ancient of animal laws, that commanding order, and acts as a necessary inhibition and sublimation of predatory energies that would otherwise long ago have destroyed our species. I regard it as anything but a coincidence that the rate of civilization's rise has corresponded so closely with man's ascendant capacity to kill. Civilization is a compensatory consequence of our killing imperative; the one could not exist without the other.

We shall consider the power of civilization to influence the human outcome after we have considered the power of conscience. For while I regard the one as humanity's most reliable ally, I regard the other as its least.

My third assertion, far less speculative, is that conscience as a guiding force in the human drama is one of such small reliability that it assumes very nearly the role of villain. Conscience has evolved directly from the amity-enmity complex of our primate past. But unlike civilization it has acted as no force to inhibit the predatory instinct. It has instead been the conqueror's chief ally. And if mankind survives the contemporary predicament, it will be in spite of, not because of, the parochial powers of our animal conscience.

I expect nothing but flying chairs as reward for such an assertion. But I do not believe that an investigation such as we have pursued into the far reaches of our animal nature may be properly closed without a statement of the observer's personal conclusions: that the rational storehouses of civilization rest on forces that may save us, and that the irrational storehouses of conscience rest on forces that may destroy us.

The limitation of conscience lies in its territorial nature. It is the mechanism whereby an animal society mobilizes its members against an enemy and commands individuals to make sacrifices for the common good. So far as conscience deepens the amity channels of social partners it is a force for tolerance, for compassion, and for mercy. And so far as the capacity of a species to form territorial coalitions results in the formation of larger and larger territorial societies, the expression of tolerance and compassion and mercy comes to be extended to an increasing number of individuals. In this sense, conscience in human behaviour has acted as a building block in the edifice of civilization.

But conscience is a two-sided coin, and one side is black. Territory commands unremitting hostility for territorial neighbours. The primate amity-enmity complex cannot exist without enemies. Conscience organizes hatred as it organizes love. And with the coming of the predatory way the force of conscience has taken on an awful power lacking in the societies of non-aggressive primates. Conscience may direct the Christian martyr to die for the brotherhood of man. But that same conscience directs Christian armies to go forth and slaughter the same fellow man. It is a phenomenon that has not passed unnoted.

The conscience of social man differs from that of the social animal chiefly in its complexity. If I am a white American Protestant Southerner from the State of Georgia, my conscience may be compounded of a state loyalty directing me to defend regional interests against the territorial interests of other states and even the territorial claims of the American nation; yet at the same time my conscience as an American will direct me to defend my country in any conflict abroad, and will press me to subordinate regional demands to such national demands as are not in conflict with local purposes. But this will not by any means end the complex facets of my conscience. I shall defend the white race against the black, stand for the Christian world against what I deem to be the godless, and oppose any adventures on the part of Rome which seem to threaten my Protestant preserve. And few other than my Georgian social partners will understand that in every instance I am acting according to my conscience.

My conscience is provincial in nature, in that its origins are territorial. I shall invariably delude myself, however, that it is universal and thus bring to my actions the authority of universal law. It does nothing, of course, of the sort. It commands me simply to act in the interest of my society or societies.

My conscience is totally amoral. I shall delude myself that it directs me to act in the interests of human good, and well it may. But with equal force it will direct me to act in the interests of human evil, if such evil is in the interests of my society.

My conscience, I may tell myself, is my own. It is anything but my own. Nothing I seem to possess is so little my own. It is the exclusive property of those territorial or social institutions of which I am a part.

The conscience of social man differs from that of the social animal in a way other than its complexity. Self-awareness presses us to identify our conscience with the highest power available. I do not tell myself that my conscience is the voice of America; I assume it to be the voice of God. The member of a Communist Party does not permit his conscience to be identified with the interests of a country named Russia; he must believe that he acts for mankind. Similarly, the greater is the pressure on the individual for sacrifice, the higher must be the power invoked. God is never so fashionable as during wartime. Even the atheist society of the Soviet Union, during the ravages of the Second World War, found it necessary to reinstate God temporarily to assure full sacrifice on the part of its citizens.

The animal nature of the human conscience demands images, not reason, to invoke the amity-enmity complex. If I am a jackdaw, then whatever my unsatisfied hunger I go the way of my flock in response to a certain call. If I am a baboon, then I leap to the defence of my social partner not at the sight of his danger but in response to my troop's special cry. And though I be a man with certain reasonable endowments, I too must have my images.

The continuity of the amity-enmity complex as it has evolved into the human conscience is nowhere better illustrated than in its dependence upon symbols. The sight of a cross in the gleam of morning or the sounds of a marching band; the ripple of a flag against a clear blue sky or the voice of a choir in a village church: such sights and sounds are enough to still my most anarchistic moments. Words: Valley Forge, home and mother, Abraham Lincoln, right and wrong, Remember Pearl Harbour, pioneers, traitor, spy, Benedict Arnold, Alger Hiss; all are symbols invoking with varying success my peculiarly American amity-enmity complex.

Society in its ancient wisdom does not appeal to my conscience through reason, for my conscience being of animal inheritance will respond with a minimum of force. And so conscience in human society becomes an essentially antirational power. Its symbols must not be questioned too closely: they will lose their magic. The divine or universal origins of conscience must not be subjected to scrutiny: if I am to risk my life, then the cause must be superb. Above all, conscience must exist in one form only, my own. To grant that my enemy acts as a matter of conscience is to surrender the whole preposterous game.

The limited jurisdiction of the human mind is well demonstrated by its relations with the instinctual conscience, into which our reason in the past has possessed not even investigative powers. Yet deeply imbedded in the contemporary predicament lies the power of conscience over human action. Parochial in its very nature, it cannot grapple with universal problems. Complex and contradictory, it offers no sure direction through even a local maze. Traditional in its symbolic responses, it offers no sure direction through even a local maze. Traditional in its symbolic responses, it offers to the present no magic but the past's. Instinctual in its demands, it greets enlightenment as its enemy. Delusive in its necessities, it tends to strengthen the foolish and weaken the wise. And monopolistic in its territorial grip, it denies even communication between antagonists.

Without question conscience has led men forward along many a hard trail from his Pleistocene beginnings. But through how many hours on how many battlefields has conscience supported and made possible man's blackest adventures? In the parochial neighbourhoods of human necessity conscience still plays a part in effecting universal demands. But in the predicament that challenges man's survival as a species, conscience becomes a sometime friend.

Yet conscience is not ours to dismiss. It is a portion of our animal nature, and can no more be discarded than can the adoration of things that go boom. Raise four generations of human beings under anarchistic canary birds, and we shall resume our belief, given access to traditional materials, that our conscience is the voice of God or the people. It is the way we are. And we cannot, as social creatures, get along without it.

I conclude my third assertion. The power of conscience, blind, anti-rational, and acting in alliance with the weapons fixation, will be the responsible force if self-annihilation be the human outcome. The amity-enmity complex is a command of the kind perfected by natural selection in the interests of species survival. But allied to the instincts of an armed predator, it has gone awry. Evolution does not anticipate. Natural selection, weeding the forgotten gardens of our African emergence, could not foresee the lightning or pre-hear the thunder. And so an instinct safeguarding the survival of species has with cosmic irony become in *Homo sapiens* a prime mover towards destruction.

But no animal compulsion stands alone in the debate of our instincts. And so I return to my second assertion, that civilization is a product of evolution and an expression of nature's most ancient law. Far antedating the predatory urge in our animal nature, far more deeply buried than conscience or territory or society lies that shadowy, mysterious, undefinable command of the kind, the instinct for order. And so, when a predatory species came rapidly to evolve its inherent talent for disorder, natural selection favoured as a factor in human survival the equally rapid evolvement of that sublimating, inhibiting, super-territorial institution which we call, loosely, civilization.

It is a jerry-built structure, and a more unattractive edifice could scarcely be imagined. Its greyness is appalling. Its walls are cracked and eggshell thin. Its foundations are shallow, its antiquity slight. No bands boom, no flags fly, no glamorous symbols invoke our nostalgic hearts. Yet however humiliating the path may be, man beset by anarchy, banditry, chaos and extinction must in last resort turn to that chamber of dull horrors, human enlightenment. For he has nowhere else to turn.

If man is to survive without war, a gloomier conclusion could not be written than that this fragile, despicable, unattractive structure must become our court of last appeal. It has failed us consistently in the past. It tends to fall down every thousand years or so. Nobody wants to go into it anyway. Its libraries are as loaded with trash as they are with wisdom; its custodians are as burdened with folly as they are with fruit. From its crumbling archways have emerged, so far, few but shouting schoolboys, their hats shot full of learning and their heads unscathed. If the corridors of human enlightenment are to provide us with salvation, then a drearier whimper, one might almost conclude, could scarcely be imagined. Let us have the bang.

But the choice is not ours. Never to be forgotten, to be neglected, to be derided, is the inconspicuous figure in the quiet back room. He sits with head bent, silent, waiting, listening to the commotion in the streets. He is the keeper of the kinds.

Who is he? We do not know. Nor shall we ever. He is a presence, and that is all. But his presence is evident in the last reaches of infinite space beyond man's probing eye. His presence is guessable in the last reaches of infinite smallness beyond the magnification of electron or microscope. He is present in all living beings and in all inanimate matter. His presence is asserted in all things that ever were, and in all things that will ever be. And as his command is unanswerable, his identity is unknowable. But his most ancient concern is with order.

You may sense his presence in a star-scattered sky as silenced you stand on a lonely hill. There above you floats in tightly-packed grandeur the Milky Way, your galaxy, your celestial home. And there, beyond Andromeda's faint indication, floats your nearest brother in space. Twenty-six quintillion miles away revolves your galaxy's twin in all manner of description and behaviour.

You may sense his presence in the kind of matter called helium, that has always and will forever behave according to the rules and regulations of helium. You may sense his word in the second law of thermodynamics, or the patterned behaviour of brook trout in a clear New Zealand pool. You may feel his command in the choice of the reed bunting to defend his territory before his young; or in the pause of a jewel fish that saves his dinner and his small fry too. You may find his word in the forms of cities and symphonies, of Rembrandts and fir trees and cumulus clouds. You may read his command in the regularity of turning things, in stars and seasons, in tides and in striking clocks. Where bursts the green of the apple-orchard, all of a springtime day, there passes his presence. And here, too, he passes, in the windy fluttering of scarlet leaves and the calls of the harvesters.

Where a child is born, or a man lies dead; where life must go on, though tragedy deny it; where a farmer replants fields again despoiled by flood or drought; where men rebuild cities that other men destroy; where tides must ebb as tides have flowed; there, see his footprints, there, and there.

He does not care about you, or about me, or about man for that matter. He cares only for order. But whatever he says, we shall do. He is rising now, in civilization's quiet back room, and he is looking out the window.

7

South of the moon, where man was born, all values and all symbols seemed upside down. And the man of the north long conditioned to other skies, other winds, other ways and other faces, finds himself continually lost. By day my shadow falls to the south, for the sun is where it does not belong. I turn to the left, which should be to the west, and it is to the east. I turn to the right, which should be to the east, and it is to the west. And by night I am no better off. The African moon rides the cloud-wisps of a northern sky, and Orion goes to sleep on his head. No friendly Dipper points to a steadfast moment in space. The stars are unfamiliar.

I am lost. Which way is east? Which way is up? Yet here is the place where I was born.

The south wind adds to my predicament. There is a chill on the mile-high African savannah, for it is June and winter will soon be here. Out of the Antarctic sweeps a south wind bitter with the ice of its origins. There is the smell of Christmas shopping in the lengthening nights and the frosty mornings. But when Christmas comes we shall be sweltering in the sun, taking iced drinks in the shade, and

turning on the electric fan before we open our presents. It is almost enough to make one disbelieve in Santa Claus.

And there is the matter of my white face. It is a face, I presume, that has been too long accustomed to being a member of a majority. It has come to assume that all other faces should be like itself. Now and again in the northern crowd I can recall a face of strange shape or colour. That face however seemed always a freak. But south of the moon it is my face that is freakish and the sensation lacks comfort. I look at that face in the morning mirror and it is the face I have always known. For a moment I recapture the rightness. But in the street I lose it, and my face is a tiny white sailboat tossed on a dark, surging sea. My compass is out of order and the winds are all wrong. Loneliness oppresses me. I am afraid.

And that is another thing. I am unaccustomed to mortal fears. I have lived my life in the shelter of too many northern alliances. I have made alliance with the gentle cow, the health department, the local policeman. In the shelter of such alliances I have got out of bed in the morning with moderate assurance that I shall still be alive at bedtime. But south of the moon my allies vanish, and I have an emptiness in my stomach. I fear the cobras in the garden. I lack a treaty with the lioness. I dread the crocodiles of Lake Victoria, the tsetse fly in the Tanganyika bush, the little airplane with the funny engine, and the mosquito in the soft evening air. But most of all, I am afraid of the African street.

There are smiles, broad and white. But what lies behind the smile? I do not know. There is laughter, like small old cymbals ringing. But what lies behind the laughter? There is thoughtfulness in the depth of dark eyes. But what are the thoughts? Of the tribe in the hills? My tribe is a thousand years lost. Of the witch-doctor's magic? I know nothing of witch-doctors. Do the thoughts concern the uniqueness of man, his innocence and innate nobility? I doubt it. Only the northern soldier with his superior northern arms has suppressed in these thoughts the pleasure of massacre, the desirability of human slavery, the practicality of castrating one's captured enemy, and the ritual satisfaction of consuming a stranger, preferably alive. No debate of the instincts has contributed to the inhibition of such pleasures. No slow accretion of experience, and social wisdom, has turned these thoughts in other directions. The conscience I face in the African street bears no resemblance to my own. And the northern soldier is taking ship.

I am alone in the African street, lost, afraid, and without allies. I understand nothing. Yet this is the street where I was born. I too once delighted in massacre, slavery, castration, and cannibalism, and my conscience told me that these things were right. I too once consulted the witch-doctor, and accepted his magic, and it was not very long ago. What prevents me today? Nothing prevents me, excepting only the wisdom of my civilization and the conditioning it has brought to my instincts in my lifetime.

There was a time, I have been told, when to conceive of the earth's being round came with utmost difficulty to the minds of men. Yet slowly we have grasped the concept, and we have made it a part of human thought. There was a time, I have also been told, when to see our planet as a body revolving about the sun was equally difficult, and what is more, a heresy subject to the most lavish of punishments. But somehow, slowly, the sanctions were removed, enlightenment spread, and we came to accept the earth as other than the centre of all things. Now man must face an enlightenment concerning his own nature. It will come slowly, and with difficulty. There will be sanctions, and punishments for the heretic. The new enlightenment will spread, because it must.

The south wind blows cold, and we shall have frost. Slowly the seasons become acceptable. My shadow falls south, and east is on my left. Gradually the compass begins to make sense. *Australopithecus africanus* lies buried not in limey caves, but in my heart and your heart, and in the black man's down the street. We are Cain's children, all of us. Slowly, ever so slowly, comprehension and compassion become possible things, and the transparent curtain is gone and faces are no longer strange. Old tides pull at me and ancient swells sweep in from forgotten seas and support me, and I have a lightness, and I take my coat because these June nights can be bitter, and there is a star in the southern sky, the most magnificent star that I have ever seen, and I am beginning to know its name, Alpha Centauri.

Bibliography

FOR THE GENERAL READER, I recommend a selected list of books which have contributed material and illumination to my own investigations of our animal inheritance and so may interest him. They vary in point of view, some scientific, some philosophical, some orthodox, some *avant garde,* and together form a fairly rounded portrait of our present knowledge and convictions:

ALLEE, WARDER CLYDE, *Social Life of Animals,* New York, W. W. Norton & Company, 1938.

ALVERDES, FRIEDRICH R., *Social Life in the Animal World* (trans., K. C. Creasey), New York, Harcourt, Brace & World, Inc., 1927.

DART, RAYMOND ARTHUR, *Adventures with the Missing Link,* New York, Harper & Brothers, 1959.

HOOTON, EARNEST ALBERT, *Man's Poor Relations,* Doubleday & Company, 1942.

HOWARD, ELIOT, *Territory in Bird-Life,* London, William Collins Ltd., 1920.

HOWARD, LEN, *Birds as Individuals,* New York, Doubleday & Company, 1953.

HUXLEY, JULIAN S., *Man Stands Alone,* New York, Harper & Brothers, 1941.

KEITH, SIR ARTHUR, *Evolution and Ethics,* New York, G. P. Putnam Sons, 1947.

LACK, DAVID LAMBERT, *Evolutionary Theory and Christian Belief,* London, Methuen & Co. Ltd., 1957.

LEAKEY, LOUIS SEYMOUR BAZLETT, *Adam's Ancestors,* New York, Longmans, Green & Company, Inc., 1935.

LE GROS CLARK, SIR WILFRID EDWARD, *A History of the Primates,* Chicago, University of Chicago Press (Phoenix Books), 1957.

———— *Fossil Evidence for Human Evolution,* Chicago, University of Chicago Press, 1955.

LORENZ, CONRAD Z., *King Solomon's Ring* (trans., Marjorie

Kerr Wilson), New York, Thomas Y. Crowell Company, 1952.

MARAIS, EUGÈNE NIELEN, *My Friends the Baboons*, New York, McBride Co., 1940.

—————— *Soul of the White Ant* (trans., Winifred De Kok), New York, Dodd, Mead & Company, 1937.

OAKLEY, KENNETH PAGE, *Man the Tool-Maker*, London, British Museum, 1956.

SIMPSON, GEORGE GAYLORD, *The Meaning of Evolution* (Terry Foundation Lectures), New Haven, Conn., Yale University Lectures, 1949.

SMITH, SIR GRAFTON ELLIOT, *Human Nature* (Conway Memorial Lectures), London, Watts & Co., Ltd., 1927.

ZEUNER, FRIEDRICH EBERHARD, *Dating the Past*, New York, Longmans, Green & Company, Inc., 1951.

ZUCKERMAN, SOLLY, *Social Life of Monkeys and Apes*, New York, Harcourt, Brace & World, Inc., 1932.

FOR THE SPECIALIST READER weighing evidence either controversial or unfamiliar, I include a supplementary list of selected sources. In some cases I attach a phrase in italics to describe the papers' pertinence to my own investigations. The abbreviation AP will be understood to refer to the australopithecines.

ALLEE, W. C., "Social Dominance among Vertebrates," Biological Symposia, v. 8, 1942.

—————— "Dominance and Hierarchy among Vertebrates," Colloques internationaux du Centre National de la Recherche Scientifique, v. 34, March, 1950.

BARBOUR, G., "Makapanssat," Scientific Monthly, September, 1949. AP *site and summary*.

BARTHOLOMEW, G. A., and BIRDSELL, J. B., "Ecology and Protohominids," American Anthropologist, October, 1953. *Environmental interpretation of* AP.

BAUMGÄRTEL, W., *König in Gorillaland*, Stuttgart, Franckh'sche Buchhandlung, 1960.

BINGHAM, H., "Gorillas in a Native Habitat," Carnegie Institution, August, 1932.

BOND, G., "Geology of the Khami Stone-Age Sites," Occasional Papers, Nat. Museum of Southern Rhodesia, June, 1957. *Pleistocene climates*.

BRAIN, C. K., Bulletin, South African Museums Association, May, 1956. AP *sites and climates*.

———— "New Evidence for Cave Deposit Correlation," Third Pan-African Congress, Livingstone, 1955.

———— "The Transvaal Ape-Man-Bearing Cave Deposits," Memoir, Transvaal Museum, September, 1958. AP *sites, climates, chronology.*

BROOM, R., and SCHEPERS, G. W. H., "The South African Fossil Ape-Men," Memoir, Transvaal Museum, 1946.

BROOM, R., and ROBINSON, J. T., "The Swartkrans Ape-Men," Memoir, Transvaal Museum, 1952.

CARPENTER, C. R., "Behavior and Social Relations of the Howling Monkey," Comparative Psychology Monographs, Johns Hopkins University, May, 1934.

———— "Societies of Monkeys and Apes," Biological Symposia, v. 8, 1942.

———— Transactions, New York Academy of Science, 1942. *Evolutionary interpretation of human behaviour.*

———— "Field Study in Siam of the Behavior and Social Relations of the Gibbon," Comparative Psychology Monographs, Johns Hopkins University, December, 1940.

———— "Social Behavior of the Primates," Colloques internationaux du Centre National de la Recherche Scientifique, v. 34, March, 1950.

CARR, D. R., and KULP, J. L., "Potassium-Argon Method of Geochronometry," Bulletin, Geological Society of America, June, 1957.

CHANCE, M. R. A., and MEAD, A. P., "Social Behavior and Primate Evolution," Symposia, Society for Experimental Biology, 1953. *Animal dominance.*

CHARDIN, P. T. de, Transactions, New York Academy of Science, March, 1952. AP *summary.*

COLE, S., An Outline of the Geology of Kenya, London, Pitman, 1950.

———— "Zinjanthropus," New Scientist, October, 1959.

———— "Third Pan-African Congress," Antiquity, 1955. *The Livingstone meeting.*

DARLING, F., "Social Life in Ungulates," Colloques internationaux du Centre National de la Recherche Scientifique, v. 34, March, 1950. *Territory, sex, dominance.*

DART, R. A., "Predatory Implemental Technique of the Australopithecines," American Journal of Physical Anthropology, March, 1949. *The baboon skulls.*

———— "Adolescent . . . Mandible from Makapanskat," South African Science, October, 1948. *The fractured jaw.*

———— "The Predatory Transition from Ape to Man," International Anthropological and Linguistic Review, v. 1, no. 4, 1953.

——— "Cultural Status of the South African Man-Apes," Annual Report, Smithsonian Institution, 1955.

——— "Myth of the Bone-Accumulating Hyena," American Anthropologist, February, 1956.

——— "The Osteodontokeratic Culture of Australopithecus Prometheus," Memoir, Transvaal Museum, 1957. *Statistical distribution of Makapan fossils.*

DART, R. A., ET AL., "Africa's Place in the Human Story," South African Broadcasting Co., 1953. *Summary evolution on African continent.*

ERRINGTON, P. L., "Predation and Vertebrate Population," Journal of Mammology, 1946. *Territory.*

EVERNDEN, J. F., ET AL., "Potassium-Argon Dating of Pleistocene Volcanics," Quaternaria, 1958.

EWER, R. F., "Fossil carnivores of the Transvaal caves," Proceedings, Zoological Society, London, 1954, 1955, 1956. AP *fauna.*

——— "Dating of the Australopithecines, Faunal Evidence," South African Archaelogical Bulletin, June, 1956.

FERUGLIO, E., "Las Terrazas Marinas de la Patagonia," International Geological Congress, 1948. *Pleistocene climates.*

GREGORY, W. K., American Naturalist, November, 1946. AP *summary.*

HALICKA, A., and HALICKI, B., "Le Stratigraphie du Quaternaire dans le Bassin du Nieman," International Geological Congress, 1948. *Pleistocene climates.*

HEAPE, W., "Emigration, Migration, and Nomadism," 1931. *Territory.*

HOWELL, F. C., American Journal of Physical Anthropology, December, 1955. AP *dating, African climates.*

HUGHES, A. R., "Habits of Hyenas," South African Journal of Science, December, 1954. *Field investigation of contemporary hyena.*

ILLINGWORTH, F., "The Wolf as a Hunter," Field, January 8, 1953. *Predatory society.*

KOHLER, W., *The Mentality of Apes,* 1925.

LEAKEY, L. S. B., "Environment of Kenya Lower Miocene Apes," Actes du Congrès Pan-Africain de Préhistoire, Algiers, 1952.

——— *Report on Handaxe Sequence, Beds I–IV, Olduvai Gorge,* Cambridge University Press, 1951.

——— "New Finds at Olduvai Gorge," Nature, February 25, 1961.

LE GROS CLARK, W. E., "Importance of Fossil Australopithecines," Science Progress, July, 1947. AP *dentition.*

——— "New Paleontological Evidence on Evolution of the

Hominoidea," Quarterly Journal of the Geological Society, London, 1950. *Proconsul summary*.

—————— "Hominid Characters of Australopithecine Dentition," Journal, Royal Anthropological Institute, 1952.

——————and LEAKEY, L. S. B., "The Miocene Hominoidea of East Africa," British Museum (Natural History), 1951.

MOVIUS, H. C., Journal of Geology, July, 1949. *Pleistocene climates with attention to Villafranchian*.

MULLER, H. J., Report, Bulletin of the Atomic Scientists, June, 1955. *Mutation and radiation*.

NICE, M. M., "The Role of Territoriality in Bird-Life," American Midland Naturalist, November, 1941.

NISSEN, H. W., "Psychology of Great Apes," in M. Burton, *Story of Animal Life*, 1949. *Chimpanzees*.

OAKLEY, K. P., "Dawn of Man in South Africa," Lecture, Royal Institute of Great Britain, November, 20, 1953. AP *summary*.

—————— "Skill as a Human Possession," in *History of Technology*, v. 1, 1954, Oxford, The Clarendon Press. *Evolution of skill*.

—————— "Tools Makyth Man," Antiquity, 1957. *Cultural evolution in Africa*.

—————— "Study Tour of Early Hominid Sites," South African Archaeological Bulletin, September, 1954. AP *sites*.

—————— Report, International Geological Congress, 1948. *Definition of Villafranchian*.

—————— "Earliest Tool Makers," Antiquity, March, 1956. AP *summary*.

—————— "Dating of the Australopithecinae," American Journal of Physical Anthropology, March, 1954. AP *sites, relative dating and suggested species reclassification*.

PEABODY, F., "Cave Deposits of Kaap Escarpment," Bulletin, Geological Society of America, July, 1954. *Taungs lime deposits and Pleistocene climates*.

ROBINSON, J. T., "Telanthropus and its Phylogenetic Significance," American Journal of Physical Anthropology, December, 1953.

—————— Report, Official Journal, Dental Association of South Africa, March, 1952. AP *dentition*.

—————— "Affinities of the New Olduvai Australopithecine," May 7, 1960. *Analysis of Zinjanthropus*.

—————— and MASON, R. J., Report, Nature, September 14, 1957. *The Sterkfontein handaxes*.

SCHEIN, M., and FOHRMAN, M., "Social Dominance . . . in a Herd of Dairy Cattle," British Journal of Animal Behaviour, April, 1955.

SIMPSON, G. C., "World Climate during the Quaternary Period,"

Quarterly Journal, Royal Meteorological Society, October, 1934.

——— "Further Studies in World Climate," Quarterly Journal, Royal Meteorological Society, October, 1957.

SMITH, W. I., and ROSS, S., "Social Dominance in Male Mice," Physiological Zoology, July, 1951.

VON KOENIGSWALD, G. H. R., "Pithecanthropus and the Australopithecinae," Congres Geologique International, Algiers, 1953. AP *from Asian view.*

——— "Australopithecus and Pithecanthropus," Amsterdam Nederl Akademie van Wetenschappen, Meeting, September 26, 1953. *Hyena responsibility for Makapan bones.*

WASHBURN, S. L., "Australopithecines: the Hunters or the Hunted?" American Anthropologist, August, 1957. *Hyena responsibility for Makapan bones.*

——— ET AL., "The Human Species," Scientific American, September, 1960.

WEIDENRICH, F., "Morphological Character of Australopithecine Skull," Royal Society of South Africa, 1948. AP *from Asian view.*

WEINER, J. S., ET AL., "Solution of the Piltdown Problem," Bulletin, British Museum (Natural History), 1953.

WELLS, L. H., and COOKE, H. B. S., "Fossil Bovidae from . . . Makapan," Paeontologia Africana, 1956. AP *fauna.*

ZAPFE, H., "Fossil Traces of Bone-Crushing Predatory Animals," Research and Progress, November, 1940. *Hyena feeding habits.*

ZEUNER, F. E., "Domestication of Animals," Scientia, 1956.

ZUCKERMAN, S., ET AL., *The* AP *dentition controversy*: Nature, April 22, 1950; June 3, 1950; July 22, 1950; November 4, 1950; December 2, 1950; November 3, 1951; December 29, 1951.

Index